DRUG DISCOVERY TECHNOLOGIES

ELLIS HORWOOD SERIES IN PHARMACEUTICAL TECHNOLOGY

Editor: Professor M. H. RUBINSTEIN, School of Health Sciences, Liverpool Polytechnic, U.K.

* In preparation

DRUG DISCOVERY TECHNOLOGIES

Editors:

C. R. CLARK Ph.D.
Department of Molecular Bioscience
Parke-Davis Pharmaceutical Research Division
Warner-Lambert Co., Ann Arbor, Michigan, USA

W. H. MOOS A.B., Ph.D.
Department of Chemistry
Parke-Davis Pharmaceutical Research Division
Warner-Lambert Co., Ann Arbor, Michigan, USA

ELLIS HORWOOD LIMITED
Publishers · Chichester

Halsted Press: a division of
JOHN WILEY & SONS
New York · Chichester · Brisbane · Toronto

First published in 1990 by
ELLIS HORWOOD LIMITED
Market Cross House, Cooper Street,
Chichester, West Sussex, PO19 1EB, England
The publisher's colophon is reproduced from James Gillison's drawing of the ancient Market Cross, Chichester.

Distributors:

Australia and New Zealand:
JACARANDA WILEY LIMITED
GPO Box 859, Brisbane, Queensland 4001, Australia

Canada:
JOHN WILEY & SONS CANADA LIMITED
22 Worcester Road, Rexdale, Ontario, Canada

Europe and Africa:
JOHN WILEY & SONS LIMITED
Baffins Lane, Chichester, West Sussex, England

North and South America and the rest of the world:
Halsted Press: a division of
JOHN WILEY & SONS
605 Third Avenue, New York, NY 10158, USA

South-East Asia
JOHN WILEY & SONS (SEA) PTE LIMITED
37 Jalan Pemimpin # 05–04
Block B, Union Industrial Building, Singapore 2057

Indian Subcontinent
WILEY EASTERN LIMITED
4835/24 Ansari Road
Daryaganj, New Delhi 110002, India

© 1990 C.R. Clark and W.H. Moos/Ellis Horwood Limited

British Library Cataloguing in Publication Data
Drug discovery technologies.
1. Drugs. Development
I. Clark, R. (Colin Roy), *1955–* II. Moos, W.H. (Walter H.)
615′.191

Library of Congress Card No. 89–24425

ISBN 0–7458–0625–2 (Ellis Horwood Limited)
ISBN 0–470–21604–2 (Halsted Press)

Typeset in Times by Ellis Horwood Limited
Printed in Great Britain by The Camelot Press, Southampton

Table of contents

Preface

The discovery and development of drugs or pharmaceuticals to treat human diseases has undergone a profound change over the last century. No longer are drugs discovered by one-man, back-room operations — at the physician's or pharmacist's office. Rather, drug discovery and development now involves large, and in many cases multinational, research organizations. Thus a wide variety of scientific and non-scientific expertise and know-how is and must be applied to the discovery, development and eventual commercialization of new pharmaceuticals.

A major force underlying this change within the pharmaceutical industry is a consequential and rapid change in the technologies on which the discovery of new drugs is based. The impact of this 'technological change' is evident in both chemical and biological sciences. Take, for example, the biological sciences. There has been, and continues to be, a dramatic, significant move away from drug discovery that focuses on the whole organism. The new focus centers on strategies that target specific molecular entities critically implicated in the disease process. Receptor subtypes, enzyme isotopes, etc. are, therefore, a primary focus. These changes, which of course have their origins in 'new technologies', closely mirror advances in technologies of the so-called 'new biology', for example, recombinant DNA, protein engineering and biochemistry, receptor biology, etc. In turn, 'new biology' has as its basis many aspects of the interface between biology and chemistry. The combined evolution and revolution now allow, perhaps demand, that we explore human disease at the 'molecular level'.

A book that attempts to capture the rapidly changing nature of the drug discovery process is clearly challenged by the rapid change in the technologies which form its base. To this end, and in an attempt to overcome the inherent limitations of a book focused on 'technology', we have sought to bring together a group of internationally renowned drug discovery scientists. The purpose is not only to identify current state-of-the-art technologies, but also to point the reader in the direction of those new technologies that will have a major impact on the industry in the 1990s and beyond. We have not attempted to make the book all-encompassing. Instead, we have tried to highlight areas of scientific investigation where a major impact/benefit on drug discovery can be predicted.

The book is divided into three broad sections, namely:

I.   Drug design
II.   Drug delivery
III.   Biochemistry/molecular biology
IV.   Pharmacology

This subdivision is reflective of the multidisciplinary nature of the drug discovery process. However, it should not divert the reader from appreciating the highly 'interactive' nature of innovative drug discovery, wherein divisions between scientific disciplines (e.g. protein chemistry and biochemistry, or biochemistry and molecular pharmacology) become more and more difficult to define.

Part I of this monograph covers those aspects of applied chemistry that will make drug design a true prerequisite to competitive drug discovery. Included here are molecular modeling, quantitative structure–activity relationships, and physical methods such as multi-dimensional nuclear magnetic resonance spectroscopy and crystallography.

Part II extends the discussion to chemically related techniques of site-specific drug delivery and the special problems associated with peptides. Prodrugs, carriers, absorption and distribution characteristics, and peptoids are the main topics of this section.

Part III focuses on the molecular aspects of drug discovery from a 'new biology' perspective. Herein are discussed key biochemical approaches to drug discovery involving the study of receptors and enzymes, ion-channels and second messengers. The last chapter in this section broadens the discussion of 'new biology' to recombinant technology and the special role it and associated protein engineering plays in the drug discovery process.

Part IV presents some directions for the future of animal models, paving the way toward validated, unequivocal models, perhaps those using transgenic animals.

This book is intended for individuals within and connected to the pharmaceutical industry. This means not only research personnel, but scientists and non-scientists alike to whom state-of-the-art technology has meaning. We hope the overview of selected technologies critical to success in drug discovery serves the needs not only of those in the pharmaceutical industry, but also of students in the latter years of their studies.

The student who reads the present monograph, understands the details of the chapters most closely allied with his chosen field, and comprehends the generalities of the other chapters, will be well prepared to meet the future. Each chapter is written at a high level that will challenge the best students, while providing the basics necessary for general understanding of key concepts by the non-expert.

It is hoped that the present monograph will serve the needs of certain graduate-level special topics courses in medicinal chemistry, pharmacology, and biochemistry, including the new and affiliated discipline of molecular biology.

Other monographs have dealt with both drug discovery and development, but few if any have focused on the present mix of preclinical drug discovery technologies. Even with the present focus and mix, we have omitted obvious areas from discussion. For example, a chapter on biotechnology as it relates to the generation of human protein therapies is not included; readers are referred to the many discussions of this topic already found in journals and books. And animal models are presented only for neuroscience-related areas. The latter choice is representative of issues affecting many therapeutic targets. But, more importantly, it reflects the coming age of neurosciences, wherein technologies and understanding of the brain reach the synergies necessary for major breakthroughs in drug discovery.

We have tried to avoid drug development issues in general, and clinical development issues specifically. We leave the non-discovery issues to the recipients of state-of-the-art drug discovery technologies, our colleagues in development and clinical research.

Finally, we thank our talented group of chapter authors, whose abilities will be readily apparent to those who study the book. We are indebted to them all for thoughtful, capable, and timely input.

Ann Arbor, Michigan   Colin R. Clark and Walter H. Moos
November 1989

Selected abbreviations

Ac	acetyl
AcCh	acetylcholine (also Ach)
ACE	angiotensin-converting enzyme
ACV	acyclovir
ADP	adenosine diphosphate
AIDS	acquired immunodeficiency syndrome
Ala	alanine
AMBER	assisted model building with energy refinement
AMP	adenosine monophosphate
AM1	Austin model 1
AP	action potential
APA	Ac-Ala-Pro-Ala
Ar	aryl group
Arg	arginine
Asn	asparagine
Asp	aspartate
ATP	adenosine triphosphate
ATPase	adenosine triphosphatase
BBB	blood–brain barrier
B_i	amount of ligand bound in presence of competitor
B_{max}	density of binding sites on a concentration/weight basis
BMEC	brain microvessel endothelial cells
B_0	amount of ligand bound in the absence of competitor
Boc	tert-butyloxycarbonyl
BPTI	basic pancreatic trypsin inhibitor
BUSI	bull seminal plasma proteinase inhibitor
cAMP	cyclic AMP

CAR	conditioned avoidance responding paradigm
CCK	cholecystokinin
cDNA	complementary DNA
CDS	chemical delivery system
CHARMM	chemistry at Harvard macromolecular mechanics
CHESS	Cornell high energy synchrotron source
CHO	Chinese hamster ovary
CLOGP	computer program that estimates (calculates) $\log P$
CNDO	complete neglect of differential overlap
CNS	central nervous system
COSY	correlated 2D NMR spectroscopy
CPK	Corey, Pauling, Kolton models
CPP	(2-carboxypiperazine-4-yl)propyl-1-phosphonic acid
CS	conditioned stimulus
CSF	cerebrospinal fluid
Cys	cysteine
DAG	diacylglycerol
DCV	desciclovir
DDAVP	1-deamino-8-D-arginine
DHFR	dihydrofolate reductase
DHP	dihydropyridine
DMSO	dimethyl sulfoxide
DNA	deoxyribonucleic acid
DPAT	8-hydroxy-2-(di-n-propylamino)tetralin
DRL	differential reinforcement of low rate schedule
DSCG	disodium chromoglycate
DTI	drug targeting index
E	trans geometry
EC_{50}	concentration producing half-maximal inhibition or stimulation
ED_{50}	mean or median effective dose; dose that produces the desired effect in 50% of the population; dose that produces 50% of maximal response
ECEPP	empirical conformational energy program for peptides
EDTA	ethylene diamine tetraacetate
EGF	epidermal growth factor
EHT	extended Hückel theory
ELISA	enzyme-linked immunosorbent assay
EPSP	excitatory postsynaptic potential
F_{abs}	fraction of a compound absorbed
FDA	Food and Drug Administration (USA)
F_{hkl}	structure factor
F_{non}	fraction of a drug in nonionized form
FR	fixed ratio reinforcement (schedule)
G protein	guanine nucleotide binding protein
GABA	γ-amino butyric acid
GAMESS	generalized atomic and molecular electronic structure system
GAP	program for aligning peptide sequences with gaps introduced to display maximum homology

GDS	site-specific chemical drug delivery system
GEMSA	guanidinoethylmercaptosuccinic acid
G_i	inhibitory G protein
Gln	glutamine
Gly	glycine
GM-CSF	granulocyte-macrophage colony stimulating factor
G_0	a G protein
G_s	stimulatory G protein
GTP	guanosine triphosphate
hEGF	human EGF
His	histidine
HIV	human immunodeficiency virus
HMGCoA	hydroxymethylglutaryl coenzyme A
HONDO	highest order neglect of differential overlap
HPLC	high performance (pressure) liquid chromatography
ICYP	iodocyanopindolol
IC_{50}	concentration of an agent (e.g. an antagonist) that decreases response by 50%
Ile	isoleucine
INDO	intermediate neglect of differential overlap
IOP	intraocular pressure
iPr	isopropyl
IP_1	D-myo-inositol monophosphate
IP_2	D-myo-inositol bisphosphate
IP_3	D-myo-inositol trisphosphate
IP_4	D-myo-inositol tetrakisphosphate
ITI	intertrial interval
i.v.	intravenous
J	coupling constant
K_b	dissociation constant for a competitive antagonist
K_D	equilibrium dissociation constant
kDa	kilodalton
K_i	(comparative) inhibition constant
Leu	leucine
LFER	linear free energy relationships
LI	latent inhibition
LIMS	laboratory information management system
$\log P$	log of the partition coefficient
LRTF	ligand responsive transcription factor
Lys	lysine
m1, m2, ...	muscarinic receptor subtypes (sometimes M1, M2, etc.)
MAS	human transforming protein
Met	methionine
MIF	macrophage inhibitory factor
MINDO	modified intermediate neglect of differential overlap
MITI	Ministry of International Trade and Industry (Japan)
MIR	multiple isomorphous replacement

MMx	molecular mechanics programs developed by Allinger (MM1, MM2, etc.)
MNDO	modified neglect of differential overlap
MOPAC	molecular orbital package
MR	molar refractivity
mRNA	messenger RNA
MW	molecular weight
NADPH	reduced form of nicotinamide adenine dinucleotide phosphate
NAARE	N-acyl amino acid releasing enzyme
NCE	new chemical entity
NECA	$5'$-N-ethylcarboxamide analogue of adenosine
nH	pseudo-Hill coefficient
NMDA	N-methyl-D-aspartate
NMR	nuclear magnetic resonance (spectroscopy)
nOe	nuclear Overhauser enhancement (NMR)
NOESY	application of nOe in two dimensions (2D NMR)
Nva	norvaline
P	octanol-water partition coefficient
PA	phosphatidic acid
P_{aq}	aqueous permeability of a drug
pA_2	$\log K_b$
P_c	permeability coefficient
PC	personal computer
PCP	phencyclidine
PD	prodrug
PDE	phosphodiesterase
PDM	pharmacokinetics and drug metabolism
PGE	prostaglandin E
pH	measure of acidity
Phe	phenylalanine
PI	phosphatidyl inositol
PIP	phosphatidylinositol 4-phosphate
PIP$_2$	phosphatidylinositol 4,5-bisphosphate
PK	protein kinase
PKC	protein kinase C
PLC	phospholipase C
PPE	porcine pancreatic elastase
PPI	phosphoinositide (phosphatidylinositol, phosphatidylinositol 4-phosphate and phosphatidylinositol 4,5-bisphosphate)
PNS	peripheral nervous system
Pro	proline
P_w	permeability of the gut wall to a drug
QNB	quinuclidinyl benzilate
QSAR	quantitative structure–activity relationships
R	alkyl or other group
r	correlation coefficient
R value	residual factor describing fit of model to observed data

r.m.s	root mean square (deviation)
RNA	ribonucleic acid
Sar	sarcosine
s.c.	subcutaneous
SD	soft drug
SDS	sodium dodecyl sulfate
Ser	serine
SHR	spontaneously hypertensive rat
SIMCA	partial least squares QSAR/statistical method, often considered a class modeling method or pattern recognition technique
S_0	aqueous solubility of a nonionized species
SOTA	state-of-the-art
Sta	statine
STO-3G	Slater-type orbital with 3-Gaussians
TEA	tetraethyl ammonium salt
TI	therapeutic index
TLC	thin-layer chromatogram
TRH	thyrotropin releasing hormone
Trp	tryptophan
TSA	transition state analog
TTX	tetrodotoxin
UCS	unconditioned stimulus
Val	valine
VI	(multiple) variable interval
V_L	volume of the lumenal contents
X_0	drug dosage
Y	denotes N-linked glycosylation sites
Z	cis geometry
3-PPP	3-(hydroxyphenyl)-N-propylpiperidine
5-FU	5-fluorouracil
5-HT	serotonin
6-OHDA	6-hydroxydopamine

Part I
Drug design

1

Computer-assisted drug design

Philip Loftus
ICI Pharmaceuticals Group, ICI Americas, Wilmington, Delaware, USA

1.1 INTRODUCTION

Several famous drugs, including many of the current generation of antibiotics, were discovered by developing a biological test and screening large numbers of chemical substances. These were either known chemical entities, which is how several of the major chemical companies initially became involved in the pharmaceutical business, or natural products, which were frequently mixtures of chemical substances for which precise structural information was not known.

Although this style of approach is still in use today, it is generally employed to generate an initial chemical lead in a new area. Advances in separation and characterization techniques mean that it is almost always possible to isolate and identify a substance of interest. At this point, medicinal chemists began to develop hypotheses for the underlying medicinal chemical basis of the observed biological activity and began to design and synthesize new compounds targeted at producing enhanced biological activity.

The criteria used to rationalize observed activity are the same as those used to study most basic chemical properties and consist, primarily, of shape, lipophilicity, electronic distribution, and hydrogen-bonding capability. Traditionally, organic chemists used mechanical models of chemical structures in order to study their properties and to compare one structure with another. These models fell into two major categories: the first comprised 'wire frame' or 'Dreiding' models which attempted to represent the molecular 'skeleton' of a compound, whereas the second sought to depict the volume of space occupied by the molecule itself, the most well known of this latter group being the familiar CPK (Corey, Pauling, Koltun) models.

Although still widely used, mechanical models have a number of fundamental limitations, one of the most important being a restricted ability to accurately represent sterically strained systems, other than for very simple groups such as cyclopropane rings. Another is the difficulty of constructing models of large molecules, particularly biological models, where complex framework systems are required simply to support the physical weight of the model. From the perspective of the medicinal chemist, another major limitation is the difficulty of being able to physically superimpose one chemical structure over another.

The advent of low-cost digital minicomputers and high-resolution graphics displays in the 1970s meant that it became possible to generate accurate three-dimensional displays of drug molecules and to interact with them in real time. Although computers had been used to model chemical properties in pharmaceutical companies since the 1950s, early calculations were performed on large, expensive computer systems and produced their output in terms of large volumes of numerical data. Computer graphics were used to transform such numerical results into visual images, greatly facilitating their interpretation, and the relatively low cost of a whole new generation of minicomputers meant that this technology became available in the research laboratory.

1.2 STRUCTURE-BUILDING TECHNIQUES

Early attempts at computer-assisted drug design generally began either with crystallographic coordinates, obtained directly from experimentation, or indirectly from the literature or a compendium such as the Cambridge Crystallographic Database [1]. Other attempts used a template-based approach to build up a three-dimensional representation of the drug molecule within the computer using standard functional group fragments which were joined together in a manner directly analogous to that used in assembling a conventional Dreiding model. Given the wide diversity of modern drug candidates, however, a large range of such templates is required. Hence, a number of additional techniques have also been developed for this purpose, the most common being the use of molecular mechanics [2], semi-empirical quantum mechanics [3], and distance geometry [4]. In addition to their use in defining molecular geometries, these techniques provide additional information which is also of considerable value to the medicinal chemist.

1.3 THE MOLECULAR MECHANICS APPROACH

Molecular mechanics is one of the most conceptually straightforward of the techniques employed in computer-assisted drug design, and is also one of the most widely used. In this approach, the energy of a molecule is assumed to be made up of a number of discrete components, each of which is directly attributable to the interaction between a specific pair of atoms. Hence, the overall energy of a molecule can be represented in a form similar to that shown in equation (1.1).

$$E_{molecule} = E_{steric} + E_{bond\,length} + E_{bond\,angle} + E_{torsion} \qquad (1.1)$$

The individual energy terms are calculated between all relevant pairs of atoms, and then summed to give the energy for the molecule as a whole.

This approach was initially applied to the study of the conformational stabilities of hydrocarbon molecules [5–7], in which good overall agreement between the calculated and experimentally determined values was obtained. In the case of hydrocarbon molecules, the small difference in electronegativity between carbon and hydrogen meant that the contribution of polar interactions to the total energy of the molecule was small and could reasonably be ignored.

In most drug molecules, however, the presence of a wide variety of highly electronegative heteroatoms (such as nitrogen, oxygen and the halogens) means that the polar interaction energies can be substantial and, therefore, must explicitly be taken into account. A number of different ways of accomplishing this have been proposed, including the assignment of discrete-bond dipoles followed by evaluation of the resultant dipolar interaction energies [8], and the allocation of partial charges to individual atoms. In this latter case, the polar interaction energy is then defined in terms of the sum of the pairwise electrostatic interactions, as shown in equation (1.2).

$$E_{polar} = \sum \frac{Cq_iq_j}{r_{ij}} \tag{1.2}$$

where q_i and q_j represent the partial charges on two atoms i and j, r_{ij} is the internuclear separation between them, and C is a constant. The summation is then carried out over all appropriate pairs of atoms ij (where $j > i$).

A significant effort has been invested in developing empirical models to describe the polar interactions in organic molecules [9–12]. Unfortunately, the sensitivity of these interactions to subtle changes in molecular geometry, particularly in conjugated systems, and to neighboring group effects, has so far limited the applicability of these techniques.

In particular, the close approach of one polar molecule to another can lead to a significant mutual cross-polarization, modifying the electrostatic interactions between them. A similar effect is found in conformationally flexible drug molecules containing highly polar and/or polarizable groups, where changes in conformation can give rise to directly analogous effects. Consequently, any empirically based model of electrostatic interactions, based on the concept of formalized partial charges, will be subject to such limitations. This is especially important in the case of drug molecules, which frequently contain highly electronegative functional groups in conformationally flexible or extensively conjugated environments.

Finally, the molecular mechanics approach calculates energies for molecules in isolation (i.e. in a gas phase environment). The presence of a solvent can have a significant effect, particularly on the polar interactions, which, at least from an intermolecular perspective, decrease in relative importance as the dielectric constant of the solvent increases. It is not, however, safe to assume that polar interactions can be ignored in highly polar solvents, since the interaction between a drug molecule and the solvent, itself, can influence both the stability and the preferred conformation of the drug.

Apart from its conceptual simplicity, the molecular mechanics approach has the advantage of being able to partition the energy of a molecule into readily understandable forms which can be explicitly associated with interactions between specific pairs of atoms. The computational implementation of this approach is also straightforward, and conformational minimizations for even quite large drug molecules can be solved on small minicomputers within minutes. Hence, this approach is frequently used to 'refine' drug structures entered directly from a graphics terminal, using a template-based approach, or generated from a computationally more rapid, but conformationally less dependable, technique such as distance geometry.

As a result of its popularity, a number of computational implementations of the molecular mechanics approach have been developed, one of the best known being the MMx (MM1, MM2, MMP, etc.) series of programs developed by Allinger [2,13], which have found widespread use in the areas of both chemical and pharmaceutical research.

1.4 LIMITATIONS OF THEORETICAL APPROACHES

When applied appropriately, molecular mechanics, and some of the more sophisticated computational approaches discussed subsequently, provide powerful tools for the study of molecular geometries and energies. Fundamentally, however, most of these techniques have a number of significant limitations. First, as mentioned above, most calculations are performed on single isolated molecules, giving rise to so-called *in vacuo* or 'gas phase' energies which take no account of intermolecular interactions, particularly those between a compound and its neighboring solvent molecules.

Similarly, as pointed out earlier, these calculations often make no allowance for the influence of dielectric constant on polar interaction energies. Although molecular mechanics and molecular dynamics programs designed to handle enzyme and protein molecules are now attempting to allow for the influence of solvent, most small-molecule calculations still do not take this effect into account.

Consequently, even with the more rigorous calculations, care must be exercised in interpreting the significance of the results in an experimental context. Hence, while it may be reasonable to assume that the preferred gas phase conformation for a molecule represents a realistic approximation to the corresponding state in a strongly hydrophobic environment (such as that encountered within a membrane bilayer, or hydrophobic protein-binding site from which water is known to be excluded) the conformational preference in a hydrophilic environment, such as that encountered in the plasma or cytoplasm, may be markedly different.

In most applications, an initial starting geometry for the structure under study is derived either from X-ray crystallographic data or from tables of standard molecular geometries, and the structure is then fully, or partially, optimized., Although a variety of minimization techniques are available for this purpose, varying in both computational speed and accuracy, they almost always converge on the first local energy minimum encountered.

Given the complex nature of the energy surface for many drug molecules, there is no *a priori* way of knowing whether a minimum located in this manner is the true 'global' energy minimum for the molecule or just a 'local' minimum on the energy surface. Frequently, it is the starting conformation selected which determines the final result, and considerable care in both its selection and the interpretation of the result obtained is normally required.

Inherent in the molecular mechanics approach is the assumption that all interactions are additive, i.e. that the energy of the molecule as a whole is simply the sum of the energies of interaction between the atoms from which it is formed. Most molecular-mechanics-based approaches also assume that the non-bonded interaction terms are radially symmetric. This is particularly important in the case of drug molecules since it frequently implies that there is no directional dependence for the modeling of lone pair interactions. This in turn is important in the treatment of hydrogen bonds, which have strong directional preferences, and force fields are now beginning to be extended to take hydrogen bonding specifically into account [14].

The frequently made assumption that polar interactions are independent of both conformation and environment, discussed above, is another limitation in the case of drug molecules containing conformationally flexible conjugation pathways, or highly polarizable functional groups.

The validity of a molecular mechanics calculation, being an empirical approach, is strongly dependent on the appropriateness of the force field and parameter set that is being employed. In general, approaches parameterized using a specific series of compounds, such as steroids, give good results when applied to closely related series of compounds, such as the terpenes. They may, however, give very poor results when applied to unrelated systems (such as peptides, continuing the example above). Careful parameterization is, therefore, critical to the success of any molecular-mechanics-based approach, and several pharmaceutical companies have already developed significant 'in house' collections of parameters applicable to their specific areas of research.

1.5   QUANTUM-MECHANICS-BASED APPROACHES

One of the earliest methods used for calculating the resonance energy of a delocalized system involved the application of extended Hückel theory (EHT). Although now largely superseded, many of the currently used quantum mechanics programs have evolved from this simple approach.

A very widely used program, at the semi-empirical level, has been the CNDO/2 (complete neglect of differential overlap) method of Pople and Segal [15]. Though still ultimately based on empirical parameters, these programs calculate atomic interactions in terms of the overlap of localized atomic orbitals and take electronic delocalization effects, such as conjugation and aromaticity, explicitly into account. They are normally fully parameterized for both first- and second-row elements, so that the major parameterization problems found with many of the molecular mechanics programs are avoided.

One of the principal advantages of the semi-empirical approach over molecular mechanics is its ability to take specific account of the effects of electron delocalization. This is particularly important in the case of drugs containing heteroaromatic ring systems and other highly conjugated systems. The basic CNDO method was later extended to give INDO (intermediate neglect of differential overlap) [16]. Dewar *et al.* also developed a semi-empirical approach known as MINDO (modified intermediate neglect of differential overlap) [17–19]. This has now been incorporated into the MOPAC (molecular orbital package) program [20], together with the more recently developed MNDO method [3] and its successor, AM1 (Austin model 1) [21]. MINDO, MNDO, and AM1 were all parameterized to reproduce experimental enthalpies of formation, and both MNDO and AM1 have now found widespread acceptance as general-purpose semi-empirical routines.

Programs at this level generally give good agreement with experimentally determined molecular geometries (bond lengths and bond angles), but do less well in the area of conformational energy, even to the extent of sometimes failing to reproduce experimentally determined rank orders of conformational stability. Similarly, the assignment of partial charges to specific atoms, generally achieved using Mulliken population analysis [22], occasionally produces partial charge distributions for which there is little direct experimental support, such as the well known prediction of the alternation of induced charge given by CNDO/2 for saturated molecules [23,24].

Although offering a number of significant advantages over molecular-mechanics-based approaches, semi-empirical programs are computationally intensive to run, with geometry optimizations for even relatively small drug molecules taking several hours of dedicated minicomputer time to complete. The advent of a new generation of super-minicomputers, incorporating advanced vector architectures, may cause this situation to change significantly in the near future, however, and there is currently work being carried out in a number of laboratories to tune the existing programs to take full advantage of this new hardware technology.

Despite the general utility of semi-empirical programs, their weakness in certain energetic areas, such as the failure to correctly rank order the major conformations for a compound and their limited ability to handle hydrogen-bonding interactions, has led to a gradual but growing use of a number of more theoretically rigorous computational programs based on the *ab initio* quantum mechanical approach.

These programs, such as Gaussian-80 [25], Gaussian-82 [26], HONDO [27], and GAMESS (generalized atomic and molecular electronic structure system) [28] are among the most sophisticated and accurate that are currently available. Unfortunately, however, they are also the most computationally intensive to use. In practice, this means that geometry optimizations, for all but the smallest of drug molecules, performed using anything other than a minimal basis set quickly become impracticable in most pharmaceutical environments. Since the size of the calculation increases as the fourth power of the number of orbitals involved, further advances in the algorithms and computational techniques employed are required [29] before the use of calculations at this level, on a routine basis, becomes a practical proposition.

1.6   GRAPHICAL DISPLAYS OF MOLECULAR STRUCTURE

In the modern drug discovery process, a medicinal chemist typically works from an initial lead structure and attempts to improve it in order to meet some targeted level of biological selectivity and activity. This initial lead may have come from a variety of sources, such as clinical trials, an unanticipated side effect of a current drug undergoing testing, or the random screening of either synthetic or natural products. In a few favorable cases, there may be a known enzyme to be inhibited for which the X-ray crystallographic coordinates of the enzyme, or a closely related analog, are already known.

In many cases, however, there is only a lead compound and the details of the biological mode of action at the molecular level are unknown; this is particularly true in areas such as the central nervous system. In either event, the rational drug discovery process involves the medicinal chemist in formulating a hypothesis of the chemical basis of the observed biological activity and then designing, synthesizing and testing compounds which exemplify and test such hypotheses.

On the basis of the observed biological activity, these hypotheses are either expanded, or abandoned, and the process repeated in an iterative manner until a compound with the desired biological profile is finally obtained. It is important to realize from the outset that computer modeling frequently tells us nothing about the validity of the biological model *per se*. Its power lies in the ability to examine the accuracy with which a proposed drug candidate exemplifies the chemical hypothesis which it was designed to test.

Since the medicinal chemist is working on the basis of the derived biological test result, a failure to achieve an enhanced level of activity may arise either from an invalid hypothesis, or from the fact that the selected compound does not exemplify the hypothesis under test. Traditionally, it could be difficult, if not impossible, to differentiate between these two possible situations. Molecular modeling is already making a significant contribution by improving the probability that a chosen compound accurately reflects the chemical hypothesis under test.

A simple illustration of one of the most basic uses of molecular modeling is presented in Fig. 1.1 (see color section). This shows trimethoprim **1**, a known inhibitor of dihydrofolate reductase (DHFR), superimposed on itself in two different orientations. This particular image, along with the others used in this chapter, was generated using the Enigma™ program developed at ICI [30], but is illustrative of the display capabilities supported by most modern molecular graphics systems. In Fig. 1.1, one molecule of trimethoprim, laid out in a planar conformation, has been 'turned over' and placed over a second molecule in the same initial conformation. As can be seen, the two pyrimidine nitrogen atoms in the red structure superimpose reasonably well onto a pyrimidine and exocyclic amine nitrogen in the blue one. The overall outline of the two structures, superimposed in this manner, is also reasonably close, leading to the possibility that trimethoprim might be able to fit into the DHFR-binding site in either orientation if it binds in a planar form.

1

A major benefit of molecular graphics is the ability to superimpose two, or more, structures and examine in detail the nature of the overlap. This is particularly useful in the case of non-planar structures where this operation is generally difficult to perform using mechanical models. In this particular example, however, an examination of even the simplest of models would readily have shown that there is a severe steric interaction between two of the hydrogens on the adjacent aromatic rings. The question, then, is how far out of plane the rings would need to be twisted in order to produce a reasonably stable conformation.

To examine this question, trimethoprim was conformationally optimized using Aesop™ [31], a molecular mechanics program based on the Allinger [2] MM2 force field and incorporating many of the features of the BIGSTRN-3 program [32,33]. This produced a conformation in which the pyrimidine and benzene rings were rotated out of the plane defined by the bridging methylene carbon atom, and the two-ring carbon atoms to which it is directly attached, by dihedrals of 108° and 124°, respectively. The energy for this minimized conformation was calculated to be 13.4 kcal/mol.

In this form, the two aromatic rings are almost orthogonal to one another, leaving the question of how much energy it would cost to begin to rotate them back towards a more planar conformation. One of the uses of moelcular mechanics is being able to answer such 'what if' questions. Hence, to rotate the two rings so that they each made a dihedral of 45° with the original plane gave an energy of 16.0 kcal/mol (i.e. 2.6 kcal/mol above the minimum). Similarly, repeating the calculation but using dihedrals of 30° gave an energy of 21.2 kcal/mol (i.e. 7.8 kcal/mol above the minimum).

Although it is dangerous to attach too great a significance to small calculated energy differences, the high value of 7.8 kcal/mol for the 30/30° conformation means that it is unlikely that trimethoprim would bind in this form. The 2.6 kcal/mol value for the 45/45° conformation implies that this form could merit more careful consideration since the calculational accuracy is on the order of 1 kcal/mol, and, even if the 2.6 kcal/mol value is, indeed, accurate, this could be more than compensated for by favorable binding interactions to the active site.

The conformation of trimethoprim bound to the active site of *E. coli* DHFR has been determined by X-ray crystallography [34] which showed that trimethoprim did, indeed, adopt a non-planar conformation in the bound state, the specific values of the relative dihedrals depending both on the source of DHFR and on the nature of the substituents on the rings [35].

1.7   SURFACE AND VOLUME DISPLAYS

As well as using framework molecular models, such as Dreiding models, medicinal chemists have also used various models which attempt to represent the volume of space occupied by a molecule such as CPK models. Computer graphics also provide a number of ways of displaying the volume of space occupied by a molecule. The most common of these is to display a van der Waals surface. This is, typically, shown using a 'dot' or 'shaded' surface superimposed on the structural framework for the molecule giving rise to the type of display shown in Fig. 1.2 (see color section).

Another commonly used method is to display the so-called 'solvent accessible' surface for a molecule, also referred to as the Connolly [36,37] or 'probe' surface. This is the surface that would be mapped out by rolling a spherical probe molecule, usually water, over the surface of the molecule in question. This has the effect of smoothing out the many small crevices in the normal van der Waals surface, making the overall surface contours somewhat easier to see. For this reason, probe surfaces are frequently used when displaying large, complex molecules, particularly biological molecules such as proteins and enzymes.

Surface displays can be particularly useful when studying superimposed molecules, as a way of defining their relative spatial requirements. A simplified illustration of this is presented in Fig. 1.2, which shows a possible superpositioning of phenylethylamine **2** onto "diphenylethylidine" **3**, as proposed in the work of Salama *et al.* [38]. Displaying the surfaces for the two overlapped structures enables the researcher to study not only the ability of the two molecules in question to directly superimpose, but also to easily identify regions of similarity and difference in terms of their spatial requirements. Hence, even in the case of a simple photograph, it is easy to see where the two structures occupy a common region of space and where they each differ.

In the example illustrated, the conformational flexibility of the two molecules in question is fairly limited and the problem was actually addressed using conventional mechanical models. As the number of structures to be superimposed grows beyond two, however, or as the degree of conformational freedom of the structures increases, the task of manually performing the superpositioning becomes increasingly difficult. It is in just these situations that the computational approach proves its true value, since not only is it possible to superimpose large numbers of structures, but, even in the case of highly flexible molecules, it is not necessary to know in advance the conformations in which they can most effectively be superimposed.

1.8   DISPLAY OF ELECTRONIC PROPERTIES

The chemical properties of a drug, and, hence, ultimately, its biological activity, are determined by basic steric and electronic requirements. In designing drug candidates, medicinal chemists have long been sensitive to the importance of the role played by steric considerations. This is due, in no small part, to the ready availability of mechanical models which can be used to study and predict potential steric interactions.

In the case of electronic properties, no corresponding set of mechanical models is available, with the result that these have been much more difficult to study effectively. Since it is not normally practical to measure the electronic properties for most drug candidates experimentally, theoretical models have, traditionally, been used. A common method is to calculate the excess electron densities (partial charges) for the individual atoms within a molecule using a semi-empirical approach. For most such calculations, the partial charge information is derived by performing a Mulliken [22] population analysis, which partitions the electron density in the molecular orbitals between the individual atoms. The largest partial charges (generally those on the most highly electronegative atoms, or on the hydrogens attached to these atoms) are used to model the polar interactions for the molecule, particularly the hydrogen-bonding interactions.

There are, however, a number of limitations with this approach. Even when the molecular orbital densities have been obtained from quantum mechanical calculations, the validity of assigning partial charges on the basis of a Mulliken population analysis has been subject to question [39]. This approach also assumes that the charge distribution around an atom is radially symmetric so that the directional effects of hydrogen-bonding interactions are lost.

1.9 ELECTROSTATIC POTENTIALS

Unlike steric interactions, which drop off rapidly with distance, polar interactions have only a linear distance dependence. Hence, atoms other than immediate close neighbors can make a significant contribution to the polar interaction energy for a given atom. Because of this, it is, generally, necessary to take the contributions of all of the atoms in a molecule into account when determining its polar interactions.

This is most effectively accomplished using the concept of an electrostatic potential or field. The field at any given point around an isolated molecule is simply the sum of the contributions made by each of the atoms in the molecule to the potential, and is defined as the force that would be experienced by a unit positive charge positioned at that point. Note that the electrostatic potential is defined for a single isolated molecule. Bringing any form of charged species up to a molecule will induce some degree of polarization which will, in turn, serve to modify the overall potential. A similar effect would also be produced by surrounding a molecule by a polar solvent, even though both the molecule and the solvent might be formally uncharged.

Hence, it is dangerous to attach too rigorous a quantitative significance to the use of electrostatic potential displays or, for that matter, to polar interactions in general. They do, however, provide a very powerful qualitative tool, particularly in terms of studying the hydrogen-bonding capabilities of a molecule.

A common way of depicting electrostatic potentials is to calculate them for points lying on either the van der Waals or solvent-accessible surfaces and to display them as a series of color-coded dots or bands. This tends to give the impression, however, that the most important polar interactions all take place on the steric surface. Since electrostatic interactions attenuate only linearly with distance, this is not always the case and an alternative means of display is to determine the surface corresponding to a given electrostatic potential. Since the value of the potential is the same at all points on such a surface, this potential is commonly referred to as an isopotential.

By way of illustration, Fig. 1.3 (see color section) depicts the 15 kcal/mol isopotential surfaces for amiloride and its deschloro analog, the positive isopotential being shown in red and the negative one in blue. These were derived from an *ab initio* approach in which the isopotentials were calculated directly from the STO/3G (Slater Type Orbital 3-Gaussians) wave function. The basis set (STO-3G) generally reflects the degree of sophistication of the mathematical treatment of the atomic orbitals in the molecule and STO-3G represents a widely used minimal basis set for general-purpose calculations.

By calculating the isopotentials directly from the wavefunction, without performing a Mulliken population analysis, the directional orientation of the lone pair contributions is preserved, reflecting a more accurate description of the hydrogen-bonding capabilities of the molecule. In the figure, the isopotential surface has been suppressed where it penetrates the van der Waals surface of the molecule, since it would not be accessible in this region.

It has long been known that the presence of substituents on a conjugation pathway can have significant chemical consequences, and electrostatic and isopotential displays provide a sensitive means of studying such effects. As can be seen, the removal of the chlorine produces significant changes not only at the point of substitution, but also in more remote parts of the molecule. Hence, the size of the negative isopotential lobes around the carbonyl oxygen and *meta* pyrazine nitrogen atoms, which reflect principally the lone pair electron densities, are enhanced, considerably, in the deschloro analog. Similarly, a small isopotential lobe appears on the amine nitrogen *para* to the chlorine position. These changes imply corresponding differences in hydrogen-bonding ability and provide an additional insight into the marked loss of activity observed for the deschloro compound.

Used with appropriate discretion, isopotentials provide a powerful and sensitive way of comparing the hydrogen-bonding capabilities of a series of compounds and of systematically studying the influence of substituents. This can be particularly useful when attempting to compare molecules of substantial structural diversity which give rise to similar biological activity. As mentioned earlier, however, it is important to remember that these displays are only qualitative and that the calculations from which they are derived pertain to isolated molecules in the gas phase.

1.10   MACROMOLECULAR SYSTEMS

The theoretical calculation of the secondary and tertiary structures of even the smallest enzyme systems from the experimentally determined peptide sequence is a formidable task that is still, generally, well beyond the scope of current computer systems. Hence, although molecular modeling has been extensively applied to the study of proteins and enzymes, and more especially to the study of enzyme substrate interactions, almost all such studies have used X-ray crystallographic coordinates for the enzyme or protein under study, or a closely related analog, as their starting point.

Notwithstanding this limitation, where such information is available, molecular modeling can play an important role by making available a wide range of sophisticated structural displays. Fig. 1.4 (see color section) shows the X-ray crystallographic structure of tosyl-porcine pancreatic elastase [40,41]. To simplify the display, the normal convention of showing only the alpha carbon backbone has been adopted, although individual amino acid side chains are shown for residues close to the active site.

Although displays of this type provide detailed information on the precise nature of the active site and its steric and electronic requirements, the application of rigorous calculations to systems of this size is generally not feasible. In particular, the more stringent quantum mechanical techniques are almost always excluded. Hence, most of the computational techniques applicable to macromolecules have their origins in the molecular mechanics approach. Many of them use additional simplifying assumptions in an attempt to reduce the level of computational complexity, such as the united-atom approach in which a carbon and its directly attached hydrogens are treated as a single composite atom. Most of them have also been extensively parameterized to handle peptides, and often contain extensions to their force fields to provide more realistic treatment of hydrogen-bonding interactions.

Among the more widely used systems are the ECEPP (Empirical Conformational Energy Program for Peptides) of Momany *et al.* [42] (1975), the CHARMM (Chemistry at Harvard Macromolecular Mechanics) program of Brooks *et al.* [43] and the closely related AMBER (Assisted Model Building with Energy Refinement) of Weiner and Kollman [44]. These are used both for the study of enzyme substrate interactions and for the geometry optimization of structures derived by modifying the peptide sequence, or conformation, of an experimentally determined structure.

From a pharmaceutical perspective, one of the major applications of these systems lies in the study of enzyme substrate interactions, where the goal is frequently to discover a suitable inhibitor of the enzyme. This process is, however, more complex than it might appear on the surface and involves the relative energetics of the enzyme and substrate, both free in solution and complexed together. One of the major difficulties lies in the fact that the substrate is usually solvated, to a greater or lesser extent, when free in solution and is frequently forced to lose all, or part, of this on binding to the enzyme. In a similar manner, the enzyme-binding site is not necessarily empty prior to binding of the substrate. It too may be solvated when free so that binding of the substrate involves the expulsion of solvent from the binding site. Hence, the overall change in free energy, which is what determines the binding constant, may be difficult, if not impossible, to define accurately. Even without the complicating effects of differential solvation, some binding processes include the cooperative binding of a cofactor, the energetics of which would also need to be considered. Despite these difficulties, significant progress has already been made in a number of areas of major pharmaceutical significance.

One of the most extensively studied enzyme systems, using these techniques, has been dihydrofolate reductase. This enzyme catalyzes the reduction of dihydrofolate **4** to tetrahydrofolate **5** by means of hydride transfer from NADPH. Tetrahydrofolate derivatives are used in a variety of one-carbon transfer reactions coupled with the action of thymidylate synthetase [45], and the inhibition of DHFR has been employed in both the treatment of cancer and the development of antibacterial agents. Methotrexate **6** is a potent DHFR inhibitor with K_i values of about 10^{-10}M [46].

$R = p-C_6H_4CONHCH(CO_2H)CH_2CO_2H$

6

Fig. 1.5 (see color section) shows the X-ray crystallographic structure for methotrexate and NADPH bound to DHFR derived from *Lacto-bacillus casei* [47], showing the alpha carbon backbone for the enzyme together with methotrexate and NADPH. There are considerable differences in DHFR derived from various species, and Hansch *et al.* [35] have used molecular modeling, together with a variety of quantitative structure activity relationship (QSAR) techniques to study the binding of methotrexate 6 and trimethoprim 1, starting from the crystallographic data for DHFR derived from both *L. casei* [47] and *Escherichia coli* [34,48].

The X-ray data show conclusively that the active site of DHFR derived from *E. coli* is considerably more spacious than that from *L. casei*. This was used to explain differences in the observed binding energies of substrates to enzymes derived from these two sources. It was also proposed that the larger binding site associated with *E. coli* might allow for at least partial retention of solvation of the substrate on binding, a factor which could contribute significantly to the observed binding constant. In particular, computer graphics were used to demonstrate the tight fit of trimethoprim to the *L. casei* enzyme and its much looser fit to that derived from *E. coli*.

In spite of the strong binding of methotrexate 6 to DHFR, Andrews *et al.* [49] have predicted that it binds in a high-energy conformation, a result which is also supported by potential energy calculations [50]. Matthews *et al.* [47] have also proposed that methotrexate binds in an orientation that is rotated by 180° from that expected by direct comparison with the natural substrate (cf. the earlier discussion of trimethoprim 1), an argument for which there appears to be significant indirect support [51,52].

Blaney *et al.* [53] have also used crystallographic data [54,55] to study the interaction of thyroxine with prealbumen, using this as a model for the interaction of thyroid hormones with the nuclear thyroid hormone receptor [56]. By carefully examining the steric fit of a series of thyroid hormone analogs, an additional unused binding pocket was observed. Four new analogs were then designed to take advantage of this and shown to bind in a manner consistent with their ability to interact with the additional site.

The zinc-containing endopeptidase, thermolysin, has also been studied by a combination of crystallographic and molecular modeling techniques [57–59]. After examining the steric and polar interactions found by visually docking substrates into the enzyme, the authors proposed a model in which the formation of the Michaelis complex involved the coordination of the substrate via a water molecule, rather than directly to the zinc atom in the enzyme. The method of cleavage was also proposed to involve the formation of an intermediate tetrahedral complex in which the substrate coordinated to the zinc in a bidentate manner, causing the zinc to become pentacoordinate. This was shown to be consistent with experimentally determined hydrolysis data for the enzyme by Morihara and Tsuzuki [60].

In each of the above studies, the enzyme was treated, primarily, as a rigid molecule whose structure had been determined crystallographically. Hence, it is becoming increasingly clear that the future potential of computer-assisted drug design depends heavily on the availability of appropriate macromolecular crystallographic data. A key source in this regard is the Protein Data Bank†, which makes available a growing number of enzyme and protein coordinates in computer-readable form. Several major pharmaceutical companies also already have significant macromolecular crystallography groups 'in house', a trend which appears certain to continue in the future.

Given the importance of X-ray crystallographic data in the study of substrate binding, a number of techniques have been developed to automate the initial 'docking' of a potential substrate into an enzyme receptor site [61]. This approach has been used by DesJarlais *et al.* [62] to study the interaction of flexible ligands with receptor sites of known molecular geometry, on the basis of molecular shape. The method was applied both to the study of the binding of methotrexate to dihydrofolate reductase, and to the study of thyroxine to prealbumen, and provided predicted binding geometries for the substrates which indicated close steric fits with the receptor sites and were in close agreement with the crystallographic results.

With the advent of more powerful computer systems, it is now possible to begin applying these techniques to both the enzyme and the substrate, allowing optimization of the intact enzyme substrate complex. Rao *et al.* [63] have applied this approach to the binding of antitumor antibiotics related to anthramycin to various deoxydecanucleotides, used as models for DNA. Energy minimizations of the bound complexes were performed using the AMBER-UCSF program [44,64], and the binding was shown to produce very little distortion in the DNA double helix and to be relatively insensitive to sequence variation close to the complexation site. The conformational features of the complexes were also found to be generally consistent with results obtained from two-dimensional NMR NOE (Nuclear Overhauser Enchancement) studies of Graves *et al.* [65,66].

1.11 MOLECULAR DYNAMICS AND MONTE CARLO TECHNIQUES

The problem of encountering 'local' and 'false' minima during structure optimizations, referred to earlier in the chapter in the context of drug molecules, becomes an

† Protein Data Bank, Chemistry Department, Brookhaven National Laboratory, Upton, New York.

even more formidable problem when macromolecular systems are considered. The number of local energy minima for even the smallest enzyme or protein is very large, making it extremely difficult to sample the energy surface for them effectively. As one response to the problem of locating the global minimum, Crippen [67] has proposed the development of empirical potentials for conformational analysis, which are parameterized to place known crystal structures near well defined local minima.

An increasingly important approach is to provide the molecule with a certain amount of thermal energy, in the form of an initial set of translational, vibrational and torsional velocities, and to then 'follow' it computationally as it moves along its energy trajectory [68]. This process is analogous to sampling the conformation and behavior of a molecule undergoing random thermal motions at different points in time and is known as molecular dynamics.

A major attraction of this approach is that the molecule is now able to move over the energy surface so that there is a finite probability that it can jump from one conformational energy minimum to another rather than automatically becoming trapped in the first minimum encountered. For this reason, one of the early applications has been in the study of cyclic peptides [69] where it is difficult to explore conformational flexibility within the ring using a conventional molecular mechanics approach. Hagler [70] has also reviewed the application of the molecular dynamics approach to a broader range of peptides and proteins.

Although computationally intensive, molecular dynamics has been applied successfully to the study of enzyme–ligand complexes. Fujita [71] carried out a 27 ps simulation of the 1:2 enzyme–ligand complex between porcine pancreatic elastase (PPE) and the tripeptide acetyl–alanine–proline–alanine (APA) which involved sampling a total of some 450 structures. The study indicated the presence of hydrogen bonding between the two APA ligands, a feature that had not been found in the 1.65 Å crystallographic analysis. Note, however, the very short simulation period used in the study. This is a frequent limitation with molecular dynamics studies, and significantly reduces the probability that the system will undergo any high-energy transitions. The higher the energy of a conformational transition, the lower its probability, for a given thermal energy level; hence, the longer the system would need to be sampled in order to give rise to a reasonable probability that such a transition might occur.

A subsequent study [72] also examined the 1:1 complex between PPE and APA. This complex has not been studied crystallographically, and the acetyl group of APA was found to be able to occupy two distinct sites. One of these corresponds to the primary specificity site found in the crystal study of the 1:2 complex, whereas the second leaves the acetyl group projecting out into solution.

Virtually all the molecular dynamics calculations carried out to date employ a modified molecular mechanics force field. The method is not, however, intrinsically limited to this approach, and alternative implementations, such as the use of a semi-empirical method [73], have also been considered. The computational demands imposed by a dynamics approach do, however, impose severe limitations on the complexity of the force field that can be employed.

An alternative way of providing an effective sampling of the energy surface in a complex system is to use Monte Carlo simulation [74]. Jayaram *et al.* [75] studied the effect of hydration on the stability of dimethylphosphate and its sodium salt. The *gauche–trans* and *gauche–gauche* forms were found to be equally preferred in the case of the hydrated anion, but the *trans–trans* conformation was found to be energetically preferred for the sodium dimethylphosphate ion pair.

The Monte Carlo approach has been widely used in studying the effects of solvation, and Margheritis and Corongin [76] have applied it to the calculation of the *ab initio* potential for acetylcholine in aqueous solution. Their calculations indicate that acetylcholine contains around 38 water molecules in its global hydration shell and that there is relatively free rotation about the choline–acetate bond. Given the importance of solvation effects in determining enzyme–ligand binding constants, this is, clearly, an area of growing future importance.

Sophisticated molecular modeling capabilities are now available in virtually every major pharmaceutical company and it is clear that theoretical and graphical techniques will continue to play an increasingly important role in the new drug discovery process. Used appropriately, these provide a powerful insight into the chemical basis of biological activity. It is important, however, whenever possible, that theoretical studies are closely supported by experimental verification. Hence, the most effective applications are likely to be those which are interdisciplinary, combining theoretical predictions and analyses with crystallographic data and data derived from other important techniques such as NMR spectroscopy [77].

ACKNOWLEDGMENT

The author would like to express his appreciation of Drs C. L. Lerman, M. Waldman, R. F. Hout Jr., and B. B. Masek for assistance in preparing the structural displays.

REFERENCES

[1] Kennard, O., Watson, D. G., & Town, W. G. (1972). Cambridge Crystallographic Data Centre. I. Bibliographic file. *J. Chem. Doc.* **12,** 14.

[2] Allinger, N. L. (1976). Calculation of molecular structure and energy by force field methods. *Adv. Phys. Org. Chem.* **13,** 1.

[3] Dewar, M. J. S. & Thiel, W. (1977). Ground states of molecules. 38. The MNDO method. Approximations and parameters. *J. Am. Chem. Soc.* **99,** 4899.

[4] Crippen, G. M. (1982). Distance geometry analysis of the benzodiazepine binding site. *Mol. Pharmacol.* **22,** 11.

[5] Hendrickson, J. B. (1961). Molecular geometry. I. Machine computation of the common rings. *J. Am. Chem. Soc.* **83,** 4537.

[6] Wiberg, K. B. (1965). A scheme for strain energy minimization. Application to the cycloalkanes. *J. Am. Chem. Soc.* **87,** 1070.

[7] Lifson, S. & Warshel, A. (1968). Consistent force field calculations of conformations, vibrational spectra, and enthalpies of cycloalkane and *n*-alkane molecules. *J. Chem. Phys.* **49,** 5116.

[8] Abraham, R. J. & Parry, K. (1970). Rotational isomerism. VIII. A calculation of the rotational barriers and rotamer energies of some halogenated compounds. *J. Chem. Soc.* **B,** 539.

[9] Del Re, G. (1958). A simple M.O.L.C.A.O. method for calculating the charge distribution in saturated organic molecules. *J. Chem. Soc.* 4031.

[10] Momany, F. A. (1978). Determination of partial atomic charges from *ab-initio* molecular electrostatic potentials. Application to formamide, methanol and formic acid. *J. Phys. Chem.* **82,** 592.

[11] Abraham, R. J. & Hudson, B. (1984). Approaches to charge calculations in molecular mechanics. 2. Resonance effects in conjugated systems. *J. Comp. Chem.* **5,** 562.

[12] Abraham, R. J. & Smith, P. E. (1988). Charge calculations in molecular mechanics IV: a general method for conjugated systems. *J. Comp. Chem.* **9,** 288.

[13] Sprague, J. T., Tai, J. C., Yuh, Y., & Allinger, N. L. (1987). The MMP2 calculational method. *J. Comp. Chem.* **8,** 581.

[14] Allinger, N. L., Kok, R. A., & Imam, M. R. (1988). Hydrogen bonding in MM2. *J. Comp. Chem.* **9,** 591.

[15] Pople, J. A. & Segal, G. A. (1966). Approximate self-consistent field molecular orbital theory. III. CNDO results for AB_2 and AB_3 systems. *J. Chem. Phys.* **44,** 3289.

[16] Pople, J. A., Beveridge, D. L., & Dobosh, P. A. (1967). Approximate self-consistent orbital theory. V. Intermediate neglect of differential overlap. *J. Chem. Phys.* **47,** 2026.

[17] Baird, N. C. & Dewar, M. J. S. (1969). Ground state of sigma-bonded molecules. IV. M.I.N.D.O. method and its application to hydrocarbons. *J. Chem. Phys.* **50,** 1262.

[18] Dewar, M. J. S. & Haselbach, E. (1970). Ground states of sigma-bonded molecules. IX. The MINDO/2 method. *J. Am. Chem. Soc.* **72,** 590.

[19] Bingham, R. C., Dewar, M. J. S., & Lo, D. H. (1975). Ground states of molecules. XXV. MINDO/3: an improved version of the MINDO semi-empirical SCF-MO method. *J. Am. Chem. Soc.* **97,** 1285.

[20] Stewart, J. J. P. & Dewar, M. J. S. (1983). QCPE program 455, University of Indiana, Bloomington, Indiana.

[21] Dewar, M. J. S., Zoebish, E. G., Healy, E. F., & Stewart, J. J. P. (1985). AM1: a new general purpose quantum mechanical molecular model. *J. Am. Chem. Soc.* **107,** 3902.

[22] Mulliken, R. S. (1962). Criteria for the construction of good self-consistent field molecular orbital wave functions, and the significance of L.C.A.O. M.O. population analysis. *J. Chem. Phys.* **36,** 3428.

[23] Pople, J. A. & Gordon, M. (1967). Molecular orbital theory of the electronic structure of organic compounds. I. Substituent effects and dipole moments. *J. Am. Chem. Soc.* **89,** 4253.

[24] Stolow, R. D., Samal, P. W., & Giants, T. W. (1981). On CNDO/2-predicted charge alternation. *J. Am. Chem. Soc.* **103,** 197.

[25] Binkley, J. S., Whiteside, R. A., Krishman, R., Seeger, R., DeFrees, D. J., Schlegel, H. B., Topiol, S., Kahn, L. R., & Pople, J. A. (1981). Quantum Chemistry Program Exchange (QCPE) Program 406. University of Indiana, Bloomington, Indiana.

[26] Binkley, J. S., Frisch, M. J., DeFree, D. J., Raghavachari, K., Whiteside, R.

A., Schlegel, H. B., Fluder, E. M., & Pople, J. A. (1983). GAUSSIAN 82. Carnegie-Mellon University, Pittsburgh, Pennsylvania.

[27] Dupuis, M., Rys, J., & King, H. F. (1976). Evaluation of molecular integrals over Gaussian basis functions. *J. Chem. Phys.* **65**, 111.

[28] Dupuis, M., Spangler, D., & Wendolowski, J. J. (1980). NRCC software catalog 1, program QGO1. Lawrence Berkeley Laboratory, University of California, Berkeley, California.

[29] Van Alsenoy, C. (1988). *Ab initio* calculations on large molecules: the multiplicative integral approximation. *J. Comp. Chem.* **9**, 620.

[30] Loftus, P., Waldman, M., Hout, R. F., Jr., & Masek, B. B. (1985). Enigma™, ICI Pharmaceuticals Group, Wilmington, Delaware.

[31] Masek, B. B., Waldman, M., & Hout, R. F., Jr. (1987). Aesop™, ICI Pharmaceuticals Group, Wilmington, Delaware.

[32] Nachbar, R. B. & Mislow, K. (1982). QCPE program 514, University of Indiana, Bloomington, Indiana.

[33] Nachbar, R. B., Hounshell, W. P., Naman, V. A., Wennerstrom, O., Guenzi, A., & Mislow, K. (1983). Application of empirical force field calculations to internal dynamics in 9-benzyltriptycenes. *J. Org. Chem.* **48**, 1227.

[34] Baker, D. J., Bedell, C. R., Champness, J. N., Goodford, P., Norrington, F. E. A., Smith, D. R., & Stammer, D. (1981). The binding of trimethoprim to bacterial dihydrofolate reductase. *FEBS Lett.* **126**, 49.

[35] Hansch, C., Li, R., Blaney, J. M., & Langridge, R. (1982). Comparison of the inhibition of *Escherichia coli* and *Lactobacillus casei* dihydrofolate reductase by 2,4–diamino-5-(substituted benzyl) pyrimidines: quantitative structure–activity relationships, X-ray crystallography and computer graphics in structure activity analysis. *J. Med. Chem.* **25**, 777.

[36] Connolly, M. L. (1983). Solvent-accessible surfaces of proteins and nucleic acids. *Science* **221**, 709.

[37] Connolly, M. L. (1983). Analytical molecular surface calculations. *J. Appl. Crystallogr.* **16**, 548.

[38] Salama, A. I., Insalaco, J. R., & Maxwell, R. A. (1971). Concerning the molecular requirements for the inhibition of uptake of racemic ^{3}H-norepinephrine into rat cerebral cortex slices by tricyclic antidepressants and related compounds. *J. Pharmacol. Exp. Ther.* **178**, 474.

[39] Wiberg, K. B. (1979). Infrared intensities. The methyl halides. Effect of substituents on charge distributions. *J. Am. Chem. Soc.* **101**, 1718.

[40] Watson, H. C., Shotton, D. M., Cox, J. M., & Muirhead, H. (1970). Three-dimensional Fourier synthesis of tosly-elastase at 3.5 angstrom resolution. *Nature* **225**, 806.

[41] Shotton, D. M. & Watson, H. C. (1970). Three-dimensional structure of tosyl-elastase. *Nature* **225**, 811.

[42] Momany, F. A., McGuire, R. F., Burgess, A. W., & Scheraga, H. A. (1975). Energy parameters in polypeptides. VII. Geometric parameters, partial atomic charges, nonbonded interactions and intrinsic torsional potentials for the naturally occurring amino acids. *J. Phys. Chem.* **79**, 2361.

[43] Brooks, B. R., Bruccoleri, R. E., Olafson, B. D., States, D. J., Swaminathan,

S., & Karplus, M. (1983). CHARMM: a program for macromolecular energy minimization and dynamics calculations. *J. Comp. Chem.* **4**, 187.

[44] Weiner, P. K. & Kollman, P. A. (1981). AMBER: Assisted model building with energy refinement. A general program for modeling molecules and their interactions. *J. Comp. Chem.* **2**, 287.

[45] Hitchings, G. H. & Roth, B. (1980). Dihydrofolate reductases as targets for selective inhibitors. In: M. Sandler (ed.) *Enzyme Inhibitors as Drugs.* Macmillan, London.

[46] Colwell, W. T., Brown, V. H., Degraw, J. T., & Morrison, N. E. (1979). Inhibition of microbacterial dihydrofolate reductase by 2,4-diamino-6-alkylpteridines and deazapteridines. *Dev. Biochem.* 215.

[47] Matthews, D. A., Alden, R. A., Bolin, J. T., Filman, D. J., Freer, S. T., Suon, R., & Kraut, J. (1978). Dihydrofolate reductase from *Lactobacillus casei.* X-ray structure of the enzyme–methotrexate–NADPH complex. *J. Biol. Chem.* **253**, 6946.

[48] Matthews, D. A., Alden, R. A., Freer, S. T., Xuong, N. H., & Kraut, J. (1979). Dihydrofolate reductase from *Lactobacillus casei.* Stereochemistry of NADPH binding. *J. Biol. Chem.* **254**, 4144.

[49] Andrews, P. R., Craik, D. J., & Martin, J. L. (1984). Functional group contributions to drug–receptor interactions. *J. Med. Chem.* **27**, 1648.

[50] Spark, M. J., Winkler, D. A., & Andrews, P. R. (1982). Conformational analysis of folates and folate analogues. *Int. J. Quantum Chem., Quantum Biol. Symp.* **9**, 321.

[51] Fonticella-Camps, J. C., Bugg, C. E., Temple, C., Jr., Rose, J. D., Montgomery, J. A., & Kisliuk, R. L. (1979). Absolute configuration of biological tetrahydrofolates. A crystallographic determination. *J. Am. Chem. Soc.* **101**, 6114.

[52] Armarego, W. L. F., Waring, P., & Williams, J. W. (1980). Absolute configuration of 6-methyl-5,6,7,8-tetrahydropterin produced by enzymatic reduction (dihydrofolate reductase and NADPH) of 6-methyl-7,8-dihydropterin. *J. Chem. Soc., Chem. Commun.*, 334.

[53] Blaney, J. M., Jorgenson, E. C., Connolly, M. L., Ferrin, T. E., Langridge, R., Oatley, S. J., Burridge, J. M., & Blake, C. C. F. (1982). Computer graphics in drug design: molecular modeling of thyroid hormone–prealbumin interactions. *J. Med. Chem.* **25**, 785.

[54] Blake, C. C. F. & Oatley, S. J. (1977). Protein–DNA and protein–hormone interactions in prealbumin: a model of the thyroid hormone nuclear receptor. *Nature* **268**, 115.

[55] Blake, C. C. F., Geisow, M. J., Oatley, S. J., & Rerat, C. J. (1978). Structure of prealbumin: second, tertiary and quaternary interactions determined by Fourier refinement at 1.8 angstroms. *J. Mol. Biol.* **121**, 339.

[56] Eberhardt, N. L., Ring, J. C., Latham, K. R., & Baxter, J. D. (1979). Thyroid hormone receptors. Alterations of hormone binding specificity. *J. Biol. Chem.* **254**, 8534.

[57] Monzingo, A. F. & Matthews, B. W. (1984). Binding of N-carboxymethyl dipeptide inhibitors to thermolysin determined by X-ray crystallography: a

novel class of transition state analogues for zinc peptidases. *Biochemistry* **23,** 5724.

[58] Hangauer, D. G., Monzingo, A. F., & Matthews, B. W. (1984). An interactive computer graphics study of thermolysin-catalyzed peptide cleavage and inhibition by *N*-carboxymethyl dipeptides. *Biochemistry,* **23,** 5730.

[59] Bush, B. L., (1984). Interactive modeling of enzyme–inhibitor complexes at Merck Macromolecular Modeling graphics facility. *J. Comp. Chem.* **8,** 1.

[60] Morihara, K. & Tsuzuki, H. (1970). Thermolysin: kinetic study with oligopeptides. *Eur. J. Biochem.* **15,** 374.

[61] Kuntz, I. D. (1982). A geometric approach to macromolecular–ligand interactions. *J. Mol. Biol.* **161,** 269.

[62] DesJarlais, R. L., Sheridan, R. P., Dixon, J. S., Kuntz, I. D., & Venkataraghavan, R. (1986). Docking flexible ligands to macromolecular receptors by molecular shape. *J. Med. Chem.* **29,** 2149.

[63] Rao, S. N., Singh, U. C., & Kollman, P. A. (1986). Molecular mechanics simulations on covalent complexes between anthramycin and B DNA. *J. Med. Chem.* **29,** 2484.

[64] Weiner, P. K., Singh, U. C., Kollman, P. A., Caldwell, J. W., & Case, D. (1985). AMBER (UCSF) *Version 2.0,* Department of Pharmaceutical Chemistry, University of California, San Francisco, California.

[65] Graves, D. E., Pattaroni, C., Balakrishnan, M. S., Ostrander, J. M., Hurley, L. M., & Krugh, T. R. (1984). The reaction of anthramycin with DNA. Proton and carbon nuclear magnetic resonance studies on the structure of the anthramycin–DNA adduct. *J. Biol. Chem.* **259,** 8202.

[66] Graves, D. E., Stone, M. P., & Krugh, T. R. (1985). Structure of the anthramycin–d(ATGCAT)$_2$ adduct from one and two dimensional proton NMR experiments in solution. *Biochemistry* **24,** 7573.

[67] Crippen, G. M. (1987). Determination of an empirical energy function for protein conformational analysis by energy embedding. *J. Comp. Chem.* **8,** 972.

[68] Hermansson, K., Lie, G. C., & Clementi, E. (1988). On velocity scaling in molecular dynamics simulations. *J. Comp. Chem.* **9,** 200.

[69] Hagler, A. T., Osguthorpe, D. J., Dauber-Osguthorpe, P., & Hempel, J. C. (1985). Dynamics and conformational energetics of a peptide hormone: vasopressin. *Science* **227,** 1309.

[70] Hagler, A. T. (1985). Theoretical simulation of conformation, energetics and dynamics of peptides. *Peptides* **7,** 213.

[71] Fujita, T. (1987). A specific inhibitor design approach by means of molecular dynamics calculation for porcine pancreatic elastase. *J. Comp. Chem.* **8,** 645.

[72] Fujita, T. & Meyer, E. F., Jr. (1987). Molecular dynamics simulation of the 1:1 enzyme–ligand complex between porcine pancreatic elastase and acetyl-alanine–proline–alanine. *J. Comp. Chem.* **8,** 801.

[73] Stewart, J. J. P., Davis, L. P., & Burggraf, L. W. (1988). Semi-empirical calculations of molecular trajectories: method and application to some simple molecular systems. *J. Comp. Chem.* **8,** 1117.

[74] Metropolis, N., Rosenbluth, A. W., Rosenbluth, M.N., Teller, A. H., & Teller, E. (1953). Equation-of-state calculations by fast computing machines. *J. Chem. Phys.* **21,** 1087.

[75] Jayaram, B., Mezei, M., & Beveridge, D. L. (1987). Monte Carlo study of the aqueous hydration of dimethylphosphate conformations. *J. Comp. Chem.* **7,** 917.

[76] Margheritis, C. & Corongiu, G. (1988). Acetylcholine in water: ab-initio potential and Monte Carlo simulation. *J. Comp. Chem.* **9,** 1.

[77] Moos, W. H., Humblet, C. C., Sircar, I., Rithner, C., Weishaar, R. E., Bristol, J. A., & McPhail, A. T. (1987). Cardiotonic agents. 8. Selective inhibitors of adenosine 3′,5′-cyclic phosphate (cAMP) phosphodiesterase-III (PDE-III). Elaboration of a 5-point model for positive inotropic activity, *J. Med. Chem.* **30,** 1963.

2

Quantitative structure–activity relationships

W. J. Dunn III
University of Illinois at Chicago, College of Pharmacy, Chicago, Illinois USA

2.1 INTRODUCTION AND HISTORICAL DEVELOPMENT OF THE STUDY OF QUANTITATIVE STRUCTURE–ACTIVITY RELATIONSHIPS, OR QSAR

During the period of the middle to late nineteenth century some of the most significant discoveries in chemistry were made. It was just prior to this time that urea was synthesized and organic chemistry had its beginnings. This was followed by a period where chemists were involved in characterizing elements and compounds by studying their physical properties. From this came the various mathematical laws which chemists, such as van't Hoff and Arrhenius, discovered to explain the behavior of chemical systems. These laws were stated explicitly in mathematical form.

It was also at this time that chemists became interested in the effects that various naturally occurring compounds had on biological systems. It was only natural for Crum-Brown and Frazer to propose in 1868 that the basis for the physiological action of organic compounds was their physicochemical structure [1]. In this paper, it was also proposed that relationships between physiological activity and chemical structure could be expressed within the framework of mathematics in the same way that structure–property relationships could be expressed.

The first workers to systematically study relationships between chemical structure and biological activity were Meyer [2] and Overton [3,4] who, independently, were studying the relationship between structure and potency of general anesthetics. There was much interest in the use of general anesthetics, such as chloroform, methylene chloride, etc., in surgery. Using such species as goldfish, they showed that narcotic potency, defined operationally as an observable, reversible anesthetic effect, was proportional to the distribution coefficient of the compounds between water and olive oil. These relationships were not demonstrated mathematically, either in equation or in graphic form. It should be pointed out that the relationship proposed here is between biological activity and a physichochemical property of the active agents. This assumes that measured physicochemical properties contain information about the structure of the compound and that this information can be used to explain biological effects. This assumption is fundamental to early QSAR development.

The first published QSAR, to this author's knowledge, was included in a report by Furukawa [5] who showed that the local anesthetic effect of salicylate esters was a function of molecular size. Furukawa defined molecular size as the number of carbon atoms in the ester function. This QSAR is significant for two reasons: (1) it is the first mathematical expression of a structure–activity relationship and (2) the structures of the members of the series of active compounds are not expressed as a measured, physicochemical property but as a parameter obtained directly from the chemical structures of the compounds.

There was no significant work in the area of structure and activity until the work of Hansch et al. [6] on the relationship between structure and plant growth regulating activity of phenoxyacetic acids (1) was published in 1962. Hansch and his coworkers were trying to explain the variation in activity of these compounds and proposed that

1

activity was a function of the Hammett σ-constant [7] and a new substituent constant π. This is shown in equation (2.1). The term $\log 1/C$ is the biological activity, where C is the molar concentration required to give a standard, predetermined response from the biological system. This convention was suggested by Hansch. Expressed in this way, biological activity is obtained from dose–response data and it puts biological activity on an increasing scale. Other indices have been proposed and used, but this parameter is the one of choice.

$$\log 1/C = a + b\sigma_k + c\pi_k \tag{2.1}$$

Here the Hammett σ-constant is a substituent constant derived from the ionization constant, K_H, of benzoic acid and that of an appropriate benzoic acid derivative, denoted by k, as shown in equation (2.2).

$$\log K_k - \log K_H = \rho\, \sigma_k \tag{2.2}$$

Substituents with $\sigma_k > 0$ are electron withdrawing and acid strengthening while those with $\sigma_k < 0$ are electron-donating and acid-weakening. Hammett found that this effect of substitution on benzoic acid ionization could be extended to a large number of organic reactions through what were termed linear free energy relationships, LFERs.

π_k is a substituent constant analogous to σ_k and is related to the partition coefficient, P, for a compound between 1-octanol and water by equation (2.3). Hansch suggested that 1-octanol be used as a model for lipoidal phases in the biological system, as this solvent was much more convenient to work with than naturally occurring solvents such as olive and other vegetable oils that were used in earlier studies. Other solvents, such as hexane, chloroform and ether, have been used, but 1-octanol is the solvent of choice. In addition, it seems to work, and a very convincing case has been made for considering minimal hydrophobicity, as defined by the 1-octanol model, in the drug design process [8].

Substituents with $\pi_k > 0$ are said to be lipophilic (relative to the substituent H) and those with $\pi_k < 0$ are hydrophilic.

$$\log P_k - \log P_H = \pi_k \tag{2.3}$$

Equation (2.3) was not completely satisfactory in explaining the activity of the phenoxyacetic acids. It was, however, consistent with Hammett relationships and the current thinking of electronic effects on organic reactions as held by physical organic chemists at that time.

Only when a second-order term in π was added to equation (2.3) was there satisfactory agreement between observed and predicted values of activity [9]. This leads to equation (2.4)

$$\log 1/C = a + b\sigma_k + c\pi_k + d\pi_k^2 \tag{2.4}$$

which has been termed the Hansch model for QSAR. The theoretical origin of the second-order term has been shown to result from a mechanism in which there is differential transport to the active site [10], and this transport is related to the relative lipophilicity of the members of the series. This can also be explained by proposing competing equilibria for binding of the compounds at the active site [11].

The Hansch model, in its simplest form, i.e. $b = 0$ in equation (2.4), is a parabola. This function has a maximum in log P which can be obtained from the appropriate mathematical operations on equation (2.4). There have been several proposals made to improve the modeling of structure with activity which are essentially alternatives to the Hansch model, and the two most notable of these are by Martin [12] and Kubinyi [13]. Martin's model is essentially hyperbolic whereas Kubinyi's model is termed 'bilinear'.

During an approximate period of 15 years following the publication by Hansch *et al.* [6] of their parabolic model for QSAR, many examples of the use of this model were published. A review of these examples has appeared [14]. However, the Hansch approach has one major shortcoming and that is that it cannot deal with the inactive case. It will be shown in following discussions that it is basically a special case of the overall general QSAR problem, which, in its broadest sense, includes a solution to the problem of the relationship between chemical structure and activity but also a solution to the problem of chemical structure and inactivity.

The basic question Hansch was trying to answer was what quantitative change in activity would be associated with a change in chemical structure in (**1**). A more general approach would be to first determine if an analog of **1** would be active or inactive and then to predict its level of activity if it were predicted to be active. This makes the problem of QSAR first one of classification followed by prediction of a level of activity. Classification problems were first studied by the great English statistician, Fisher, who proposed in 1928 [15] a method for discriminating one group or category of objects from another. This method is now referred to as linear discriminant analysis [16]. It has found some use in QSAR [17,18], but it is now considered to be of very limited utility [19] here. However, it will be discussed later but mainly because of its historical significance.

In the early 1970s, reports of the use of classification methods in QSAR began to appear [20–23]. Classification techniques will be referred to as pattern recognition methods. Early reports of applications of methods of pattern recognition, mainly with linear discriminant analysis or its variant, the linear learning machine [24], are significant only because they were efforts to extend the traditional QSAR methodologies to the problem of classification. It was not until the late 1970s with the development of the SIMCA method of pattern recognition [25] that there was a general solution to the QSAR problem. Until this time, approaches to the problem of classification had been based on linear discriminant analysis and the linear learning machine. These methods *discriminate* between classes of object as opposed to modeling class *similarities*. Understanding the difference is a critical and important point for those who wish to obtain QSAR models with optimal predictability. In the next sections, the QSAR data set and the data making it up, which includes biological activities and chemical descriptors, will be discussed. This will be followed by a discussion of the various data-analytic methods which can be applied and the information which can be extracted.

2.2   THE QSAR DATA SET

It is instructive here to discuss the point at which QSAR enters into the drug design process. At the beginning of a drug design project, a lead compound is identified. The problem of identifying lead compounds is usually considered to be outside the realm of classical QSAR but the recent work of Martin [26] has shown that computer-assisted database searching for substructures can be used to discover leads. While substructure searching is not a traditional QSAR study, it is worthy of mentioning here since it is a form of pattern recognition. Computer-assisted methods are necessary when visual inspection of a large number of structures becomes impractical. Substructure searching is used to find a set of atoms with geometries similar to those found in compounds which are confirmed to have a given type of activity. The searching is done on a large data base, and, depending on the conditions placed on the searching algorithm, can be fast or very time-consuming. It can find compounds which have a higher than chance probability of having a given type of activity, and once a lead compound is identified, a set of compounds is designed and synthesized for further testing.

Following lead identification, an efficient lead optimization study based on methods of experimental design [27] should be carried out. This has only recently been realized, and while this should be considered a formal part of QSAR studies, only a few reports have appeared in the literature on this subject [28–30] and thus will not be discussed here. For optimal predictability, the QSAR should be based on data from a well designed study.

The basic QSAR data set is given in Fig. 2.1. The compound index is k. The

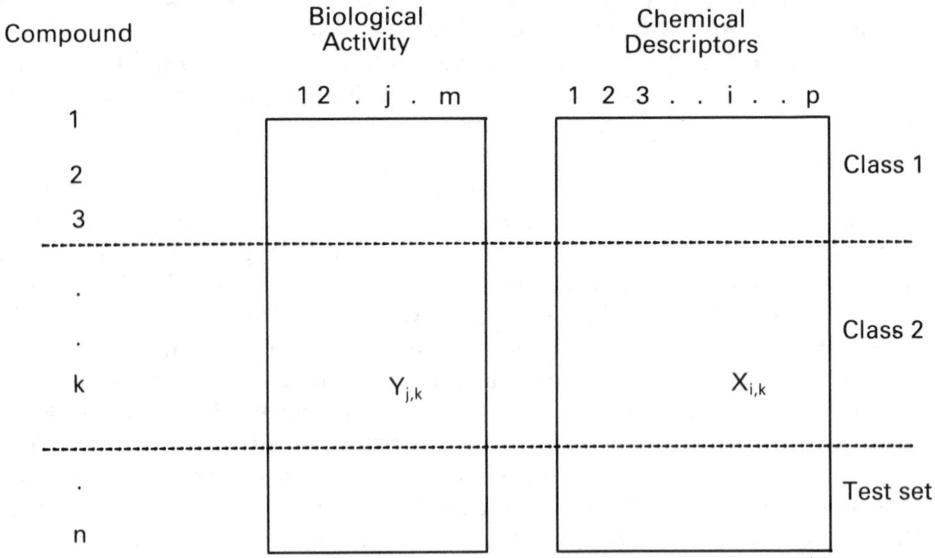

Fig. 2.1.

chemical data are noted by **X** and the biological data are noted by **Y**. The data are presented in bold print to indicate matrix notation. The elements of the matrices are indicated as x and y with i an index for chemical variables whereas index j is for a specific biological activity measurement. Thus $x_{i,k}$ is the chemical descriptor i for compound k and $y_{j,k}$ is the biological activity in system j for compound k. There are m biological activity measurements and p chemical descriptors for n compounds. Thus the order of the biological activity matrix is n(rows) $\times$ m(columns) whereas the order of the chemical descriptor matrix is n(rows) $\times$ p(columns).

If the QSAR study involves classification, the compounds can be divided into categories or classes with the division guided by the researcher's prior knowledge of their category. The objective of classification studies is to use the chemical data alone or the chemical and biological data together to derive rules which can be used to classify compounds of unknown activity. The classes in Fig. 2.1 are called, in pattern recognition terminology, the *training sets*. The compounds of unknown activity are called the *test sets*. The training and test sets are usually congeners or chemically similar compounds. There is no requirement in QSAR or the statistical literature that this be the case, however, and with the use of appropriate descriptors, compounds of diverse structure can be placed in the training and test sets. In addition to chemical similarity, pharmacological similarity is also assumed for the training compounds. Pharmacological similarity implies that the compounds exert their effect by the same mechanism. This assumption is rarely satisfied in most QSAR studies.

The terms above also apply if the data analysis involves classical Hansch modeling. Here the objective is to derive a predictive regression model from the training set and predict the activities of the test compounds. The difference in classification and Hansch modeling is that different data-analytic methods are applied in each case. Also, a Hansch analysis requires the assumption that all of the compounds in the data matrix have a measurable activity while pattern recognition techniques can be applied even if some of the training and test compounds are inactive.

In the classical Hansch analysis there is usually only one **Y** variable which will lead to a predictive model as in equation (2.1). There is no reason that more than one **Y** variable be measured on each compound resulting in more than one model if the data analysis is done using multiple regression.

2.2.1   Information obtained from a QSAR study
Once a lead compound has been identified and a series of congeners has been designed and tested, the next step in a drug design project is to propose a new compound or new compounds for evaluation. These are now the test set, and if QSARs have been developed for the training set(s), these can be applied to the test set.

Four levels of information are possible from QSAR [19]. At the first level the objective of a QSAR study is to predict whether a new compound will be a member of one of two or more defined classes of pharmacological agents. An example is whether a new compound will be an agonist or antagonist of a specific receptor or a substrate or inhibitor for an enzyme. It must be known in advance that the test compound is a member of one of the training sets.

At level two, the objective is to predict that a test compound is a member of one of the training sets with the additional possibility that it may be an outlier to the training sets. Therefore additional information is obtained at this level.

At levels one and two, only a class assignment is known for the training set members. At level three, in addition to having the class assignments for the training compounds, one continuous activity is available for each compound. Here the objective is to first classify test compounds as at level two and in a subsequent analysis predict the level of activity.

If more than one measure of biological activity is available for each member of the training sets, an activity matrix results. At level four, a classification at level two is formulated and this is followed by prediction of the activity matrix. An example of a QSAR study which is a level-four analysis is prediction of the carcinogenic potential for a compound based on its profile in a battery of tests [31].

When designing a QSAR study, it is helpful to consider the problem in terms of these four levels, since the level of information required must be considered when selecting a method of data analysis to be used. This will be discussed in a later section.

2.2.2   The biological activity data
In the strictest interpretation of the Hansch approach to developing QSARs, the biological activities for the compounds under study should come from dose–response

data. This is not always possible, and relative response data from a single treatment of the same concentration are frequently reported for each member of a series. This is much less expensive than using dose–response data but can introduce error into the data if the measurement to which the data are normalized contains error. If classification methods are to be applied to the data, only binary data, such as active or inactive, are necessary.

2.2.3   The chemical descriptor data

The chemical descriptor data are the most critical aspect of the QSAR problem. It may be argued that the biological activity data are more important, but this is true only when highly accurate activity data are required. Such data are very difficult and expensive to obtain. Even with binary biological activities or qualitative ranking data such as $+ + +$, $+ +$, $+$, for a series, considerable information can be obtained from a QSAR study with appropriate data-analytical techniques, since the analysis can be carried out on the chemical descriptor data alone.

In developing a strategy for chemical description, one must consider the structures of the compounds. The assumption of chemical similarity discussed above requires that the compounds be described so as to be similar. In general, two types of descriptor can be used. The first are descriptors which are derived from a consideration of the total structure of the compound. An example would be log P, boiling point, molecular weight, etc. A disadvantage of the use of molecular descriptors such as log P is that they are experimental data. In some cases, reliable estimates can be obtained from empirical calculations, but these estimates are, at times, suspect owing to approximations which must be made. An advantage of the use of these descriptors is that if the compounds they describe do not appear to be similar in a classical sense, they are defined or described to be similar.

The partition coefficient is perhaps the most important parameter used in drug design and QSAR studies. Therefore, many methods have been explored for its estimation. One such method is the Hansch π-constant approach based on equation (2.3), which assumes that the π-constant from one parent system can be used in another. This extrapolation has been shown to fail in many cases. An alternative has been proposed by Rekker [32] based on hydrophobic fragment constants. This approach is also based on equation (2.5), and assumes additivity as the π-constant method does.

$$\log P = \sum a_n f_n \tag{2.5}$$

Using this equation, a structure is broken down into defined fragments, n, and their contribution to log P is the product of its fragmental value and the number of times, a, it appears in the structure. The fragmental constants are obtained from experimental log P data and are the averages of their contributions in a number of solutes. Equation (2.5) provides much better estimates of log P, since the fragmental constants used are usually obtained from a large number of log P values. A variation of this approach is used in the log *P* estimation program, CLOGP, which is available from the Pomona College Medicinal Chemistry Project [33].

More recently, a new method of estimating log *P* for a compound has been proposed [34] based on a cavity model and solute surface area. The solvent accessible surface area as defined by Lee and Richards [35] is calculated for the solute supermolecule [36]. Two solute surface areas are significant. The first is the isotropic surface area, which is defined as that associated with the non-polar part of the super molecule. The second surface is the fraction of the solute surface which is hydrated. The log *P* for the solute is calculated from regression models with these two variables. The models are calibrated from over 400 experimental log *P* values in six water–non-polar solvent systems.

If the compounds in the series are analogs of a parent structure, such as **1** above, substituent constants such as Hammett σ, Hansch π, group molar refractivity (MR), molecular shape analysis, MSA, parameters [37], etc., can be used. Most of these parameters can be obtained from tabulations [33], which is a distinct advantage.

$$^{+}H_3N-CH(R_1)-CONH-CH(R_2)-CONH-CH(R_3)-COO^{-}$$ **2**

One class of molecules which has proved difficult to treat using classical QSAR methology is the peptides. The main reason for this is that descriptors are not readily available describing the structural variation within a class of peptides, in this case tripeptides such as **2**. It has not been possible to obtain a universal set of descriptors for the R-groups in **2**. This problem has been solved, in part, by Hellberg *et al.* [38] who compiled 29 measured experimental variables for the 20 naturally occurring amino acids. The result was a 20×29 matrix from which the three largest principal components (principal components analysis will be discussed later) were extracted. The resulting three principal component scores, which represent the projection coordinates of each amino acid side chain from a 29-dimensional hyperspace to 3-dimensional space, are called latent variables. Hellberg *et al.* [38] refer to them as principal properties, as they are the result of a linear combination of the original 29 variables. The principal properties can be used as independent variables in classical QSAR studies or with other data-analytic techniques to derive predictive models for peptides [38].

2.3   DATA ANALYTIC METHODS FOR QSAR STUDIES

Once a lead compound has been identified and a series of analogs has been synthesized and tested, a data table such as Fig. 2.1 will result. In the next phase of the design project, QSAR methodology can be used to explore and develop relationships between the two data blocks. Selecting the appropriate method is a function of the type of information required for the drug design project. Also the nature of the data which is to be analyzed must be considered if models with optimal predictability are to result. In the next sections are discussions of two of the most useful data-analytic methods: multiple linear regression and principal components analysis and its variation, partial least squares regression analysis.

2.3.1 Multiple linear regression

There are many approaches one can take when discussing a technique such as multiple linear regression which is so commonly used in chemistry. One can take the point of view of a statistician and dwell on the more mathematical aspects of the method. One of the best discussions of multiple linear regression from this direction is by Bergman and Gittins [39]. This discussion also contains some very useful advice regarding the use and misuse of multiple linear regression. Some of these will be pointed out here.

Multiple linear regression and its use will be developed with an emphasis on that of the chemist as discussed recently by Geladi and Kowalski [40]. One must be cautious here, however, because developing QSAR has its unique problems and some of the more significant misuses of multiple linear regression in QSAR have resulted from researchers not paying heed to these.

There are some key assumptions understood when multiple linear regression is applied to data. The first is that the x_is are independent and relevant to the problem. It is also assumed that the x_is can be measured or determined precisely relative to the dependent variables, y_k. The first assumption is seldom met and the result is some degree of collinearity in the descriptor data. It is well known that the biological activities observed have more uncertainty than the chemical data, especially if the biological response is from an *in vivo* assay. This may not be the case if the **Y** data are from an *in vitro* system such as an enzyme assay or receptor preparation.

In statistical terminology, the Hansch model for QSAR is a general linear model. This assumes from a column in Fig. 2.1 that there are n dependent variables y_1, $y_2, \ldots, y_k, \ldots, y_n$. Each y is assumed to be linearly related to a set of p observations, $x_{i,k}$. This general linear model is given in equation (2.6).

$$y_k = \beta_1 x_{1,k} + \beta_i x_{i,k} + \beta_p x_{p,k} + \varepsilon_k \tag{2.6}$$

The βs are coefficients for the x terms and the εs are the error terms for each y. The x_i are called independent variables and the y_k are the dependent variables. There are n dependent and p independent variables.

Equation (2.6) can be expressed graphically in matrix form as equation (2.7)

$$
\begin{array}{cccc}
n \times 1 & n \times p & p \times 1 & n \times 1 \\
\boxed{y} & = \boxed{\mathbf{X}} & \boxed{\beta} & + \boxed{\varepsilon}
\end{array}
\tag{2.7}
$$

where y is an $n \times 1$ column vector, $\mathbf{X}$ is the $n \times p$ chemical descriptor matrix, β is the $p \times 1$ coefficient vector and ε is the $n \times 1$ vector of residuals. The key to using multiple linear regression is to find a stable solution to the coefficient vector.

Recalling that there are n compounds and p descriptors it can be shown that the stability of the coefficient vector depends on the number of compounds relative to the number of descriptors. If $p > n$, there are more variables than compounds and the number of solutions for β in equation (2.7) is infinite. This is certainly not ideal, but examples have appeared in the QSAR literature of use of multiple linear regression under these conditions.

In the case where $p = n$, the number of compounds and variables is the same. The least squares treatment gives a unique solution for the β vector provided that the x_is are independent. In QSAR development there is almost always some redundancy in the independent variables so very seldom are the x_is truly independent.

The last case is that with $p < n$ or there are fewer independent variables than compounds in the regression analysis. An exact solution for β cannot be obtained, but a 'best' estimate can be by minimizing the length of the residual vector, ε. Multiple linear regression estimates the set of coefficients, β, which minimizes the residual sum of squares, $\Sigma(\varepsilon)^2$ thus the 'least squares method'.

This least squares solution is given in equation (2.8),

$$\beta = (\mathbf{X}'\mathbf{X})^{-1}\mathbf{X}'y \tag{2.8}$$

where $\mathbf{X}'$ is the transpose of $\mathbf{X}$. If there is a high degree of collinearity in the $\mathbf{X}$ data, $(\mathbf{X}'\mathbf{X})^{-1}$ may not exist, which is one of the most serious problems with multiple linear regression. If the inverse, $(\mathbf{X}'\mathbf{X})^{-1}$, exists and a stable estimate of the β vector is obtained, a QSAR is obtained.

It is instructive at this point to develop some tools for evaluating the significance of the QSAR. The first is based on the variance, which is defined as a sum of squares of residuals per degree of freedom in a calculation. In the case of the y_ks, a sum of squares of residuals, ss_1, about the mean, y, can be calculated from equation (2.9). This is the total variation in the data.

$$ss_1 = \sum(y_{j,k} - y)^2 = ss_2 + ss_3 = \sum(y_{j,k} - y)^2 + \sum(y_{j,k} - y_{j,k})^2 \tag{2.9}$$

The total variation is composed of two parts: a systematic part explained by regression, ss_2, and the unexplained variation, ss_3. The residual variance from regression can also be calculated as in equation (2.10) where p is the number of variables in the regression. $y_{j,k}$ is the regression prediction for $y_{j,k}$. Variance is the variation per degree of freedom; thus the total variance is given in equation (2.10).

$$\mathbf{S}_1 = ss_1/(n-1) \; ss_1 = \sum(y_{j,k} - y)^2/(n-1) \tag{2.10}$$

The explained variance from regression, $\mathbf{S}_2$, and the residual variance, $\mathbf{S}_3$, can also be calculated as in equation)2.10) where the denominator is the appropriate number of degrees of freedom for the calculation.

The F-test can be used in hypotheses testing to determine the significance of a particular variable in a regression model. This is equivalent to the null hypothesis, $\beta_i = 0$. The F-test is a comparison of the variance explained by regression after variable i is added to the model to that explained before it is added.

$$F = [(ss_2)_{after}/(ss_2)_{before}](n - p) \tag{2.11}$$

If the null hypothesis is true, i.e. $\beta_i = 0$, the F ratio approaches 1 and there is no statistical basis for including the new variable. If the ratio is greater than 1, the level of significance in the variance explained by the new variable can be obtained from standard F tables in statistics texts or handbooks. In many QSAR reports, the significance of a regression model has been based on an overall F-test which is a comparison of the variance explained by the regression model with that of the mean. This can be misleading, as a significant equation can contain an insignificant variable. It is recommended here that only the sequential F-test be used. This is significant to using the t-test for variable significance. Also, the 95% confidence interval can be used to determine the significance of a term in the model.

Another statistic which is used to test the significance of a QSAR is the correlation coefficient, r, or its square, r^2. This statistic is a ratio of the variance explained by a model to that about the mean. It can be interpreted intuitively since as the residuals in equation (2.7) go to zero, ss_2 goes to 0 and r^2 goes to 1.

$$r^2 = (ss_1 - ss_2)/ss_1 \tag{2.12}$$

Using the correlation coefficient alone to justify a model should never be done. The initial assumptions made when multiple linear regression is selected should be recalled. It is assumed that the relationship between y_k and the x_is is linear and that y_k may contain error of measurement. Therefore, the residuals can have variation from two sources: model error and measurement error. Measurement error can be determined, but model error cannot; one never knows whether the correct model has been selected. Therefore, an observed $r^2 > 0.95$ in QSAR studies is probably fortuitous.

The most significant result from a QSAR study is a predictive model. This makes model validation an important part of QSAR research. The predictability of a model should be tested on compounds that were not used in its derivation as is done with the jack-knife methods [39]. Such techniques insure the internal consistency of the training data. It is best to select a test set from the set of active congeners prior to model development and use these compounds for model validation.

One of the main problems with multiple linear regression is its tendency in QSAR to give spurious or chance correlations. This has been discussed by Topliss and Edwards [41] and it results from beginning with too many independent variables relative to dependent variables in the model development step. Referring to Fig. 2.1, there should be no fewer than five compounds for each chemical descriptor, or $n > 5p$, used in the model development phase. Some researchers interpret this to mean that there should be five compounds for each descriptor found to be significant in the final model.

2.3.2 Principal components regression
One of the most powerful data analysis techniques for use in QSAR is principal components analysis. It has not received much attention for a number of reasons, the

main one being that it is not a technique familiar to chemists. Principal components analysis is a data reduction method, which compresses data into abstract, 'latent' variables which are difficult to interpret. This is a disadvantage if the objective of the QSAR study is to obtain indirect evidence for a particular mode of action for the series of compounds under analysis. An advantage of principal components analysis is that it can be used as a basis for pattern recognition [25] in classification studies at levels 1, 2 and 3 as discussed above [19]. This use of the method will be discussed later.

The problem of too many variables leading to overfitting with multiple linear regression can be circumvented by the use of methods which are not sensitive to chance or spurious correlations. One of these techniques is principal components regression [40]. This procedure works by first applying principal components analysis to the **X** matrix to extract latent variables. These latent variables are then used as the independent variables with multiple linear regression to derive QSARs. This is diagrammed below and given as equation (2.13).

$$n \times p \quad 1 \times p \quad n \times 1 \quad 1 \times p \quad n \times 1 \quad 1 \times p \quad n \times p$$

$$\mathbf{X} = \mathbf{x} + t\, b + t\, b + \mathbf{E}$$

$$x_{i,k} = \mathbf{x} + \sum_{a=1}^{A} t_{i,a} b_{a,k} + e_{i,k} \tag{2.13}$$

In equation (2.13), A is the number of principal components or product terms in the model, $\mathbf{x}$ is the mean vector of the columns and e the residuals. The method has least squares properties since the residuals become small as A approaches p. Principal components analysis reduces the elements of the residual matrix, $\mathbf{E}$, to some predetermined small value. In equation (2.13), two principal components of a possible p are calculated from $\mathbf{X}$. The ts are then used in multiple linear regression as independent variables.

As mentioned above, the problem with principal components analysis is that it tends to convert variables which the chemist is comfortable with, to abstract variables which are linear combinations of the original data. Therefore, the latent variables seldom have a straightforward interpretation. The other side of this is that, in a number of cases, a unique physical interpretation of physicochemical data is usually not possible. It is well known that variables such as log P and molar refractivity, for example, are highly correlated and can in many cases be used interchangeably in regression models.

Another problem with principal components analysis is that the ts are extracted from $\mathbf{X}$ along the principal axes of variation in $\mathbf{X}$. In QSAR studies, the variables of interest are those correlated with the variation in the **Y** data, and the latent variables are not necessarily those of interest in QSAR. The next technique, partial least squares regression, has been developed to address this problem in QSAR [42].

2.3.3 Partial least squares regression
Partial least squares regression is outlined in equations (2.14)–(2.16) below.

$$x_{i,k} = \sum_{a=1}^{A} t_{i,a} b_{a,k} + e_{i,k} \qquad\qquad (2.14)$$

$$y_{i,j} = \sum_{a=1}^{A} u_{i,a} q_{a,j} + e_{i,j} \qquad\qquad (2.15)$$

$$u = d^* t \rightarrow y = t^* d^* q \qquad\qquad (2.16)$$

It is assumed with this method that there is systematic variation in **X** and **Y** that is correlated. The ts and us are principal components like latent variables and the bs and qs the corresponding loadings. The latent variables are extracted along the axes of greatest variation within the two data matrices, **X** and **Y** from Fig. 2.1, that are both *systematic and correlated*. With partial least squares regression, the ts and us can be thought of as principal components scores which have been weighted by the correlation between the two blocks. This differs from principal components analysis which extracts only systematic variation from the two matrices and does not consider correlation. This leads to equation (2.16), the inner relation for the correlation between the ts and us which can be used to predict y_ks from the x_js.

An advantage of partial least squares regression is that it can be used in the case in which there are more independent variables than compounds, or when $p > n$. Under these conditions, multiple linear regression gives unstable estimates of the β-vector. Partial least squares regression is the method of choice in QSAR when biological data are obtained in several screeens for the members of a series of compounds. It can also be used as a basis for pattern recognition when classification is desired. This aspect of QSAR studies will be discussed in the next sections.

2.4 PATTERN RECOGNITION AND CLASSIFICATION
Pattern recognition is an important aspect of drug design and development. Those trained in medicinal chemistry and pharmacology, in most cases, can recognize the type of activity a compound will have from its two-dimensional structure. The process of recognition is based on the researcher's experience and knowledge of receptors and the endogenous substances which interact with them in biological systems.

There are three basic types of pattern recognition as used in QSAR. They have recently been discussed in detail [43]. The first group of methods are the hyperplane or class discrimination methods. Examples are the linear learning machine [24] and linear discriminant analysis [16]. This first group of methods can only operate at level 1 as discussed earlier. This requires that the test compounds be members of the training sets, a condition seldom met in QSAR. As with multiple linear regression, they cannot be used when the number of descriptors, p, approaches the number of compounds, n, in each training set. The hyperplane methods select variables which *discriminate* between classes. In QSAR, the objective is to model the variation about the means of classes, not to discriminate between class means. This is an important point when a QSAR problem is formulated.

The second group of methods are the distance methods which make a class assignment on the basis of the distances of a test compound to its known nearest neighbors. The most commonly used method is the k-nearest-neighbor method [44]. This method operates at level two, and has been used in a number of early QSAR studies. Since it cannot be used to predict the level of activity of a test compound it has limited utility in QSAR.

The third group of pattern recognition methods is the class modeling methods. The only one of this group in use in QSAR is SIMCA pattern recognition [25], which incorporates classification and prediction of the level of activity in its methodology. These results are classification at levels three and four. SIMCA is the only method which operates at levels three and four.

2.4.1 How pattern recognition methods work

After a problem has been formulated as one of classification, and relevant chemical descriptors have been selected for the training and test sets, pattern recognition methods can be applied to the data. Pattern recognition studies are done in discrete steps. The **X** data in Fig. 2.1 are the *features*, and from these a p-dimensional coordinate system can be established which defines *feature space*. The data for each compound form a vector called the *pattern vector*. Projection of the pattern vectors into the feature space will result in the training sets clustering in different regions of the pattern space. This is shown in Fig. 2.2 for two classes in three dimensions for convenience.

Up to this point all methods of pattern recognition work in the same way. The problem from Fig. 2.2 is to develop a set of rules which can be used to determine where a test compound lies relative to the defined classes in feature space. On this point the three methods differ significantly and these are discussed in the following sections.

2.4.1.1 *Hyperplane and class discrimination methods*

The basis of the hyperplane and discrimination methods is linear discriminant analysis [16] which was developed first by Fisher [15]. The classification rule, or discriminant function, used by the hyperplane methods is a line, plane or hyperplane which can be constructed to separate the two classes. To illustrate how the discriminant function is calculated, consider a two-class problem in which compounds in the groups are described by two variables x_1 and x_2 as shown in Fig. 2.3. The variables for the two groups are y_1 and y_2 which may be categorical, i.e. 2 for active and 1 for inactive compounds or continuous in which the two classes are weakly active and strongly active. The two groups are clustered in the figure with

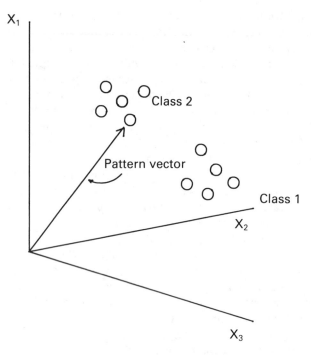

Fig. 2.2 — Two classes represented in feature space. Each member of the class is represented by a pattern vector.

some overlap of the two classes. Discriminant analysis, and the so-called hyperplane methods, calculate a discriminant function which is a linear combination of x_1 and x_3 as shown in equation (2.17).

$$y = v_1 x_1 + v_2 x_2 \tag{2.17}$$

The discriminant function passes through the origin as shown in Fig. 2.4. An infinite number of discriminant functions can be calculated. The orthogonal projection of the two classes onto the discriminant function shows that some separation occurs, but it follows that other functions are possible, and some will be better than others. The optimal one is the one that gives minimal overlap of the training sets so that the two classes are on either side of the function.

Fig. 2.4 contains a hint as to the difficulties with the hyperplane methods in QSAR. Any test compound will be on either side of the discriminant function, so unless it is known in advance that the test compound is a member of one of the defined classes, an erroneous classification will result.

2.4.1.2 Distance methods
An example of distance-based methods is the k-nearest-neighbor [44] technique, where k is a small, odd integer, usually 3 or 5. The k-nearest-neighbor method of

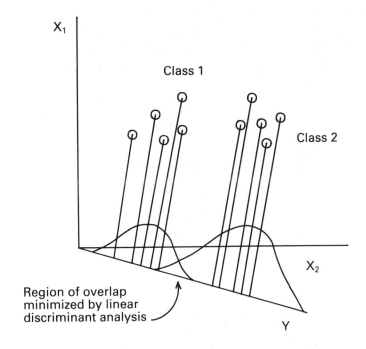

Fig. 2.3 — Two classes problem for linear discriminant analysis.

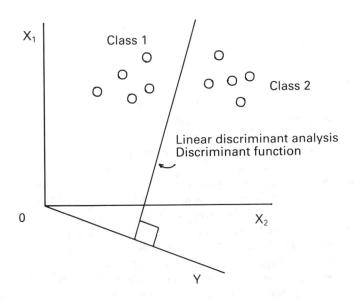

Fig. 2.4 — Discriminant function derivation for linear discriminant analysis.

pattern recognition is one of the most easily applied and widely used classification techniques. It is based on the premise that an unknown pattern vector will be most similar biologically to the pattern vectors it is nearest. The distance is usually Euclidean, but if the data are binary, the Hamming distance is used. The method is illustrated in Fig. 2.5.

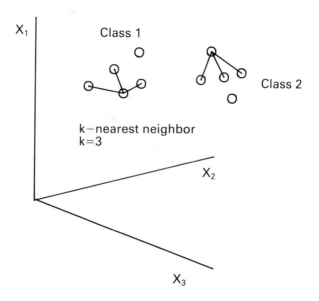

Fig. 2.5 — k-nearest-neighbor applied to a two-class problem.

2.4.1.3   Class modeling methods

Class modeling methods are based on modeling the training sets with principal components. These models approximate the regular variation of the data within a class by a point, line or plane. Around the model, a tolerance interval is constructed from the statistical scatter of the data. The result is that the volumes occupied by the classes are defined mathematically so that classification of test compounds is based on where in pattern space they are located. An advantage of projection methods is that the models, i.e. points, lines and planes, can be defined to satisfy different criteria depending on the objective of the data analysis.

The projection of the data for two classes from a p-dimensional space onto a lower-dimensional (hyper)plane is illustrated geometrically in Fig. 2.6. This is equivalent to deriving disjoint principal components models (equation (2.13)) for the two classes with the position in pattern space of each compound approximated by the class mean, $\mathbf{x}$, and their principal component scores, ts. The number of principal components required to approximate the data structure for each class corresponds to whether the classes are approximated by a point, $A = 0$, a line, $A = 1$, a plane, $A = 2$,

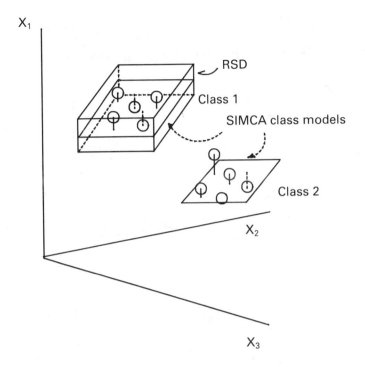

Fig. 2.6 — SIMCA representatiion of two classes. Class 2 is approximated by a 2-component model (plane), while Class 1 illustrates confidence intervals around the class.

or a hyperplane, $A \geqslant 3$. The residuals, $e_{i,k}$, are used to construct tolerance intervals around each class, and these define volumes within which members of each class have the highest probability of being observed. Classification of test set compounds is based on where they are situated relative to the training sets 'volumes'.

The partial least squares method operates at level three and therefore provides qualitative and quantitative estimates of biological activity. It can also operate at level four as illustrated graphically in Fig. 2.7.

A recent application of the partial least squares regression technique which illustrates a number of its advantages is the method comparative molecular field analysis (CoMFA) by Cramer *et al.* [44]. The **Y** data in Fig. 2.1 are binding constants for a series of steroids to their carrier protein. The **X** data are parameters derived by developing a three-dimensional grid to represent the binding site of the carrier protein. Each point in the grid is parameterized to represent a 'probe atom', which in this study is a methyl group assumed to be an sp^3 carbon with charge $+ 1.0$. Each steroid ligand is placed in the grid in an orientation which is determined by the root-mean-square difference in interaction energies, and the non-covalent interaction potential is calculated for the probe and positions in the lattice which correspond to the atoms which compose the ligands. The result is what is termed a 'three-way' descriptor matrix [45]. This matrix is then 'unfolded' to a two-way table which is the

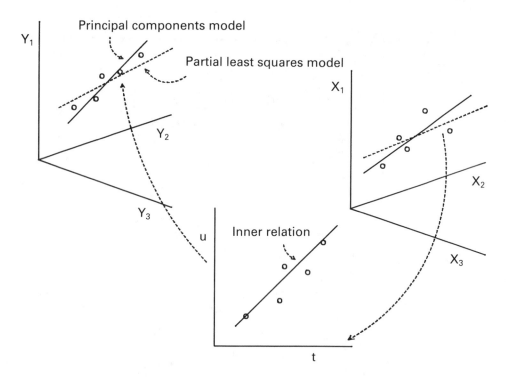

Fig. 2.7 — Geometric interpretation of the partial least squares method in pattern recognition. Only one class is shown, but extension to several classes is obvious.

X data in Fig. 2.1. Partial least squares is used in a regression analysis of the **X** and **Y** data. High and significant correlations were found between the binding and interaction potentials at specific sites.

This method seems to hold much promise. Partial least squares regression is the only method which can be applied in such cases because of the very large descriptor matrix that results. Multiple linear regression could never be applied here. There should be some discussion in the QSAR research community about the unfolding of the three-way data table, as this is the critical step in the analysis.

REFERENCES

[1] Crum-Brown, A. & Fraser, T. (1868). On the connection between chemical constitution and physiological action I. On the physiological action of the salts of the ammonium bases, derived from strychnia, brucia, thebaia, codeia, morphia and nicotia. *Proc. Roy. Soc. Edinburgh* **25**, 151.
[2] Meyer, H. H. (1899). On the theory of alcohol narcosis I. Which property of anesthetics gives them their narcotic activity. *Arch. Exp. Pathol. Pharmakol.* **42**, 109.

[3] Overton, E. (1899). Ueber die allgemeinen osmotischen Eigenschaften der Zelle, ihre vermutlichen Urachen und ihre Bedeuting für die Physiologie. *Vierteljahressch. Naturforsch. Ges. Zürich* **44**, 88.

[4] Overton, E. (1901). *Studien uber die narkose.* Fischer, Jena, Germany.

[5] Furukawa, S. (1918). Biological activity of perfumes. *J. Tokyo Chem. Soc.* **39**, 584; Furukawa, S. (1918). Biological activity of perfumes. *ibid.* **39**, 809; Furukawa, S. (1919). Biological activity of perfumes. *ibid.* **40**, 42.

[6] Hansch, C., Maloney, P. P., Fujita, T., & Muir, R. (1962). Correlation of the biological activity of phenoxyacetic acids with Hammett substituent constants and partition coefficients. *Nature* **194**, 178.

[7] Hammett, L. P. (1940). *Physical Organic Chemistry.* 1st edn, McGraw-Hill, New York.

[8] Hansch, C., Björkroth, J. P., & Leo, A. (1987). Hydrophobicity and central nervous system agents: on the principle of minimal hydrophobicity in drug design. *J. Pharm. Sci.* **79**, 663.

[9] Hansch, C. & Fujita, T. (1963). ρ-σ-π analysis. A method for the correlation of biological activity and chemical structure. *J. Amer. Chem. Soc.* **86**, 1616.

[10] Penniston, J. T., Beckett, L., Bentley, D. L. & Hansch, C. (1969). Passive permeation of organic compounds through biological tissue; a non-steady-state theory. *Mol. Pharmacol.* **5**, 333.

[11] Higuchi, H., Richards, J. H., Davis, S. S., Kamada, A., Hou, J. P., Nakano, M., Nakano, N. I., & Pitmann, I. H. (1969). Solvency and hydrogen bonding interactions in nonaqueous systems. *J. Pharm. Sci.* **59**, 1376.

[12] Martin, Y. C. (1978). *Quantitative Drug Design.* Marcel Dekker, New York.

[13] Kubinyi, H. (1977). Quantitative structure–activity relationships of the bilinear model, a new model for nonlinear dependence of biological activity on hydrophobic character. *J. Med. Chem.* **20**, 625.

[14] Hansch, C. & Clayton, J. (1973). Lipophilic character and biological activity of drugs II: the parabolic case. *J. Pharm. Sci.* **62**, 1.

[15] Fisher, R. A. (1928). *Statistical Methods for Research Workers.* 2nd edn, Oliver and Boyd, Edinburgh.

[16] Lachenbruch, P. A. (1975). *Discriminant Analysis.* Hafner Press, New York.

[17] Martin, Y. C., Holland, J. B., Jarboe, C. H., & Plotnikoff, N. (1974). Discriminant analysis of the relationship between physical properties and the inhibition of monoamine oxidase by aminotetralins and aminoindanes, *J. Med. Chem.* **17**, 409.

[18] Dunn III, W. J. & Greenberg, M. (1977). Synthesis, physicochemical properties and antitumor activities of 1-aryl-3-benzyl-3-methyltriazenes. *J. Pharm. Sci.* **66**, 1416.

[19] Albano, C., Dunn III, W. J., Edlund, E., Johansson, E., Norden, B., Sjöström, M., & Wold, S., (1978). Four levels of pattern recognition; computers and optimization in analytical chemistry. *Anal. Chim. Acta* **103**, 429.

[20] Ting, K. H., Lee, R. C. T., Milne, G. W. A., Shapiro, H., & Guarino, A. M. (1973). Applications of artificial intelligence: relationship between mass spectra and pharmacological activity of drugs. *Science* **180**, 417.

[21] Chu, K. C., Feldman, R. J., Shapiro, M. B., Hazard, B. F., & Geran, R. I. (1975). Pattern recognition and structure activity studies. Prediction of antitumor activity in structurally diverse drugs in an experimental mouse brain tumor system. *J. Med. Chem.* **18**, 539.

[22] Kowalski, B. R. & Bender, C. F. (1972). Pattern recognition. A powerful approach to interpreting chemical data. *J. Amer. Chem. Soc.* **94**, 5632.

[23] Stuper, A. J. & Jurs, P. C. (1975). Classification of psychotropic drugs as sedatives or tranquilizers using pattern recognition. *J. Amer. Chem. Soc.* **97**, 182.

[24] Nilsson, N. J. (1965). *Learning Machines*. McGraw-Hill, New York.

[25] Wold, S. (1976). Pattern recognition by disjoint principal components models. *Pattern Recognition* **8**, 127.

[26] Martin, Y. C. (1989). Personal communication, Abbott Laboratories.

[27] Box, G. E. P., Hunter, W. G., & Hunter, J. S. (1978). *Statistics for Experimenters*. Wiley, New York, Chapter 16.

[28] Austel, V. (1982). A manual method for systematic drug design. *Eur. J. Med. Chem.* **17**, 9.

[29] Austel, V. (1982). Selection of test compounds from a basic set of chemical structures. *Eur. J. Med. Chem.* **17**, 339.

[30] Hellberg, S., Sjöström, M., Skagerberg, B., & Wold, S. (1987). Peptide structure activity relationships, a multivariate approach. *J. Med. Chem.* **30**, 1126.

[31] McCann, J. & Ames, B. N. (1976). *Proc. Natl. Acad. Sci. USA* **73**, 950.

[32] Rekker, R. (1977). *The Hydrophobic Fragmental Constant*. Elsevier, Amsterdam.

[33] Hansch, C. & Leo, A. (1982) Partition coefficient data bank, Pomona College Medicinal Chemistry Project, Claremont, California.

[34] Koehler, M. G., Grigoras, S., & Dunn, W. J. (1988). The relationship between chemical structure and the logarithm of the partition coefficient. *Quant. Struc. Act. Rel.* **7**, 150.

[35] Lee, B. & Richards, F. M. (1971). The interpretation of protein structures: estimation of static accessibility. *J. Mol. Biol.* **55**, 379.

[36] Pullman, A. & Port, B. (1974). Molecular orbital study of the conformation of histamine: the isolated molecule and solvent effect. *J. Mol. Pharmacol.* **10**, 505.

[37] Koehler, M. G., Rowberg-Schaefer, K., & Hopfinger, A. J. (1988). A molecular shape analysis and quantitative structure activity–relationship investigation of some triazine–antifolate inhibitors of leishmania dihydrofolate reductase. *Arch. Biochem. Biophys.* **266**, 152.

[38] Hellberg, S., Sjöström, M., Skagerberg, B., & Wold, S. (1988). Peptide quantitative structure–activity relationships, a multivariate approach. *J. Med. Chem.* **30**, 1126.

[39] Bergman, S. W. & Gittins, J. C. (1985). *Statistical Methods for Pharmaceutical Research Planning*. Marcel Dekker, New York, Chapter 1.

[40] Geladi, P. & Kowalski, B. (1986). Partial least squares: a tutorial. *Anal. Chim. Acta* **185**, 1.

[41] Topliss, J. G. & Edwards, R. P. (1979). Chance factors in studies of quantitative–structure activity relationships. *J. Med. Chem.* **22**, 1238.

[42] Dunn III, W. J. & Wold, S. (1989). Pattern recognition techniques in drug design. In: C. A. Ramsden (ed.) *Comprehensive Medicinal Chemistry*. Pergamon Press, Oxford.

[43] Varmuza, K. (1980). *Pattern Recognition in Chemistry*. Springer-Verlag, Berlin.

[44] Cramer III, R. D., Patterson, D. E. & Bunce, J. D. (1988). Comparative molecular field analysis (CoMFA). 1. Effect of shape on binding of steroids to carrier proteins. *J. Amer. Chem. Soc.* **110**, 5959.

[45] Wold, S. & Geladi, P. (1987). Local principal component models, rank maps and contextuality for curve resolution and multi-way calibration inference. *Chemomet. Intell. Lab. Sys.* **2**, 273.

[46] Wold, S., Wold, H., Ruhe, A., & Dunn III, W. J. (1984). The collinearity problem in linear and nonlinear regression. The partial least squares (PLS) approach to general inverses. *SIAM, J. Sci. Stat. Comp.* **5**, 735.

3

Physical methods in drug discovery

Steven D. Young
Merck Sharp & Dohme Research Laboratories, Division of Merck & Co., Inc.,
West Point, Pennsylvania, USA

3.1 INTRODUCTION

It has been 40 years since X-ray crystallography was used to solve the structure of penicillin [1]. This landmark achievement in the history of drug development was accomplished without the aid of digital computers. Not until the late 1950s would the first practical computers begin to affect the way crystallographers viewed organic molecular structure problems. The use of these early computers allowed for the first macromolecular structure solution at atomic resolution (2 Å). In 1960, the structure of sperm whale myoglobin [2], a relatively small protein, was solved using the EDSAC II, a state-of-the-art digital computer at the University of Cambridge [3]. The analysis required the development of computer programs from scratch and hundreds of hours of computer time to run them on a machine with a tiny fraction of the computational power of a modern personal computer (PC).

With the ability to examine the structure of small molecules, i.e. drugs, at the atomic level and at the same time period examine the structure of some of their target proteins, namely enzymes, the science of drug design had entered a new era.

Drug design has benefited from the development of another technology to probe molecular structure at the atomic level, nuclear magnetic resonance (NMR) spectroscopy. The phenomenon of nuclear magnetic resonance was first observed in the 1940s, and its application to organic molecules was laid out in the 1950s by Bloch and others [4]. NMR spectroscopy as applied to small molecules has been familiar to medicinal chemists since the early 1960s. Only recently have the combined advances in probe design, digital computer and cryomagnet technologies as well as the theoretical understanding of the NMR phenomenon led to the use of NMR spectroscopy to study drug–receptor interactions. The action of a drug on its receptor, whether a membrane-bound protein or free enzyme, is a dynamic process, and information gathered from NMR spectroscopy about interatomic distances, both intermolecular and intramolecular, can tell us a great deal about the function of a drug.

This chapter is an attempt to provide a brief overview of the application of these two technologies to the process of drug design.

3.2 X-RAY CRYSTALLOGRAPHY

The concept of employing X-rays to examine the structure of crystalline material began with von Laue in the early part of this century. Von Laue discovered that crystals would diffract X-rays in an orderly fashion, forming interference fringes on photographic plates much the way a diffraction grating produces an interference pattern with visible light. The explanation that von Laue correctly gave to this observation was that the spacing between the atoms in the crystal lattice must be approximately the same as the wavelength of the X-rays. The diffraction phenomenon in crystals is a three-dimensional analogy to the two-dimensional effect seen within an optical diffraction grating. Shortly after von Laue's experiments, Bragg developed a simple equation relating the angle of reflection of the X-ray to its wavelength and the distance between the planes of atoms within the crystal.

$$\text{Bragg's Law:} \qquad n\lambda = 2d \sin \theta \qquad\qquad (3.1)$$

The incident angle of the X-ray beam, θ, on the crystal lattice when the interplanar spacing d satisfies Bragg's law for a given wavelength of X-rays, λ, will be equal to the reflection angle of the diffracted beam. Information about atoms in a lattice may be gathered by observing the intensity of the diffracted X-ray beam at the total deflection angle 2θ relative to the incident beam. It is possible to develop a geometrical analogy to Bragg's law where the point (or atom) of diffraction is placed at the center of a sphere. If the radius of the sphere is defined as $1/\lambda$ then the distance between any two points on this sphere separated by the total reflection angle 2θ will be $1/d$. This reciprocal distance construction is credited to P. P. Ewald and is useful in reconstructing the arrangement of atoms in the unit cell from the diffraction data [5]. The intensity of the diffracted X-rays is dependent on the electron density of the atoms in the crystal, the number of atoms within the unit cell and the angle of the incident X-ray beam. For a given crystal, this information is related by a function called the structure factor, F_{hkl} [6].

Mathematically, functions can be mapped between reciprocal coordinate systems by the Fourier transform. This relationship, developed by the mathematician Joseph Fourier, is useful in both crystallography and spectroscopy. Using the Fourier transform, a two-dimensional function relating amplitude with frequency may be mapped into an amplitude versus time function, time being reciprocal units of frequency. In crystallography, the function of amplitude with reciprocal space (Ewald's analogy) may be transformed into a function representing amplitude (electron density) with space (distances within the crystal matrix). It is this concept that leads to the realization that an X-ray diffraction pattern is in reality the Fourier transform representation of the observed crystal.

If a crystal were a single type of atom, then the amplitude of the scattered X-rays could be related directly to the structure factor F_{hkl}. Since a crystal is composed of a large number of diffracting atoms, the structure is also related to the phase of the diffracted beam. Experimentally the phase of the X-ray beam cannot be measured and constitutes what is known as the phase problem in X-ray crystallography. X-ray crystallographers have developed several methods to overcome the phase problem. The method of Patterson avoids the problem of phase by relating the distance between atoms to the square of the observed amplitude. This calculation results not in a structure itself but rather a map (Patterson map) which relates the distances between atoms. For N atoms in a unit cell there will be N^2 peaks in the map [7]. If the unit cell has no dominant atom, as in a simple organic compound, the Patterson peaks will overlap and thus cannot be interpreted. However, if a heavy atom is present, the intense scattering by this atom will produce dominant peaks in the map. The positions of the light atoms can be determined by using the phases approximated from the positions of the heavy atom peaks.

A second method for solving the phase problem is known as the isomorphous replacement method [5,6]. This technique relies on the ability, in the case of macromolecules, to bind a heavy atom. If the native crystal can bind a heavy atom without significant perturbation to its structure then the bound structure is considered in isomorphous heavy atom derivative. The diffraction patterns of the isomorphous heavy atom derivative and the native crystal are obtained. The difference between the patterns is in principle a representation of the diffraction pattern of a crystal of the heavy atoms alone. This difference diffraction pattern for heavy atoms can be used to locate the positions of the heavy atoms using the Patterson method or 'direct methods' where the phases are approximated from the amplitudes of the structure factors. Once the positions of the heavy atoms are known, exact phases for the structure factors may be worked out. The assumption is made that the structure factor for the heavy atom derivative is the sum of the structure factors for the native crystal and the theoretical heavy atom crystal. The measurement of the amplitudes of the structure factors for both crystals combined with the phase information from the theoretical heavy atom crystal will give two possible values for the phase of the native crystal. Measurement of a second heavy atom derivative would remove the ambiguity. The difficulty with this method lies in finding at least two heavy atom derivatives that are truly isomorphous with the native crystal.

For small molecule structure analysis the preparation of heavy atom derivatives is usually not possible. The approach to determining the phases for the structure factors without the aid of heavy atoms is commonly referred to as direct methods. The direct methods rely on the fact that everywhere within a crystal, the electron density must be positive and that the electron density surrounding the individual atoms is approximately spherical. Knowledge of the space group of the crystal and the structure factor amplitudes allows statistical guesses of the sign of the phase for the structure factors to be made. (A complete description of the origin of direct methods may be found in [5].) The routine solution of small molecules by direct methods is a result of combination computer programs such as MULTAN [8], published in 1974. Commercial X-ray diffractometers and minicomputers now allow for collection of data and structure solution of small molecules in a matter of days. An example of such a small molecule structure solution is shown in Fig. 3.1.

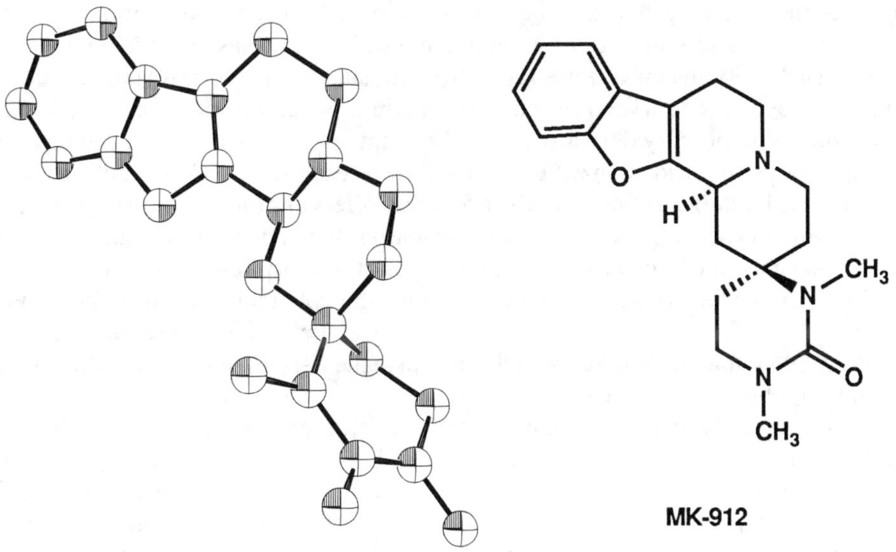

MK-912

Fig. 3.1 — Ortep representation of the crystal structure of MK-912, an alpha-2 antagonist. Crystal structure by J. Hirshfield.

3.2.1 Structure determination

The process of X-ray structure determination for both small molecules and macromolecules begins with growing well formed crystals suitable for mounting, and characterization of their space group. In the case of small organic molecules typical of drugs, an ideal well formed crystal, approximately 0.2 mm on an edge, is often grown by evaporative or cooling methods. For macromolecules such as proteins, the problem is often considerably more complex, as the crystals typically contain as much as 35% water. Protein crystals are grown from many different solvent systems, and a variety of salts have been used to precipitate crystals [9]. The most widely used salt in this regard is ammonium sulfate owing to its efficient ability to 'salt-out' proteins. Organic solvents have been used to crystallize proteins but often cause denaturation, limiting their usefulness. The choice of precipitating media affects the way the protein will crystallize, altering the areas of contact between hydrophobic regions of the molecule and the intercalated solvent. When viewed in terms of drug design, the way in which a protein is crystallized is critical to interpretation of the structure obtained. Often the availability of material for crystallization restricts the number of precipitant systems that may be tried. Microdialysis in capillary tubes [10] against the gradient of precipitant allows crystallization of tiny amounts of protein from 5 to 50 µl of solvent. Crystals obtained in this manner may be mounted in the diffractometer directly without further manipulation.

For macromolecules the next step in structure determination is often preparation of one or more heavy atom derivatives. The heavy metal atom to be incorporated into the protein may either be co-crystallized as a complex or be diffused into pre-existing crystals. The latter method is more likely to result in an isomorphous crystal, but has the risk of collapsing the delicate crystal lattice by desorption of water molecules necessary for hydration. Non-metallic heavy atoms of sufficient electron density such as iodine may be used. Electrophilic substitution on tyrosine residues by iodine has been used [11] and cysteine residues may be reacted with mercuric nitrates to produce thiomercury derivatives [12]. Of great interest to medicinal chemists are the structures of various enzymes involved in disease states. Co-crystallization of enzymes with inhibitors bound to the active site offers another method of producing heavy atom derivatives. A number of heavy-atom-labeled inhibitors may be bound to the enzyme under study to produce the series of isomorphous derivatives needed.

With the necessary set of crystals in hand, the collection of diffraction data is begun. The crystals are mounted in or on a quartz capillary, and a set of precession photographs is made. By precessing the crystal in the X-ray beam and simultaneously moving the film around a circle with the crystal at the origin and having a narrow metal slit screen between the film and the crystal, a photograph of the diffraction pattern for a single crystal plane is obtained. Examining the pattern provides information on the geometry of the unit cell. The density of the spots is proportional to the intensity of the diffracted X-ray beam and provides information about the location of the atoms within the unit cell. In the very early days of X-ray crystallography the intensities of the reflections were measured with densitometers directly from the diffraction photographs. This method is finding new uses in X-ray diffraction with high-intensity sources and will be discussed later. With film, measurement of the intensity of a reflection is determined from the optical density and size of the spot on the recording film. The limitations of film, namely dynamic range and susceptibility to background fogging, are avoided with the modern single-crystal four-circle diffractometer. The computer-driven diffractometer with a single detector, either scintillation or ionization, records the intensity of a reflection by integrating X-ray photons over a set period of time. In principle the dynamic range is not limited, as the time per integration is variable. Practically, X-ray damage to the crystal and the need to record many reflections limit the time available to record a single reflection. The ability of film to record many reflections simultaneously in some instances gives it an advantage over the single-detector diffractometer. Once the crystal being observed is mounted in front of the incident X-ray beam, the diffractometer is programmed to seek out the strongest reflections and record their intensities. Periodically during the collection of data from the weaker reflections, the detector returns to one of the strongest reflections for calibration. Radiation damage to the crystal results in a measurable loss in intensity of the calibration reflection. With film methods the decaying intensity of the reflections from a damaged crystal are recorded simultaneously, and no decay correction is needed. However, the damaged crystal begins to produce a diffuse background fogging of the film. When a crystal is damaged beyond usefulness, it must be replaced. Alignment and recalibration of the new crystal is a much simpler task with a single-detector diffractometer, and the new crystal is easily reoriented to position the calibration reflections.

The factors governing the distance resolution achievable by X-ray crystallography are many. Briefly, the number of observed reflections is inversely proportional to the cube of the crystal lattice spacing d. The intensity of the reflections is inversely proportional to the sine of the Bragg angle, and there is a proportionality with the structure factor which is dependent on the thermal motion within the crystal

[13]. Resolution is also affected by the disorder within the crystal. Even a small crystal is composed of 10^{17} molecules, and the location of atoms from one unit cell to the next is somewhat variable. With all of these considerations, the amount of time needed to collect a set of diffraction data is inversely proportional to the fourth power of the desired resolution [13]. The rate at which data can be collected is dependent on the power of the X-ray source, the sensitivity of the detector and the mechanical design of the diffractometer. More-powerful X-ray sources and the advent of area detectors, that is detectors which can measure the intensities of several reflections at once, are recent technological innovations designed to cope with the need to accumulate the data faster. More-intense conventional X-ray sources have been developed for X-ray diffractometry such as the rotating anode X-ray tube. The availability of electron synchrotrons and storage rings represent a new source of extremely intense monochromatic and polychromatic X-radiation. With increased beam power, radiation damage to the crystal becomes a major factor, limiting the useful lifetime of the crystal. Synchrotron sources have more highly collimated beams than X-ray tubes, which is another factor in their favor. A typical increase in intensity from a bending magnet synchrotron source relative to a conventional X-ray source is about 1000 fold [14]. The technological advance of the synchrotron beam now makes it possible to collect diffraction data from very large unit cells such as viruses. Analysis of a human rhinovirus as a complex with an antiviral agent has been reported at 3 Å resolution using the synchrotron X-ray source at the Cornell High Energy Synchrotron Source (CHESS) facility [15].

The advances in X-ray sources have been paralleled with advances in detection systems. Photographic techniques and single-counter diffractometers are still widely used for the accumulation of diffraction data. Diffractometers have been designed that exploit a linear array of conventional counters to simultaneously measure groups of reflections, thus speeding up data collection [16]. The area detector represents a new technology combining the advantages of both film and electronic proportional counters. There are two basic designs of X-ray area detectors: multiwire and television devices. Both devices count multiple X-ray photon events over a two-dimensional area simultaneously. Area detectors typically cover 10 to 40% of the diffraction pattern at a time, requiring data still be taken at several crystal–detector orientations. Macromolecular crystals with their large unit cells can have over 100 000 reflections to measure. Diffractometers employing a single proportional counter waste much of these data, as crystal decomposition occurs long before all of the reflections can be measured. Photographic methods suffer from poor efficiency, dynamic range, fogging, etc. The multiwire proportional counter was developed to overcome these deficiencies. Multiwire proportional counters for crystallography evolved from detectors used by physicists studying high-energy subatomic particle collisions produced in accelerators [17]. The first multiwire area detector for crystallography was developed at the University of California, San Diego. Named the Mark I, it has been used for solving the structure of dihydrofolate reductase from *E. coli*, among several other proteins [17]. The area detector is mounted a fixed distance from the crystal such that a significant portion of the diffraction pattern falls on the 30 by 30 cm window of the detector. To avoid attenutation of the diffracted X-rays by the air between the crystal and the detector, a box containing helium gas may be placed in front of the detector. The helium gas is much less efficient at absorbing X-ray photons relative to air. The detector itself consists of an $X-Y$ matrix of stainless steel wires, one axis of wires operating as the anode, the other as the cathode. The detection wires are housed in a box with a beryllium window which the X-rays pass into the detection chamber. The inside of the chamber is pressurized to one atmosphere with a 90:10 mixture of xenon and carbon dioxide. An incident X-ray photon entering the chamber is absorbed by a xenon atom, resulting in an ionization event. Since the anode and cathode wires are held at a potential difference of several kilovolts, the ionized electrons are accelerated toward the anode wires, causing a cascade of ionizations. The ions of this secondary event produce a positive current on the cathode wires recording the event on one axis. A negative current is produced on the anode wires corresponding tom the other axis. The description of the Mark I detector shows a spacing of the anode wires of 2.13 mm with 144 wires across the window. The 288 cathode wires are spaced along the y-axis at twice the anode wire density [18]. The wires along each axis are separated by delay lines. The $X-Y$ location of the ionization event is then read out from the delay time of the arriving electrical pulse. This method of measuring the data greatly reduces the amount of electronics that would be needed if the events were to be recorded individually, one wire at a time. The spatial resolution of a flat multiwire detector is limited by the number of pixels generated from the two electrode planes. The detector must be positioned far enough away from the diffracting crystal such that individual reflections do not overlap on the detector array. The parallax created at the outer edges of the detector severely limits the spatial resolution of a detector positioned to collect data from a large solid angle. Recently, focused geometry detectors have been developed [19]. These detectors refocus a diffuse ionization event at the edges of the detector with a spherical drift chamber containing two additional electrodes.

   Television area detectors are devices also designed to overcome the shortfalls of single-crystal detectors and film by collecting a large amount of the available diffraction data simultaneously. Unlike multiwire area detectors which rely on an ionization event produced by the incident X-ray for detection, television-camera area detectors operate by converting the X-ray photons into visible light by means of a phosphor. The X-ray photons falling on a phosphor screen produce a shower of visible-light photons. The intensity of these photons is not sufficient for detection directly by commercially available television camera tubes. To overcome this problem the phosphor screen is optically coupled to an electrostatic image intensifier which provides light amplification of about 100-fold. The size of the television camera's optical input is less than the size of the phosphor screen needed to collect the diffraction data. The image on the screen is reduced by the intensifier tube and associated optical couplings. The photons focused on the television tube fall on a photosensitive cathode which emits electrons. Amplification of this signal occurs again by accelerating these electrons toward a target of silicon semiconductors. The charge deposited on the silicon is then 'read' by a scanning electron beam. A rasterized image of the diffraction pattern is obtained by controlling the sweep rate of the electron beam. To obtain statistically accurate counting data, the analog video data are digitized in such a manner that the image is divided into a matrix of 512 by 512 pixel elements. The dynamic range of the detector becomes limited by the resolution of the digitizer. (For an 8-bit digitizer the dynamic range is 2^8 or 256 discrete levels.) The digitized data are summed over a period of time which has the effect of averaging out the electronic noise [20]. The accumulated diffraction data are then treated by the controlling computer much like data from a multiwire detector. The multiple stages of the television area detector give it a sensitivity range of 10^3 X-ray photons per pixel per second [21]. The development of solid-state charge-coupled devices may eventually replace the photocathode vacuum television camera tube. Presently their small size, sensitivity and reliability limit their use in X-ray diffractometry. The inherently high signal-to-noise ratios of these devices would make them very useful if the other limitations were overcome.

3.2.2   Refinement
After the crystallographic data have been gathered from the crystal(s) under investigation, the phases are derived and together with the observed structure factors, a preliminary electron density map is produced. With small molecules, the process of fitting a proposed structure with the observed electron density map is relatively straightforward. Structure factors for the proposed model are calculated and compared with the observed factors. The difference in the observed versus calculated structure factors is minimized with a least squares approach by adjusting the positions of the atoms in the model. The accuracy of the fit of the model to the observed data is often reported as a residual or R factor. The R factor is expressed in equation (3.2) as the sum of the differences in the observed minus the calculated structure factors divided by the sum of the observed Fs. In small-molecule crystallography the refined structure is usually correct if it has an R factor less than 0.25. A very good agreement between a model and the data would have an R factor of less than 0.05 [6].

$$R = \frac{\sum_i (|F_o| - |F_c|)}{\sum_i |F_o|} \qquad (3.2)$$

The complexities in building a model for a macromolecule that fits the data can be enormous. For proteins the primary structure, i.e. the amino acid sequence, can be obtained from conventional degradative sequence analysis. This amino acid chain can be fit one residue at a time into the observed electron density map. The electron density map itself may be refined by improving the crystallographic phases calculated with the molecular replacement method of Rossmann and Blow [22]. The symmetry of the protein molecule itself is used to average the electron density map. The electron density outside the volume occupied by the protein is adjusted to an average value to account for solvent. Structure factors obtained from this map are used in conjunction with those from an MIR (multiple isomorphous replacement) map to recalculate new phases. The process can then be repeated. The improved electron density map makes the task of optimizing the model somewhat easier. Any information on the limits of covalent bond lengths and angles in peptides can be used

to rule out unreasonable placement of residues within the structure. As the model is
built up, least squares refinement and difference maps are used until a satisfactory
structure is obtained.

The regularity of larger substructures between different proteins has been
exploited in interpreting electron density maps. Large fragments of proteins such as
alpha-helices, beta-strands and beta-barrels occur with regularity in differing
enzymes. These building blocks of proteins can be used in chain tracing a protein
from its electron density map. Fragments with sequence homology can be obtained
from the protein crystallographic database and their refined coordinates matched to
a portion of the protein under examination. If the match fits, the region can be
extended and the matching process repeated. If the sequence homology is not exact
for a fragment, the anomalous amino acid residue may be modeled using one of the
many available macromolecular modeling programs. The carbon alpha chain can be
built up rapidly in this manner. For example, matching fragments from different
proteins with a one Å r.m.s. standard deviation of the carbon alpha chain of retinol
binding protein (RBP) was done by using refined coordinates of fragments from
three unrelated proteins by Jones and Thirup [23]. Using 20 fragment matches from
the structures of satellite tobacco necrosis virus, apo-alcohol dehydrogenase, and
human carbonic anhydrase C, a refined r.m.s deviation of the coordinates of RBP
was reduced to 0.95 Å from an r.m.s. deviation of 1.30 Å obtained by MIR methods
alone.

3.2.3   Advanced techniques

The synchrotron as a powerful source of polychromatic and monochromatic X-rays
has opened up new areas in X-ray crystallography. The classical phase problem is
usually solved by the preparation of two or more isomorphous heavy atom derivatives. The synchrotron has the ability to produce a wide spectrum of X-rays which are
tunable. Crystals which contain atoms exhibiting large anomalous scattering effects
such as a heavy metal can be examined at multiple wavelengths. Analysis of the
diffraction data collected at different wavelengths makes it possible to calculate the
phase information directly [24]. This is particularly useful if the protein under
investigation already contains a heavy atom [25] or when preparation of more than
one heavy atom derivative is impossible. The amplitude of X-rays scattered from an
atom is related to the incident X-ray by the scattering factor. However, if the
frequency of the incident X-ray is close to a natural resonance frequency of an
absorption edge of the atom, the normal scattering is disturbed. The scattering factor
takes on a dispersion component and an absorption component. If the absorption
component is strong enough the atom will scatter anomalously. The anomalous
scattering is observed as differences in reflection intensities, which are used to
calculate the phases. In practice, the difference in intensity in anomalous scattering is
much smaller (9% versus 39%) [26] than the intensity differences seen in MIR
experiments. The constraint this difference imposes experimentally is that reflection
intensities must be measured with a higher degree of accuracy [27].

Polychromatic X-ray beams of high intensity are available at synchrotron sources
with the aid of devices which subject the circulating electrons to a series of
accelerations between closely spaced magnets known as wigglers [28]. Such broad
spectrum X-radiation is useful to crystallographers for performing time-resolved

diffraction experiments with biological macromolecules. Polychromatic irradiation of protein crystals produces a Laue diffraction pattern which may be recorded on film. Laue diffraction makes it possible to record a large proportion of the data needed for 3 Å resolution in a single exposure of a stationary crystal. Further, because of the high intensity of the beam, exposure times can be limited to the millisecond timescale. Sufficient data to solve a complete structure may be accumulated with just a few Laue photographs. The thermal and radiation damage inflicted on the crystals during exposure to the high-intensity beam makes it neccessary to move an undamaged portion of the crystal into the beam with each successive photograph. A single 3 mm long crystal can provide up to 20 Laue photographs by indexing the sample [29,30]. The Laue method has recently been used successfully to examine ligand binding in the enzyme glycogen phosphorylase b [31]. Three angular Laue photographs of the 97 kDa protein bound to the oligosaccharide maltoheptose, a substrate, were taken with a total data collection time of 3 s. From these data, 15,000 unique data were obtained. Using the Laue data alone to obtain structural information would have given only modest resolution. However, a monochromatic data set of the native protein to 1.9 Å resolution was available. This information provided a solution of the bound structure from the Laue data by difference methods.

3.2.4 Neutron diffraction

Neutron diffraction of organic crystals bears many similarities to X-ray diffraction. Scattered neutrons obey Bragg's law and are subject to Lorentz conditions. Neutrons are electrically neutral and do not generate free radicals within the bombarded crystal. The result is a great saving in labor, as the reduced amount of radiation damage usually makes it possible to collect the diffraction data needed from a single crystal. Neutron scattering is not dependent on atomic number in the way X-ray scattering is. In fact hydrogen and its next heaviest isotope, deuterium, have large scattering factors. A significant difference is that hydrogen has a negative scattering factor. This fact translates to a negative density level in the Fourier map. The negative scattering factor is attributed to resonance with hydrogen nuclei which retards the phase of the scattered neutron abnormally [32]. Such interaction is not observed with deuterium which has a large, but positive, scattering factor. Further, the absorption of neutrons by organic systems is less than that of X-rays, hence larger crystals may be used. The advantage is offset, however, by the fact that available neutron sources have much lower beam intensities than X-ray sources [33]. To elicit useful structural information from protein crystals, neutrons must have wavelengths of about 1 Å. Conveniently, thermal neutrons from the fission of uranium-235 have a distribution of wavelengths centered on 1 Å. Experimentally, neutrons are extracted from a reactor and passed through a monochrometer to remove unwanted high-energy particles. Neutrons are not primary ionizing radiation. In order to be detected a neutron must collide with a suitable target producing an ionizing particle which is then counted. Gas-filled multiple wire area detectors are useful for counting and can be operated under higher pressures with a suitable target gas such as helium-3 [32].

The fact that the neutron diffraction can discriminate between hydrogen and deuterium atoms is particularly attractive to those studying protein structure. Since proteins have a large water content the background scattering from the intercalated hydrogens must be reduced. Soaking the crystals in D_2O exchanges the interstitial water molecules, leaving only covalently bound hydrogens and those water molecules so strongly hydrogen bonded to the protein that exchange is slower than the soaking time. Interestingly, the side chain nitrogen in lysine residues exhibits strong neutron scattering when they are deuterated and no scattering when they possess only hydrogens [32], making it easy to trace out the lysines along the carbon-alpha backbone. Neutron diffraction has been used to study a number of enzymes including trypsin [34] and lysozyme [35]. The sites of interaction of ethanol on lysozyme were deduced by the neutron diffraction of a crystal of non-deuterated lysozyme soaked with a 25% aqueous solution of perdeuterated ethanol [36]. This study provided insight into the mechanism of ethanol-induced denaturation of the enzyme.

3.2.5   Drug design

Knowledge of the interaction of an effector substance with a protein is central to the process of drug development. The promise of X-ray crystallography to allow those who design drugs to 'see' the active site of an enzyme, alone or interacting with a substrate or inhibitor, has become a common occurrence. It is difficult to quantify the contribution of crystallography to the drug design process. Certainly small-molecule structure solution aids the medicinal chemist with everyday problems of relative and absolute stereochemistry not readily evaluated by spectroscopic methods. Protein crystallography can only tell us about the interaction of enzyme inhibitors with enzymes once an inhibitor is known. That information, however, may be invaluable in the eventual design of other inhibitors which embody the necessary physical and metabolic properties to become drugs. Often the key enzyme involved in a human disease is not available in sufficient quantity and purity, or refuses to crystallize. In some of these cases the crystal structure of enzymes with similar homology and mechanism have provided insight and understanding of the disease-related enzymes. For example, the zinc peptidase carboxypeptidase A has served as a guideline for the design of angiotensin-converting enzyme (ACE) inhibitors, useful in the treatment of hypertension and other cardiovascular disorders [37]. Another enzyme important in the control of blood pressure, renin, an aspartic protease, has been a long-sought-after target. The crystal structures of the related enzymes penicillopepsin and mouse renin have given a detailed view of how inhibitors based on the transition state analog (TSA) approach bind to human renin and other aspartic acid proteases [38,39]. The retroviral protease from the human immunodeficiency virus (HIV), the causative agent in the disease AIDS, is another aspartic acid protease [40]. Knowledge from previous forays into designing renin inhibitors may one day lead to a treatment for this serious disease. X-ray crystallographic examination of several dihydrofolate reductases has helped to explain the mechanism of such important drugs as the anti-cancer agent methotrexate, the antibacterial trimethoprim, and the anti-malarial pyrimethamine [41]. Human leukocyte elastase is an attractive target as a treatment for emphysema. The porcine enzyme structure is helping in the design of drugs which inhibit the human enzyme [42]. The list of contributions that X-ray crystallography has made to drug design is long and continues to grow as new targets for old and new diseases are uncovered.

3.3   NMR SPECTROSCOPY

Advances in the theory and technology of nuclear magnetic resonance spectroscopy in the last several years have made it possible to determine the tertiary structure of small proteins in solution. From the technological standpoint, the advances in field strength, that is the availability of commercial persistent field spectrometers operating at field strengths of 12 to 14 T, probe design and the associated rf electronics, and fast, high-resolution analog-to-digital converters make it possible to obtain high-resolution spectra on small quantities of biological macromolecules. The theoretical understanding of through-bond and through-space relaxation phenomena resulting in a multitude of two-dimensional (2D) NMR experiments [43] has helped overcome the main obstacle in assigning the ^{1}H resonances in a macromolecule, namely spectral overlap. Advances in NMR spectroscopic structure determination of protein structure complement the structural information available from X-ray crystallography. NMR spectroscopic structure information differs from crystallographic data primarily in that the intramolecular distances reflect the spatial structure of a completely solvated molecule. This information is attractive because effects of temperature, pH, denaturing agents, and host–guest complexation can be examined under conditions which more accurately reflect the physiologic state. Also, NMR spectroscopy can deduce the structure of the molecules which simply do not form crystals suitable for X-ray analysis. For molecules whose crystal structures are obtainable, NMR techniques can provide useful information on the conformational changes which occur when the crystalline compound is solvated. The limitations of the current technology are such that proteins with molecular weights in excess of 15,000 daltons have spectra too complex to be unraveled [44]. In early 1988 the tertiary structure for 10 small proteins which did not have a corresponding X-ray structure had been determined [45]. By the end of the year it was reported that the structures of approximately 50 macromolecules in that molecular weight range had been determined by NMR, and the possibility of extending the molecular weight limitation upwards to 40,000 might be possible [46]. The science of NMR structure determination of biological macromolecules is young and its potential to aid in the process of drug design is far reaching.

3.3.1   NMR experiments

The discussion here is limited to proteins, although other macromolecular systems have been studied [47]. The determination of a tertiary structure of a biomacromolecule requires forehand knowledge of its primary structure; in the case of proteins, the amino acid sequence is necessary. Chemical shift data for the 20 common amino acids have been tabulated for amino acid residues existing as part of a tetrapeptide [47]. This chemical shift information serves as a starting point for assigning all of the resonances in the NMR spectrum to their corresponding amino acid residues within the protein. Spectra may be simplified by exchanging all solvent accessible labile protons for deuterium with D_2O. The information needed for sequence assignment comes primarily from measurement of nuclear Overhauser effects (nOe's) between adjacent amino acids.

   The nuclear Overhauser effect manifests itself in NMR spectroscopy as a change in the integrated intensity of a resonance upon saturation of adjacent spin systems whose through-space interactions affect the relaxation of the nucleus undergoing resonance. It is important to realize that nOe's are a result of through-space magnetic interactions and are not through-bond effects. This fact makes nOe's useful in relating interatomic distances between portions of a protein which may be separated by many amino acid residues but whose folded structure places them in close proximity. The origins of the nuclear Overhauser effect have been explained in detail [48]. The observation of an intensity enhancement in a proton NMR from an nOe is restricted to no more than 50% and is inversely proportional to r^{-6} where r is the distance separating the interacting nuclei. The effect therefore drops off very quickly with distance and limits the measurement of nOe's to distances of less than 5 Å. Application of the nuclear Overhauser effect to NMR spectroscopy in two dimensions is referred to as a NOESY experiment [49]. In the NOESY experiment, peaks along the diagonal represent the one-dimensional frequency domain spectrum. Cross-peaks, appearing off the diagonal, arise from nuclei which are near in space. The intensities of these cross-peaks are used to assign limits to interatomic distances. The accuracy of determining interatomic distances with nOe's in proteins is limited. In practice, nOe's may arise from cross-relaxation of more than two interacting protons, so mixing times are kept short to insure nOe's develop from the strongest interacting spins. Proteins in solution are not rigid molecules and the internal motions are not necessarily linear, so nOe's do not always represent an average interatomic distance. To deal with these inherent inaccuracies, nOe data are calibrated to a known proton–proton distance, and the distances determined by nOe's are grouped into three or four distance ranges [50], rather than treating them as exact figures.

A second useful two-dimensional NMR experiment is correlated spectroscopy or COSY [51]. In the COSY experiment, the diagonal is again a representation of the one-dimensional spectrum, the off-diagonal cross-peaks representing through-bond interactions of spin-coupled resonances. The COSY experiment can show connectivity of side chains to carbon-alpha protons. An additional piece of information is obtained from the coupling constants themselves. The dihedral angle between vicinal protons is related to the coupling constant J by the Karplus equation [52]. Dihedral angles can be used to specify the positions of the side chains relative to the amino acid backbone. In some instances the coupling of the nitrogen amide proton to the carbon-alpha proton can be measured and the torsional angle for the backbone can be derived. All of the above information taken as a whole usually contains enough redundancy that a three-dimensional structure can be deduced.

3.3.2 Sequential resonance assignments

In order to access the three-dimensional structure of a protein from NMR data, assignment of individual resonance lines in the spectrum must be made. In practice, the coupling patterns from individual amino acid side chains are identified from a COSY spectrum. The connectivity between amino acid residues may be assigned from measurement of nOe's between neighboring backbone protons, amide-carbon-alpha, and amide-carbon-beta protons. The amide protons are assigned in turn to a side chain residue through carbon-alpha and carbon-beta through-bond couplings [53]. The interproton distances from the amide protons to their nearest neighbors have been tabulated for the sterically reasonable torsion angles found in globular proteins for the 20 common amino acids [54]. These values were derived from the X-ray crystallographic structures of 19 proteins determined at a resolution of at least 2 Å. Analysis of this data that carbon-alpha and carbon-beta- protons are close enough to exhibit nOe's with adjacent amide protons but rarely become close enough to amide residues farther away. These data ensure that nOe's from backbone amide protons reflect the connectivity of the protein. Statistical analysis has shown that measurement of two nOe's for each backbone amide proton, that reflect interproton distances between 2.0 and 3.6 Å, give a reliability of connectivity being assigned correctly of 99%. As the separating distance increases beyond 3.6 Å, the reliability decreases.

Once a sequence of three or four amino acid residues is identified, its location in the protein sequence can be found by inspection. Examining the COSY spectra for the specific side chain patterns provides a method of internal cross-checking, and sorting out sequences where spectral overlap occludes NH$^-$ or CH-alpha resonances [55]. Using the tripeptide or tetrapeptide embedded in the protein sequence, the connectivity-resonance assignments can be extended in two directions, that is toward the N and C termini. This general approach was first used by Wüthrich and co-workers to assign all of the resonances in the spectra of the small proteins, basic pancreatic trypsin inhibitor (BPTI, 58 amino acids) [55] and glucagon (29 amino acids) [56].

3.3   TERTIARY STRUCTURE CALCULATION

There are two calculational methods which have been used to determine the three-dimensional structure of proteins from NMR data: distance geometry [51], and restrained molecular dynamics [57].

The distance geometry method begins by setting up matrices of upper and lower limits for all interatomic distances within the protein. These limits can be defined by the van der Waals radii, standard bond lengths and angles, the diameter of the protein and nOe data from NMR. Interatomic distances for atoms are chosen at random between the upper and lower limits. The structure is then minimized by an 'embedding' algorithm which relies on constraining distances with a triangle inequality [51]. A variation on this method which operates on fixed, standard bond lengths and variable dihedral angles has been published [58]. These two distance geometry methods have been compared in their ability to calculate a structure for BPTI from the same NMR data [59]. Both of these methods produce structures in close agreement with the known X-ray structure and each other.

Calculation of the tertiary structure by restrained molecular dynamics methods begins by assembling the protein from fragments of known structure. Unknown structural elements may be incorporated as simple chains. The molecualr dynamics program then minimizes the potential energy of the structure by iteratively moving atoms and recalculating the energy. The NMR data are included as distance constraints. The quality of the structure obtained by this method depends on the quality of the force field parameters used and on the ability of the program to avoid being trapped in local minima [57].

The solution conformation of bull seminal plasma proteinase inhibitor IIA (BUSI), a 57 amino acid protein trypsin inhibitor, was derived by distance geometry methods by Wüthrich and co-workers [60]. Ten conformations of the protein were obtained using 202 distance constraints from NOESY data measured at 500 MHz in water. The backbones of all structures were in agreement to within 4 Å. No X-ray structure exists for the protein; however, there is good general agreement with the spatial arrangement for three homologous proteins whose X-ray structures have been solved.

A solution conformation for the anticoagulant hirudin, a 65 amino acid peptide from leeches, has been determined [61]. No X-ray crystallographic structure exists for hirudin, a potentially medically useful substance. NMR data provided 359 interproton distance constraints from NOESY spectra, and 10 torsional angles from carbon-alpha proton–amide proton coupling constants. The tertiary structure was determined with a combination of distance geometry and restrained molecular dynamics methods. Seven average structures were obtained with r.m.s. deviation of less than 2 Å.

The 53 amino acid protein human epidermal growth factor (hEGF) has been examined by NMR spectroscopy, and a tertiary structure calculated [62]. An X-ray structure for this protein is unknown. It is hoped that the solution structure will lend insight into the mechanism of action of hEGF and many other proteins which contain homologous sequences.

The list of NMR-based protein structures continues to grow. Recent additions include potato carboxypeptidase inhibitor, a 39 amino acid protein [63], and phoratoxin, a 46 residue hemolytic plant toxin [64]. The field is young, and as it expands, with more and more laboratories acquiring the technology and expertise, the contribution made to drug development will be significant.

REFERENCES

[1] Crowfoot, D., Bunn, C. W., Rodgers-Low, B. W., & Turner-Jones, A. (1949). The X-ray crystallographic investigation of the structure of penicillin. Oxford University Press, Oxford.

[2] Kendrew, J. C., Dickerson, R. E., Strandberg, B. E., Hart, R. G., Davies, D. R., Phillips, D. C., & Shore, V. C. (1960). Structure of myoglobin. *Nature* **185**, 422.

[3] Perutz, M. (1985). Early days of protein crystallography. *Meth. Enzymol.* **114**, 3.

[4] Becker, E. D. (1980). *High Resolution NMR, Theory and Chemical Applications*. Academic Press, New York, p. 2.

[5] Sweet, R. M. (1985). Introduction to crystallography. *Meth. Enzymol.* **114**, 19.

[6] DeRanter, C. J. (1983). Crystals, X-ray crystallography, and drugs. In: A. S. Horn & C. J. DeRanter (eds) *X-ray Crystallography and Drugs*. Clarendon Press, Oxford, p. 1.

[7] Patterson, A. L. (1935). A direct method for the determination of the components of interatomic distances in crystals. *Z. Kristallogr.* **90**, 517.

[8] Main, P., Woolfson, L., Lessinger, L., Germain, G., & Declercq, J. (1974). Multan 74: a system of computer programs for the automatic solution of crystal structures from X-ray diffraction data. Univ. of York, England.

[9] Arakawa, T. & Timasheff, S. N. (1985). Theory of protein solubility. *Meth.*

Enzymol. **114**, 49.

[10] Phillips, G. N., Jr. (1985). Crystallization in capillary tubes. *Meth. Enzymol.* **114**, 128.

[11] Sigler, P. B. (1970). Iodination of a single tyrosine in crystals of alpha-chymotrypsin. *Biochemistry* **9**, 3609.

[12] Gallwitz, U., King, L., & Perham, R. N. (1974). Preparation of an isomorphous heavy-atom derivative of tobacco mosaic virus by chemical modification with 4-sulphophenylisocyanate. *J. Mol. Biol.* **87**, 257.

[13] Wycoff, H. W. (1985). Diffractometry. *Meth. Enzymol.* **114**, 330.

[14] Prewitt, C. T., Coppens, P., Phillips, J. C., & Finger, J. W. (1987). New opportunities in synchrotron X-ray crystallography. *Science* **238**, 312.

[15] Smith, T. J., Kremer, M. J., Lao, M., Vriend, G., Arnold, E., Kamer, G., Rossmann, M. G., McKinlay, M. A., Diana, G. D., & Otto, M. J. (1986). The site of attachment in human rhinovirus 14 for antiviral agents that inhibit uncoating. *Science* **233**, 1286.

[16] Artymuik, P. J. & Phillips, D. C. (1985). On the design of diffractometers to measure a number of reflections simultaneously. *Meth. Enzymol.* **114**, 397.

[17] Matthews, D., Alden, R., Bolin, J., Freer, S., Hamlin, R., Xuong, N. H., Kraut, J., Poe, M., Williams, M., & Hoogsteen, K. (1977). Dihydrofolate reductase: X-ray structure of the binary complex with methotrexate. *Science* **197**, 452.

[18] Hamlin, R. (1985). Multiwire area X-ray diffractometers. *Meth. Enzymol.* **114**, 416.

[19] Durbi, R. M., Burns, R., Moulai, J., Metcalf, P., Freymann, D., Blum, M., Anderson, J. E., Harrison, S. C., & Wiley, D. C. (1986). Protein, DNA, and virus crystallography with a focused imaging proportional counter. *Science* **232**, 1127.

[20] Arndt, U. W. (1985). Television area detector diffractometers. *Meth. Enzymol.* **114**, 472.

[21] Arndt, U. W. (1984). Area detectors for protein crystallography at storage rings. *Nucl. Instrum. Meth. Phys. Res., Sect. A.* **222**, 252.

[22] Rossmann, M. G. & Blow, D. M. (1963). Determination of phases by the conditions of non-crystallographic symmetry. *Acta Crystallogr.* **16**, 39.

[23] Jones, T. A. & Thirup, S. (1986). Using known substructures in protein model building and crystallography. *EMBO J.* **5**, 819.

[24] Phizackerley, R. P., Cork, C. W., & Merritt, E. A. (1986). An area detector data acquisition system for protein crystallography using multiple-energy anomalous dispersion techniques. *Nucl. Instrum. Meth. Phys. Res., Sect. A.* **246**, 579.

[25] Guss, J. M., Merritt, R. P., Phizackerley, R. P., Hedman, B., Murata, M., Hodgson, K. O., & Freeman, H. C. (1988). Phase determination by multiple-wavelength X-ray diffraction: crystal structure of a basic blue copper protein from cucumbers. *Science* **241**, 806.

[26] Lindley, P. F. (1988). Crystallographic studies of biological macromolecules using synchrotron radiation. *NATO ASI Ser., Ser. C.* **221**, 509.

[27] Kvick, A. (1988). Applications of synchrotron X-rays to chemical crystallography. *NATO ASI Ser., Ser. C.* **221**, 187.

[28] Gruner, S. M. (1987). Time resolved X-ray diffraction of biological materials. *Science* **238**, 305.

[29] Hajdu, J., Achararya, K. R., Stuart, D. I., Barfield, D., & Johnson, L. N. (1988). Catalysis in enzyme crystals. *Trends Biochem. Sci.* **13**, 104.

[30] Moffat, K., Szebenyi, D., & Bilderback, D. (1984). X-ray Laue diffraction from protein crystals. *Science* **223**, 1423.

[31] Hajdu, J., Machin, P. A., Campbell, J. W., Greenough, T. J., Clifton, I. J., Zurek, S., Gover, S., Johnson, L. N., & Elder, M. (1987). Millisecond X-ray diffraction and the first electron density map from Laue photographs of a protein crystal. *Nature* **329**, 178.

[32] Schoenborn, B. P. (1985). Experimental neutron protein crystallography. *Meth. Enzymol.* **114**, 510.

[33] Wlodawer, A. (1985). Neutron diffraction: a facility for data collection and processing at the National Bureau of Standards Reactor. *Meth. Enzymol.* **114**, 551.

[34] Kossiakoff, A. A. (1982). Protein dynamics investigated by the neutron diffraction–hydrogen exchange technique. *Nature* **296**, 713.

[35] Mason, S. A., Bentley, G. A., & McIntyre, G. J. (1984). *Neutrons in Biology*. Schoenborn, B. P. (ed.), Plenum Press, New York, p. 323.

[36] Lehmann, M. S., Mason, S. A., & McIntyre, G. J. (1985). Studies of ethanol–lysozyme interactions using neutron diffraction. *Biochemistry* **24**, 5862.

[37] Cushman, D. W., Cheung, H. S., Sabo, E. F., & Ondetti, M. A. (1977). Design of potent competitive inhibitors of angiotensin-converting enzyme. *Biochemistry* **16**, 5484.

[38] James, M. N. G. & Sielecki, A. R. (1985). Stereochemical analysis of peptide bond hydrolysis catalyzed by the aspartic proteinase penicillopepsin. *Biochemistry* **24**, 3701.

[39] Navia, M. A., Springer, J. P., Poe, M., Boger, J., & Hoogsteen, K. (1982). Preliminary X-ray crystallographic data on mouse submaxillary gland renin and renin-inhibitor complexes. *J. Biol. Chem.* **259**, 12714.

[40] Nutt, R. F., Brady, S. F., Darke, P. L., Ciccarone, T. M., Colton, C. D., Nutt, E. M., Rodkey, J. A., Bennett, C. D., Waxman, L. M., Sigal, I. S., Anderson, P. S., & Veber, D. F. (1988). Chemical synthesis and enzymatic activity of a 99-residue peptide with a sequence proposed for the human immunodeficiency virus protease. *Proc. Natl. Acad. Sci. USA* **85**, 7129.

[41] Beddell, C. R. (1983). Dihydrofolate reductase: its structure, function, and binding properties. In: A. S. Horn & C. J. DeRanter (eds) *X-ray crystallography and Drug Action*. Clarendon press, Oxford, p. 169.

[42] McPhalen, C. AS., Schnebli, H. P., & James, M. N. G. (1985). Crystal and molecular structure of the inhibitor eglin from leeches in complex with subtilisin Carlsberg. *FEBS Lett.* **188**, 55.

[43] Griesinger, C., Sorensen, O. W. & Ernst, R. R. (1987). Novel three dimensional NMR techniques for studies of peptides and biological macromolecules. *J. Am. Chem. Soc.* **109**, 7227.

[44] Cooke, R. M. & Campbell, I. D., (1988). Protein structure determination by nuclear magnetic resonance. *Bioessays* **8**, 52.

[45] Kaptein, R., Bolens, R., Scheek, R. M., & van Gunsteren, W. F. (1988).

Protein structure from NMR. *Biochemistry* **27**, 5389.

[46] Abelson, P. H. (1988). New horizons in medicine. *Science* **242**, 1109.

[47] Wüthrich, K. (1986). *NMR of Proteins and Nucleic Acids*. Wiley, New York, p. 17.

[48] Noggle, J. H. & Shirmer, R. E. (1971). *The Nuclear Overhauser Effect*. Academic Press, New York, p.45.

[49] Jeener, J., Meier, B. H., Bachman, P., & Ernst, R. R. (1979). Investigation of exchange processes by two dimensional NMR spectroscopy. *J. Chem. Phys.* **71**, 4546.

[50] Braun, W. (1987). Distance geometry and related methods for protein structure determination from NMR data. *Quart. Rev. Biophys.* **19**, 115.

[51] Aue, W. P., Bartholdi, E., & Ernst, R. R. (1976). Two-dimensional NMR spectroscopy. Application to nuclear magnetic resonance. *J. Chem. Phys.* **64**, 2229.

[52] Pardi, A., Billeter, M., & Wüthrich, K. (1984). Calibration of the angular dependence of the amide-proton C-alpha proton coupling constants, $^3J_{NH}$, in a globular protein. *J. Mol. Biol.* **180**, 741.

[53] Wüthrich, K., Widner, G., Wagner, G., & Braun, W. (1982). Sequential resonance assignments as a basis for the determination of spatial protein structures by high resolution proton nuclear magnetic resonance. *J. Mol. Biol.* **155**, 311.

[54] Billeter, M., Braun, W., & Wüthrich, K. (1982). Sequential resonance assignments in protein ^1H nuclear magnetic resonance spectra. *J. Mol. Biol.* **155**, 321.

[55] Wagner, G. & Wüthrich, K. (1982). Sequential resonance assignments in protein ^1H nuclear magnetic resonance spectra. *J. Mol. Biol.* **155**, 347.

[56] Wider, G., Lee, K. H., & Wüthrich, K. (1982). Sequential resonance assignments in protein ^1H nuclear magnetic resonance spectra. *J. Mol. Biol.* **155**, 367.

[57] Van Gunsteren, W. F. and Berendsen, H. J. C. (1982). Molecular dynamics: perspective for complex systems. *Biochem. Soc. Trans.* **10**, 301.

[58] Braun, W. & Gō, N. (1985). Calculation of protein conformation by proton–proton distance constraints, a new efficient algorithm. *J. Mol. Biol.* **186**, 611.

[59] Wagner, G., Braun, W., Havel, T. F., Schaumann, T., Gō, N., & Wüthrich, K. (1987). Protein structures in solution by nuclear magnetic resonance and distance geometry. *J. Mol. Biol.* **196**, 611.

[60] Williamson, M. P., Havel, T. F., & Wüthrich, K. (1985). Solution conformation of proteinase inhibitor IIA from bull seminal plasma by ^1H nuclear magnetic resonance and distance geometry. *J. Mol. Biol.* **182**, 295.

[61] Clore, G. M., Sukumaran, D. K., Nilges, M., Zarbock, J., & Gronenborn, A. M. (1987). The conformations of hirudin in solution: a study using nuclear magnetic resonance, distance geometry and restrained molecular dynamics. *EMBO J.* **6**, 529.

[62] Cooke, R. M., Wilkinson, A. J., Baron, M., Pastore, A., Tappin, M. J., Campbell, I. D., Gregory, H., & Sheard, B. (1987). The solution structure of human epidermal growth factor. *Nature* **327**, 339.

[63] Clore, G. M., Gronenborn, A. M., Nilges, M., & Ryan, C. A. (1987). Three-dimensional structure of potato carboxypeptidase inhibitor in solution. A study using nuclear magnetic resonance, distance geometry, and restrained molecular

dynamics. *Biochemistry* **26**, 8012.

[64] Clore, G. M., Sukurmaran, D. K., Nilges, M., & Gronenborn, A. M. (1987). Three-dimensional structure of phoratoxin in solution: combined use of nuclear magnetic resonance, distance geometry, and restrained molecular dynamics. *Biochemistry* **26**, 1732.

Part II
Drug delivery

4

Chemical approaches for site-specific drug delivery

James J. Kaminski*[†] and **Nicholas Bodor**[†]
*Pharmaceutical Research Division, Schering-Plough Research, Schering-Plough Corporation, Bloomfield, New Jersey, USA
[†]Center for Drug Design and Delivery, College of Pharmacy, University of Florida, Gainesville, Florida, USA

4.1 INTRODUCTION

Clearly the most important property of a drug is its therapeutic index (TI), which represents the ratio between the toxic and therapeutic doses. Ideally, drugs should have rather large therapeutic indices, indicating a significant and safe separation between these two important dose levels. Since the development of receptor theory, attempts have been directed toward developing new therapeutic entities that would have a singular target and would be accepted by only one kind of receptor. In this way, it was hoped that aberrant toxicity would be avoided and the desired therapeutic gain would be produced. This concept would work very well if diseases would have their own specific receptors which would allow this individual design to affect only the specific disease. However, the situation is not that simple. Most receptors are generally distributed throughout the body, whereas various diseases are many times localized. This means that even if one finds a drug which binds to and agonizes or antagonizes only one specific receptor type, the therapeutic index may still not be too favorable. Recognition of this fact led to the idea that something additional had to be done to localize drugs at their desired site of action. Actually, nature has shown us some of the ways that this can be done. Neurotransmitters like dopamine are released at specific parts of the brain, producing the desired action, but they are also localized within the brain by the blood brain barrier (BBB). Moreover, once released these neurotransmitters are quickly metabolized. Taken together, these effects prevent dopamine from affecting peripheral receptors. On the other hand, when one introduces neurotransmitters, like dopamine, to the peripheral circulation, these agents cannot cross the brain barrier and therefore cannot produce central disturbances.

During the past 15 or so years, tremendous effort throughout the world has been exerted in the research and development of potentially site-specific, targeted drug delivery systems. Most of these efforts were directed to improve the delivery of currently known drugs. In most cases, the main objective was to improve the therapeutic index. However in some cases, the objective was mainly to extend proprietary protection to these known therapeutic entities. Regardless of the impetus, there are several classifications of this large field of site-specific drug delivery. One general classification differentiates first-, second- and third-order targeting [1]. First-order targeting refers to the restricted distribution of the drug to the site of action, e.g. delivery of the drug to a specific tissue or organ. Second-order targeting refers to the selective delivery of the drug to specific host cells, whereas third-order targeting refers to the directed release of the drug at predetermined intracellular sites. Excellent reviews on second- and third-order targeting as it relates to site-specific drug delivery have been presented in recent articles and a monograph [2–4].

This older classification was also used recently in an extensive review article on all kinds of drug delivery systems [5]. According to this article, site-specific drug delivery systems can be classified as prodrugs, carrier systems and mechanical pumps. In addition, the classification of carrier systems may be further delineated as macromolecular delivery systems, particulate delivery systems and cellular drug carriers.

Another very recent, comprehensive and excellent review has an entirely different and more general approach [6]. Treatment of the various drug targeting approaches here is based on consideration of the disease and the delivery of the drug in terms of site access, retention, and timing of interaction coupled to the duration of the effect of the drug and the responsiveness of the target. This approach is the most correct since it recognizes that too often carriers have been identified without any cognizance of the pathogenesis of the disease. The result of these attempts is overemphasized claims on improved site-specific delivery, although the data suggest an increase in the site access from almost nothing to marginal improvements at best.

Another classification of drug delivery systems could be *mechanism-based* — i.e. definition of the process which is the basis for their claimed or actual function. According to this classification, three global classes can be defined: *physical*, *biological* and *chemical* site-specific delivery systems. Accordingly, anything where the targeting is controlled by physical processes such as local release of pilocarpine from Ocusert (ALZA), a polymeric device inserted in the eye, to particulate delivery systems where the particles containing drugs are localized by virtue of their size in the capillaries, fall under the first group, physical delivery systems.

In the second group, the *biological* delivery systems, all attempts where the targeting is designed to be performed by biological processes should be included, e.g. targeting with monoclonal antibodies, or erythrocyte [7], leukocyte [8] or other cellular drug carriers. A large variety of carrier systems belonging to the *physical* and *biological* classes have already been extensively reviewed in the literature [4–6].

Aside from reviews describing a few specific systems [9,10] the only condensed review on *chemical* site-specific delivery systems was published in 1987 [11]. In principle, *chemical* drug delivery systems should include any system which requires a chemical reaction to produce the system, i.e. where a chemical bond connecting the active component to the carrier must be broken. Within this large class, 'polymeric prodrugs', whereby the polymeric particles or devices chemically bind the drugs, or even antibody-drug conjugates or derivatized liposomes and albumins, should all be included. However, in the strictest sense, *chemical* delivery systems refer to site-specific or site-enhanced chemical delivery forms, i.e. inactive covalently bound drug derivatives which require multistep enzymatic and/or chemical transformations to release the drug [12,13]. Again, one could simplify the overall process and separate the physical delivery from the rest by stating that in the *physical* delivery systems the drug (D) is unmodified chemically, and physical delivery of the device or the carrier to the site will provide the enhanced concentration of the drug at the active site. The other two approaches ultimately need to deliver a *precursor* which could be called a direct prodrug (PD) or a chemical delivery system (CDS). Here, either by biological means, which includes specific recognition provided by anti-bodies, macromolecular and cellular carriers, or by a chemical delivery system (CDS), in which the carrier is comparable in size to the drug, are the processes by which the *precursor* is transported to the site (Fig. 4.1).

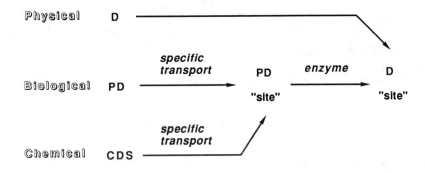

Fig. 4.1 — Mechanism-based classification of drug delivery systems.

In order to clarify some potential points of misunderstanding, certain terms need to be defined and explained. First, the term 'prodrug (PD)' will refer to the direct precursor of a drug which is just one-step removed from the drug. As shown in Fig. 4.2, a prodrug will be converted essentially in one-step to the drug. The rate of this process (k_2) is dominant over direct elimination (k_1) or other metabolism of the prodrug (k_3). It is evident that the prodrug is biologically inactive and just serves as a transport form of the drug.

We can now define a 'soft drug, SD'. A soft drug by definition is a biologically active species [14,15]. However, in general, the soft drug behaves very differently from the drug (Fig. 4.3). This behavior is by design. The soft drug will undergo a predicted and controlled singular transformation to a nontoxic and inactive metabolite, or, in some cases, will be degraded to more than one nontoxic and inactive metabolite. The main point is that by design, the soft drug simplifies the transformation–distribution–activity profile which most drugs exhibit. Soft drug design aims to

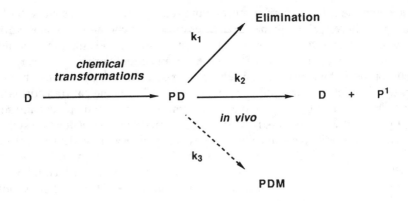

Fig. 4.2 — Prodrug definition.

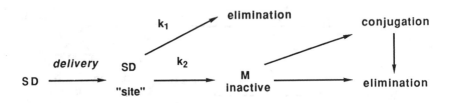

Fig. 4.3 — Soft drug definition.

produce pharmacological activity of a specific, desired kind and then predicted processes deactivate or metabolize the soft drug in one-step to an inactive species. As currently practiced, based on its general properties, a soft drug fits the definition of a *physical* delivery system the best. When applied at the desired site of action, be it topical or internal, the soft drug will elicit the desired pharmacological effect locally, but as soon as it is distributed from the site, it is susceptible to deactivation, thereby preventing any unwanted side effect which would be otherwise characteristic for this class of drug.

The most complex among all the chemically modified transport and targeted forms of a drug is the site-specific *chemical* delivery system, or simply the *chemical* delivery system (CDS). Here we can differentiate at least two major classes, the *physical–chemical–based* and the *site-specific enzyme-activated* chemical delivery systems.

The first type, the *physical–chemical-based* chemical delivery system is described in general in Fig. 4.4. Accordingly, a drug (D) is chemically transformed by covalently binding to it as many 'carrier' moieties and other functions as necessary, C and F respectively. Upon delivery to the body and overall distribution, the chemical delivery system will undergo various stepwise enzymatic conversions, both at the site

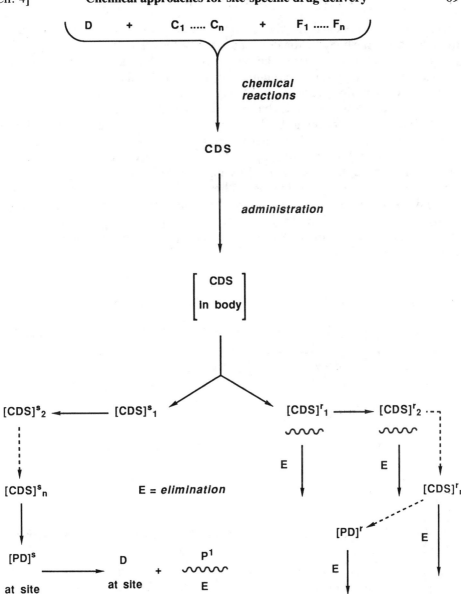

Fig. 4.4 — Physical–chemical-based chemical drug delivery systems.

(superscript s) and in the rest of the body (superscript r). These transformations can be the same type or a different type, but the main characteristic of these transformations is that they provide a predictable, significant change in the lipophilicity and distribution properties of the intermediate, allowing concentration of the inactivated intermediates, $(CDS^{1,2,...,n})$, and ultimately the direct precursor at the specific site. On the other hand, these or other enzymatic processes will convert the original chemical delivery system to inactive intermediates which will allow facile elimination from the rest of the body. Ultimately, the site-concentrated direct precursor (PD) in the last step will allow release of the active drug only at its site of action. While the process appears complicated, a number of successful examples will be described, particularly for brain-specific drug delivery. In addition, delivery to other organs besides the brain is also possible, but requires using a different chemical approach.

The second type of chemical delivery system is what one would call a medicinal chemist's dream. That is, specific enzymes at the site of action, and only at the site of action, are responsible for converting the chemical delivery system or some intermediate form of it into the active drug. This implies that this specific enzyme is absent from the rest of the body, or, for some other reason, such as selective distribution, does not affect the chemical delivery system or its intermediates elsewhere in the body. This true site-specific chemical delivery system, when successful, produces a truly dramatic separation between pharmacologic activity and toxicity. These chemical delivery systems are described schematically in Fig. 4.5.

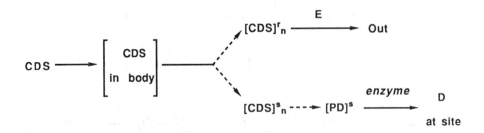

Fig. 4.5 — Site-specific enzyme-activated chemical delivery systems.

4.2 *IN VITRO* AND *IN VIVO* METHODS IN EVALUATING SITE-SPECIFIC DRUG DELIVERY

In general, a variety of *in vitro* methods are used to evaluate the chemically modified transport form of the drug, prodrug or chemical delivery system, in order to ensure that the active entity can be liberated from the transport form. For this reason, isolated enzymes, e.g. esterases, or more frequently blood and organ homogenates are used. However, many times these *in vitro* studies, intended to simulate *in vivo* conditions, can give misleading results, especially in terms of rates of enzymatic cleavage. Therefore, it is cautioned that a series of compounds must be closely related structurally in order that their relative stability be estimated reliably using these methods.

On the other hand, transport properties of prodrugs that cross various major biological barriers, such as the skin and cornea, have been evaluated *in vitro* for some time. However, these studies involve 'external' barriers which are easily accessible. Moreover, the *in vitro* results can be easily compared with *in vivo* determined data.

Recent emphasis on the potential use of peptides, proteins and neurotransmitters to be used as therapeutic entities necessitated the development of more sophisticated *in vitro* techniques to evaluate the transport properties of these, in general, more highly sensitive molecules. There are two major barriers for the delivery of these molecules: the first is the intestinal mucosa and the second is the blood brain barrier. It was long thought that the study of transport through intestinal mucosa was relatively straightforward since numerous small intestinal preparations were easily available, i.e. everted sacs, intestinal rings and vascular perfused intestine, etc. However, the potential utility of these methods is substantially reduced by the limited viability of isolated intestinal epithelial cells [16]. In addition, cell isolation procedures result in loss of cell polarity and it is difficult to delinate the potential role of the different epithelial cell components in determining membrane permeability. Nevertheless, some of these methods are useful in determining the absorption of simple molecules in particular.

By using inverted rings of the intestine, one can determine the presence of specific uptake in different segments of the intestine and these observations suggest the presence of active transport systems [17]. However, evaluation of chemically modified drugs in this model would be more difficult. Recently a model was suggested to study the transepithelial transport of peptides and protein drugs across the mucosa of the small intestine. There are two human adenocarcinoma cell lines (CACO-2 and HT-29) which have the advantageous property of being able to be grown indefinitely in culture without the loss of polarity or viability. They can be grown in monolayer intensity, and the fully developed cell layers have characteristic small intestinal enzymes [16].

In vitro studies of the blood brain barrier appear to be more difficult, as the actual barrier is the capillary wall in the brain, which is structurally different from capillaries in the rest of the body. This barrier represents a formidable physical, as well as significant enzymatic, obstacle for a wide range of blood-borne molecules, in particular peptides, proteins and neurotransmitters. Using whole animals, *in vivo* methods were the most informative for studying the unique brain 'lock-in' delivery system [9,13].

However, there is a need to investigate the transport properties of a variety of peptides, proteins and actively transported small molecules at the cellular–molecular level. Once again, the first *in vitro* test system was represented by a simple model which consisted of a suspension of isolated brain microvessel endothelial cells (BMEC) [18]. This simple model was successful in providing significant information to characterize amino acid transport systems and identifying enzymatic pathways characteristic of the blood brain barrier. However, this model suffers from the inability to study transcellular transport systems [16].

The second type of *in vitro* model for the blood brain barrier consists of brain microvessel endothelial cells grown to monolayers [18,19]. Clearly, this *in vitro* system could distinguish between uptake (endocytosis) and the transport (transcytosis) of proteins like insulin. Based on the simple microvessel suspension model, it was suggested [20] that insulin is transported intact through the blood brain barrier and, if true, this model could be used for the development of selected macromolecular delivery systems. However, recent studies demonstrate that while 60% of the bound insulin is apparently internalized, only 5% added to one side of the monolayer is transcytosed after 2 h. These results suggest significant degradation of the protein by metabolism during the experiment.

4.3 PHARMACOKINETIC CONSIDERATIONS IN EVALUATING SITE-SPECIFIC DRUG DELIVERY

A theoretical model to assess the efficiency of drug targeting was recently developed, where the value of the drug targeting index (DTI) was defined [21]. The method allows a calculation of the drug targeting index and the therapeutic availability based on the drug's total body clearance and some knowledge of the anatomy and blood flow at the target site. It was concluded that the fraction of the drug actually released from the carrier at both target and non-target sites can readily affect index values. It was also argued that most drugs already developed have a low 'potential-to-benefit' ratio from combination with a drug carrier.

A truly successful site-specific drug delivery presents an exceptional problem for the pharmacokineticist. In most cases, conventional pharmacokinetic principles based on blood level data are meaningless and cannot be used to predict pharmacologic activity. Some of the potential problems were recently addressed, but these relate more to a *physical* drug delivery system [22]. When a *chemical* drug delivery system, which is effectively localized at a specific site and futhermore is in an active form, is presented for analysis, the pharmacokinetic problems become extremely complex. For example, some of the brain-specific delivery systems are capable of producing orders of magnitude higher concentration of drug in the brain than in the periphery for as long as one month following administration of a single dose. Clearly under these circumstances, assessment of the pharmacologic and biologic parameters is the only reliable way to evaluate the effectiveness of these systems at this point in time [23].

4.4 PRODRUGS

4.4.1 Antiallergy agents

The prodrug technique has been used successfully to prolong the action of drugs in relatively few instances. A comparative study of the bronchodilator prodrug bitolterol (1) with other β_2-agonists has been reported [24] and while the prodrug prolongs the action of the bronchodilating agent calterol, after inhalation from a pressurized aerosol, bitolterol fails to give prolonged action after oral administration because of extensive first-pass hydrolysis of the ester prodrug.

Prodrugs of selective bronchodilator β-adrenoreceptor agonists have been reviewed recently with special emphasis on the development of agents with increased specificity for the lung [25,26]. Of particular interest are the *in vitro* and *in vivo* studies of two new prodrugs of tertbutaline, the cascade ester (D 2438, **2**) and bambuterol (**3**) [27].

1   R = p-CH$_3$C$_6$H$_4$CO- , *bitolterol*   2   R = p-(CH$_3$)$_3$CCO$_2$C$_6$H$_4$CO- , D 2438

      R = H , *calterol*   3   R = (CH$_3$)$_2$NCO- , *bambuterol*

                                              R = H , *tertbutaline*

D 2438 was found to be very stable in human plasma *in vitro*, exhibiting a half-life of approximately 10 h. The high hydrolytic stability of D 2438 was of an order that protection of the prodrug from extensive first-class hydrolysis could be expected. When D 2438 was given orally to dogs, both sustained action and prolonged tertbutaline plasma concentrations were observed. However, it was later determined that the hydrolysis of esters of this type occurs at a slower rate in dogs than in humans. The oral administration of D 2438 to humans resulted in neither sustained action nor prolonged tertbutaline plasma concentrations. Thus, despite its high biological stability in human plasma *in vitro* and its pharmacologic profile in the dog, D 2438 gave disappointing clinical results in man.

An alternative approach to increase the first-pass hydrolytic stability of a prodrug suggested the co-administration of an esterase inhibitor along with the prodrug; or, more desirable, the design of a prodrug that may also exhibit esterase inhibitory properties. In the latter case, the prodrug could slow down its own hydrolysis by inhibiting the esterases responsible for its own degradation.

Derivatization of phenols with an *N,N*-dimethylcarbamate moiety is known to result in compounds that exhibit esterase inhibitory properties. Thus, the bis-*N,N*-dimethylcarbamate of tertbutaline, bambuterol, was prepared as a potential prodrug that by virtue of its intrinsic esterase inhibitory activity might exhibit adequate presystemic hydrolytic stability to deliver tertbutaline upon oral administration. In man, bambuterol was found to be a selective and potent cholinesterase inhibitor with an $IC_{50} = 17$ nM for cholinesterase, whereas the corresponding value for acetylcholinesterase was 2400-fold higher, i.e. $IC_{50} = 41 \mu$M. More importantly, the *N,N*-dimethylcarbamate function appears to effectively protect bambuterol from hydrolysis during absorption and passage through the gut wall. In addition, first-pass metabolism by the liver is directed at the *N,N*-dimethylcarbamate groups where both hydrolysis and oxidative metabolism take place. Several of the metabolites generated by the two different metabolic pathways are also novel carbamate prodrugs of tertbutaline.

As a result of this presystemic stability, oral administration of bambuterol produces approximately the same proportion of tertbutaline and other urinary metabolites as an intravenous dose. In fact clinically, oral administration of bambuterol to asthmatic patients accomplishes sustained action, allowing once-a-day dosing, produces steady-state plasma concentrations of tertbutaline with little intersubject variation and exhibits some site-specific delivery of tertbutaline to the lung.

The activity profile of 2-ethoxyethyl 5-chlorobenzoxazole-2-carboxylate, eclazlast, (REV 2871, **4**) as an inhibitor of immunologically and non-immunologically mediated secretion of histamine from rat mast cells, human basophils and guinea pig lung was compared and contrasted to disodium cromoglycate (DSCG) and proxicromil. REV 2871 is taken up by rat mast cells and human leukocytes in a specific and saturable manner. The compound is hydrolysed in the mast cell to the carboxylate metabolite (REV 3579, **5**), whose *in vitro* profile is similar to DSCG. While REV 3579 is not taken up by rat mast cells or human leukocytes itself, millimolar intracellular concentration of REV 3579 is achieved when transported by the prodrug REV 2871. The unusual *in vitro* activity of REV 2871 is postulated to arise from a longer-lived inhibition of the secretory process by internalized REV 2871, rather than REV 2871 acting on exterior membrane receptors. The generality of enhanced transport across cell membranes of 'ethoxyethyl ester' prodrugs to other carboxylic acids remains to be established.

4   R = -CH$_2$CH$_2$OCH$_2$CH$_3$, REV 2871

5   R = H , REV 3579

4.4.2 Antiinflammatory agents

Most of the gastrointestinal side-effects induced by the nonsteroidal antiinflammatory agents are due to inhibition of the cyclooxygenase enzyme. Since prodrugs of nonsteroidal antiinflammatory drugs are capable of passing through the gastrointestinal tract in their inactive form, gastrointestinal disturbances caused by prodrugs are expected to be weak.

Recently the gastrointestinal ulcerogenicity of loxaprofen (CS-600, **6**) was demonstrated to be very weak. The available evidence suggests that loxaprofen is a prodrug and exerts its antiinflammatory activity only after metabolic conversion to its active metabolite (**7**) [28]. Most prodrugs are metabolized into their active forms at the gastrointestinal wall, in the liver or in the serum. However, some prodrugs can be converted into their active forms at the site of inflammation if they have an affinity for the inflammatory lesions or cells. Indofarnesylate (**8**) and proglumethacin (**9**) may be more effective prodrugs of indomethacin since they accumulate in the inflamed tissue and are converted into their active form in some parts of the inflamed tissues [29].

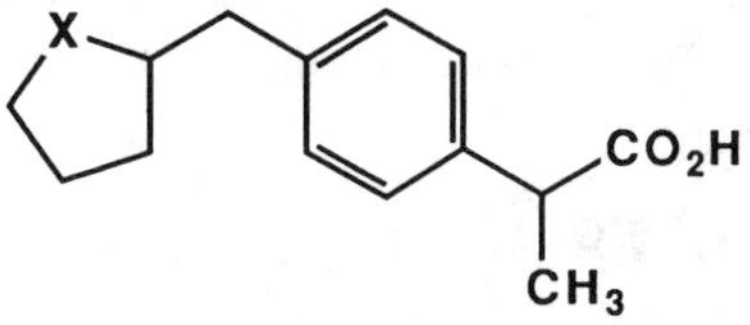
X
CO_2H
CH_3

6 X = C=O , CS-600 , *loxaprofen*

7 X = 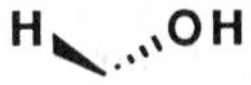
H
OH

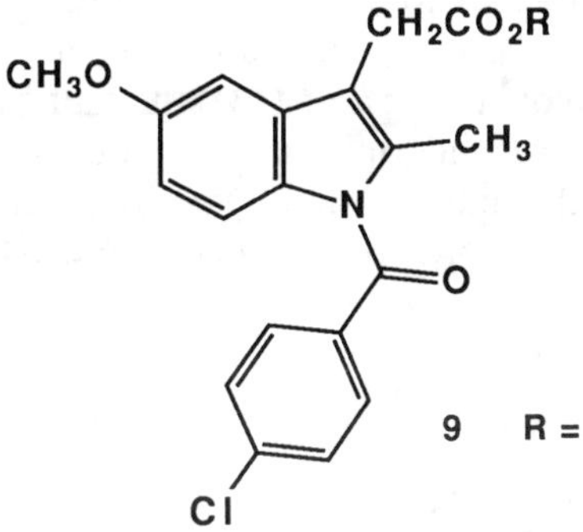
CH_2CO_2R
CH_3O
CH_3
N
O
Cl

8 R = 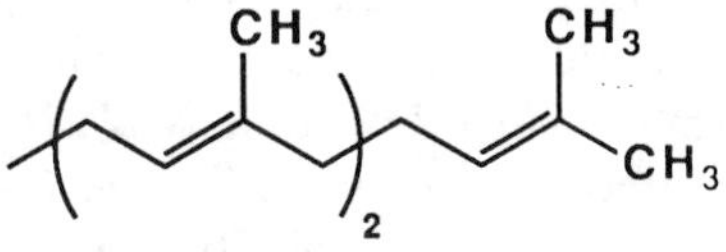
CH_3
CH_3
CH_3
2

Indofarnesylate

9 R = 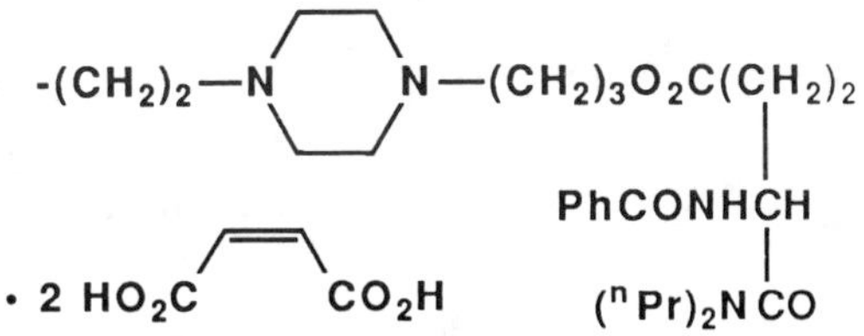
$-(CH_2)_2-N$
$N-(CH_2)_3O_2C(CH_2)_2$
PhCONHCH
$(^nPr)_2NCO$
$\cdot$ 2 HO_2C
CO_2H

proglumethacin

Arylacetic acid antiinflammatory drugs can be metabolically produced by β-oxidation of a 6-arylhex-5-enoic acid side chain. Such a mechanism has been examined for the *in vivo* sustained release of indomethacin and biphenyl acetic acid using 6-[*N*-(*p*-chlorobenzoyl)-2-methylindol-3-yl]hex-5-enoic acid (**10**), and 6-(4′-biphenylyl)hex-5- and 4-(4′-biphenylyl)but-3-enoic acids (**11**) and (**12**) respectively [30]. In a yeast-induced hyperalgesia model, the indomethacin prodrug (**10**) produced sustained analgesia for over a 12 h period. Furthermore, indomethacin plasma levels of 2 μg/ml were observed for up to 24 h post administration of the prodrug. Most importantly, when indomethacin was dosed at equipotent analgesic levels, the level of circulating drug was higher than that observed from metabolically derived drug. This observation suggests that the biologically efficacy of the drug is enhanced by site-specific tissue compartmentalization via prodrug delivery.

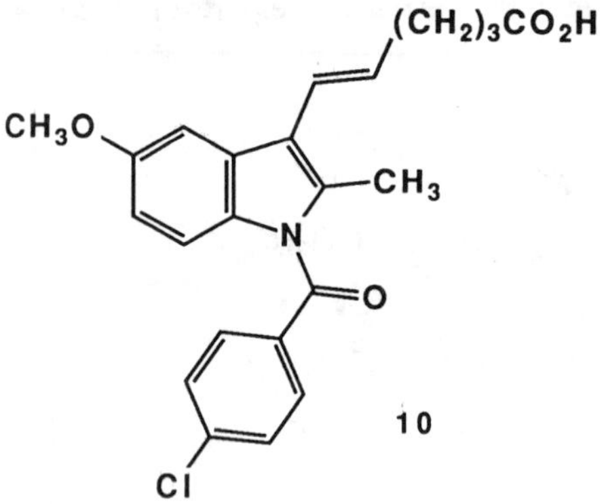

$(CH_2)_3CO_2H$

CH_3O-

$-CH_3$

10

Cl

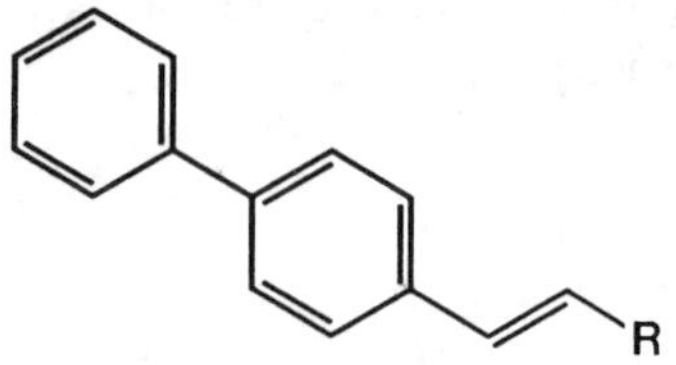

11   R = $(CH_2)_3CO_2H$

12   R = CH_2CO_2H

Novel approaches toward derivatization of the carboxylic acid function in a number of nonsteroidal antiinflammatory drugs has led to the identification of glycolamide [31–34], *N*-hydroxymethylacyl [35] and α-hydroxy-*N*-benzoylglycyl esters [35] as potential biolabile prodrugs of these carboxylic acid agents. The glycolamide esters were, in general, found to hydrolyze very rapidly in human plasma *in vitro*. For some *N,N*-disubstituted glycolamide esters (**13**), the half-lives exhibited *in vitro* were on the order of a few seconds to a few minutes while maintaining a high stability in aqueous solution. In contrast, simple methyl or ethyl esters of these carboxylic acids were found to be hydrolyzed only very slowly in the presence of human plasma.

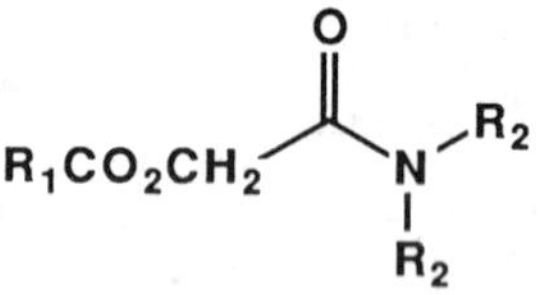

$$R_1CO_2CH_2 \overset{O}{\underset{R_2}{\overset{\|}{C}}} \overset{R_2}{\underset{|}{N}}$$

$\underline{R_1 \equiv}$ $\underline{R_2 \equiv}$

13 a   (2-hydroxyphenyl) CH_2CH_3

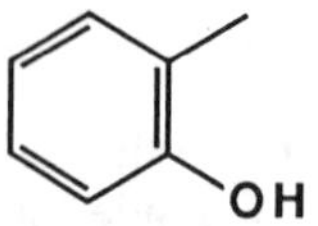

OH

CH_3

CH_3

13 b CH_3

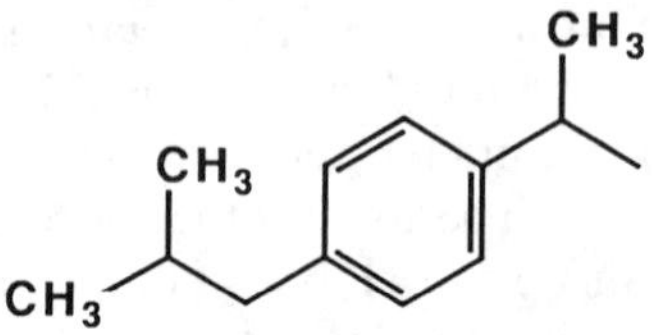

CH_3

For a number of years, many attempts have been made to develop prodrugs of aspirin. However, in the majority of cases cited, the prodrugs prepared were in fact prodrugs of salicylic acid rather than prodrugs of aspirin, acetylsalicylic acid. This situation arises since the functional moiety of the potential prodrug used to mask the carboxylic acid function cleaves slower than the acetylated phenol. Using the criteria that a 'true' aspirin prodrug must produce *measurable* plasma concentrations of aspirin, rather than salicylic acid, following *in vivo* administration of the aspirin prodrug, only two examples, **14** and **15** respectively, have been reported in the literature [36,37]. Nevertheless, several *N*- hydroxymethyl acyl (**16** and **17**) and α-hydroxybenzoylglycyl benzyl esters (**18**) have demonstrated *in vitro* hydrolysis to aspirin, rather than salicylic acid [35]. The results of the evaluation of these prodrugs *in vivo* are anxiously awaited.

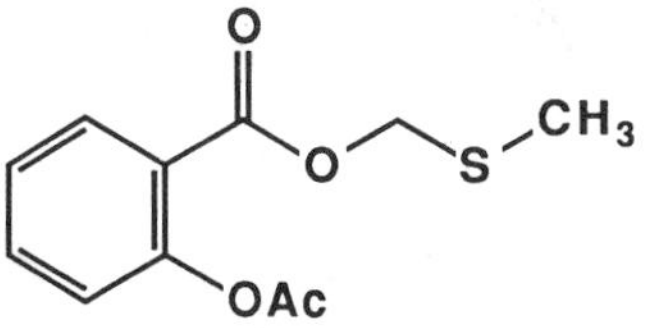
O
O
S
CH3
OAc

14

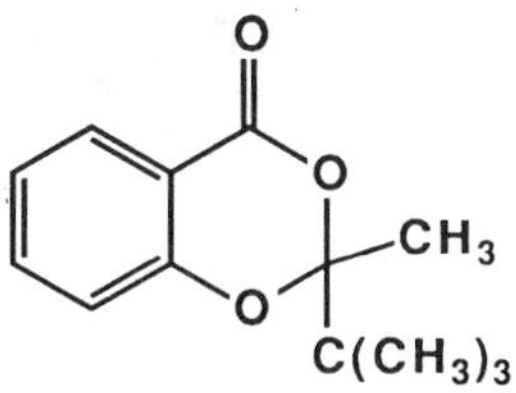
O
O
O
CH3
C(CH3)3

15

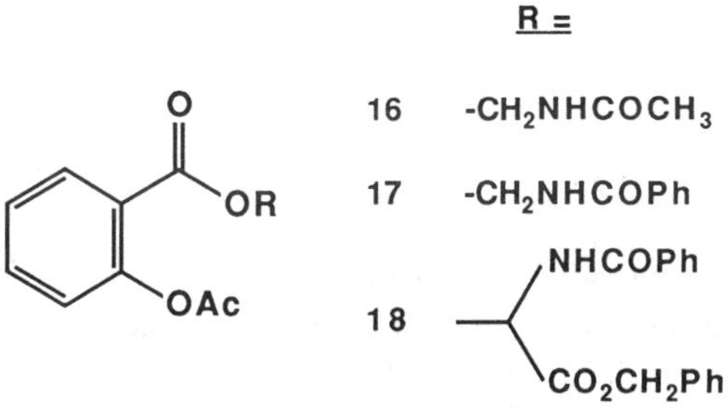
R =
O
OR
OAc
16 -CH2NHCOCH3
17 -CH2NHCOPh
18
NHCOPh
CO2CH2Ph

4.4.3 Antiulcer agents

The treatment of peptic ulcers via inhibition of the gastric proton pump enzyme, H^+/K^+-ATPase, may have intrinsic advantages over other methods of therapy such as inhibition of acid secretion by antagonism of the H-2 receptor. The intrinsic advantage of proton pump inhibitors resides solely on the specific localization of the target enzyme, H^+/K^+-ATPase, to the parietal cell of the stomach, whereas H-2 receptors are present in other organs of the body besides the stomach, e.g. the atria, etc.

Substituted benzimidazoles are potent inhibitors of the parietal cell proton pump, H^+/K^+-ATPase. The sulfide, B823-08 (**19**), inhibits gastric acid secretion in a variety of *in vivo* models, but fails to affect acid secretion in the isolated lumen perfused mouse stomach. However, the corresponding sulfoxide, B823-10 (**20**), is active both *in vitro* and *in vivo* [38]. Since the sulfide is metabolically transformed to the sulfoxide *in vivo*, the sulfide is a prodrug of the sulfoxide. Importantly, there is no indication that the functions of organs known to critically depend upon Na^+/K^+-ATPase are affected in any way. This observation is significant and consistent with the hypothesis that the sulfoxide requires activation in an acidic environment, which constitutes the basis of its specificity to inhibit stimulated parietal cells. Therefore, the sulfoxide, B823-10 (**20**), is representative of a 'site-specific' prodrug.

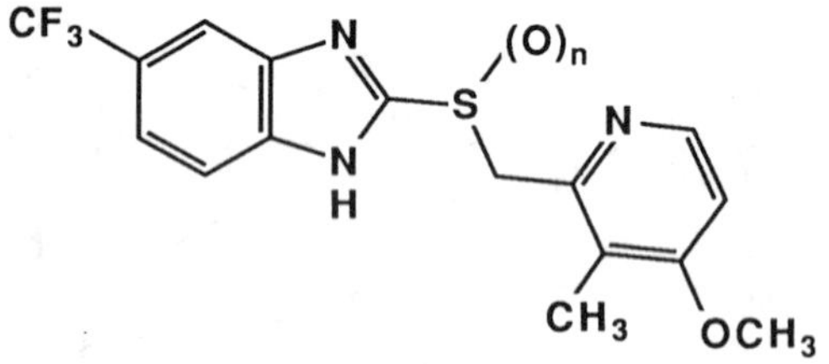

19   n = 0 , B823-08

20   n = 1 , B823-10

4.4.4   Antiinfectives

Improvement of the pharmacodynamic properties of agents used for the treatment of infectious diseases continues to be an area receiving considerable attention.

A number of acyloxymethyl esters of cefotiam (7-β-(2-2-aminothiazol-4-yl)aceta-mido)-3-(((1-(2-dimethylaminoethyl)-1-*H*-tetrazol-5-yl)thio)methyl)ceph-3-em-4-carboxylic acid (CTM, **21**) were prepared and their water solubility, lipophilicity, hydrolysis rate to CTM, isomerization to Δ^2-CTM, as well as their bioavailability following oral administration to mice were measured in order to identify a suitable prodrug for CTM [39]. In all cases studied, the plasma concentration of CTM following oral administration of the esters was higher than the oral administration of CTM, and the relative bioavailability was improved two- to nine-fold. The 2-propylvaleryloxymethyl ester (**22**) exhibited the best oral bioavailability, approximately 54%.

Quantitative structure–activity analysis of the oral absorption data in mice revealed a linear relationship between the Taft steric constant (E_s) of the ester moiety (R) and the *in vitro* hydrolysis rate of the prodrug to CTM in the presence of a homogenate of 1% mice small intestines at 37°C. A close correlation was also observed between the E_s value, the π value of R and the bioavailability of CTM as inferred from its peak plasma concentration.

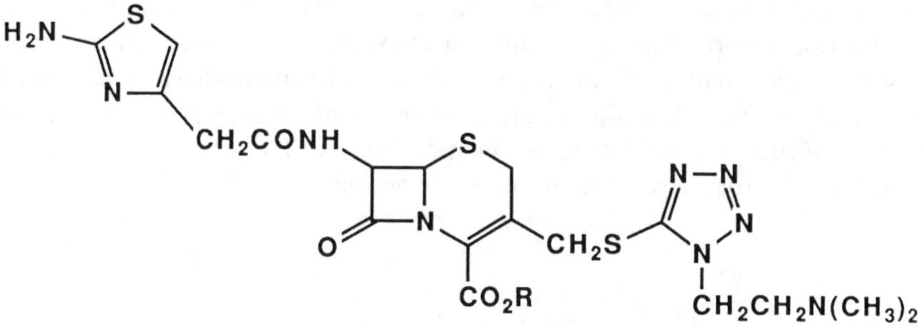

21   R = H , *cefotiam*

22   R = $CH_2O_2CCH(C_3H_7^n)_2$

3-Formylquinolone derivatives (**23**) were prepared and investigated as potential prodrugs of quinolone antibacterials [40]. These agents require metabolic activation by *in vivo* oxidation of the 3-formyl group to the 3-carboxylate in order to generate the active species following oral administration. In all cases examined, the antibacterial activity of the 3-formyl analogs determined *in vitro* was less than the corresponding 3-carboxyl compounds. *In vivo* in mice, the 3-formyl derivative of norfloxacin (**23a**) gave a two-fold higher plasma concentration of norfloxacin than oral administration of norfloxacin itself.

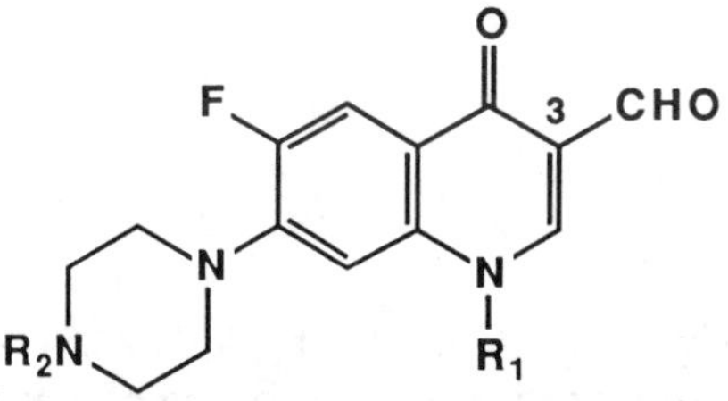

	$R_1 =$	$R_2 =$
23a	CH_3CH_2	H
23b	c-C_3H_5	H
23c	CH_3CH_2	CH_3

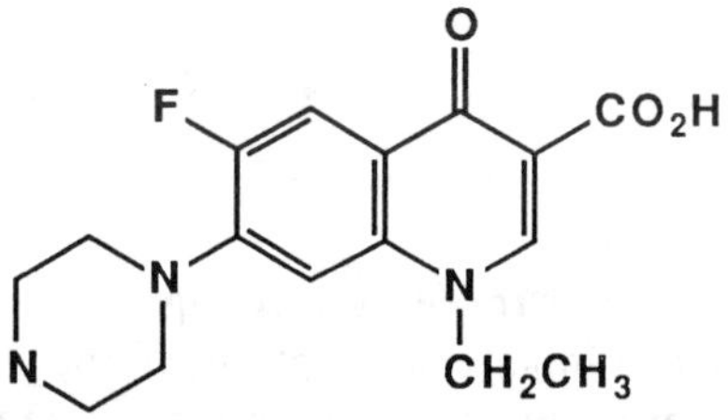

norfloxacin

Several primaquine peptides (**24**) were prepared as prodrugs of the antimalarial agent, primaquine [41]. These prodrugs were prepared as potential substrates for the enzyme plasmin. The proposed increased levels of plasmin present in antimalarial parasites might selectively release the drug at its targeted site of action and as a consequence its therapeutic index could be increased. All peptide derivatives prepared exhibited activity against *Plasmodium cynomolgi* in rhesus monkeys greater than that expected for the primaquine content of the prodrug. However, only the D-Val-Leu-Lys-primaquine peptide (24a) exhibited blood schizonticidal activity against *P. berghei* in mice. Comparison of the activity and toxicity of the D-Val-Leu-Lys-primaquine peptide (24a) relative to primaquine suggests that the peptide prodrug is more active and less toxic than primaquine. This observation is consistent with targeting of the active drug to its site of action.

	R =
24a	D-Val-Leu-Lys
24b	D-Ala-Leu-Lys
24c	L-Val-Leu-Lys
	H , *primaquine*

4.4.5 Antiviral/anticancer agents

The incomplete absorption of the antiherpes agent acyclovir (ACV, 25) when administered orally to humans prompted efforts to identify a prodrug of acyclovir that would be better absorbed from the gastrointestinal tract and then be converted to acyclovir *in vivo*. Desciclovir (DCV, 26), a prodrug of acyclovir, is converted in humans to acyclovir presumably by xanthine oxidase. Upon oral administration to humans, the absorption of desciclovir was at least 75% and approximately two-thirds of the administered dose was recovered in the urine as acyclovir [42,43]. The plasma half-life of desciclovir was 0.85 ± 0.2 h compared to 2.6 ± 0.5 h for acyclovir, indicating a facile conversion of desciclovir to acyclovir *in vivo*. Further metabolism of these two compounds was evident by the appearance of the carboxy metabolites of desciclovir (carboxy-DCV, 27) and acyclovir (carboxy-ACV, 28). The ratios of desciclovir and acyclovir to their corresponding metabolites in the urine was 4:1 and 3:1, respectively. This observation suggests that there is little difference in the efficiency of these two substrates for oxidation to their carboxylic acid metabolites. Most importantly, no serious or adverse side-effects were observed clinically following desciclovir treatment.

25	R = CH₂OH , ACV	26	R = CH₂OH , DCV
28	R = CO₂H , *carboxy*-ACV	27	R = CO₂H , *carboxy*-DCV

A variety of 1-alkoxycarbonyl, 3-acyl and 3-acyloxymethyl derivatives of 5-fluorouracil (5-FU, **29**) were investigated as potential prodrugs for 5-FU [44]. Following rectal administration to rabbits, it was determined that to achieve absorption greater than 50%, the prodrug should exhibit a partition coefficient between *n*-octanol and aqueous buffer (pH 7.4) greater than 0.5 and a solubility in water (pH 7.4) greater than 0.05 molar. 3-Propionyl and 1-*n*-butyloxycarbonyl-5-fluorouracil, **30** and **31**, respectively, were identified as the most promising prodrugs of 5-FU. The rectal bioavailability of each prodrug in rabbits was greater than 90% and the absolute oral availability of 1-*n*-butyloxycarbonyl-5-fluorouracil was 58% compared to 10% following administration of 5-FU itself.

	R₁ ≡	**R₃ ≡**
29	H	H , 5-FU
30	H	CH₃CH₂CO-
31	CH₃(CH₂)₃O₂C-	H

4.4.6 Central nervous system agents

Preclinical studies of the presynaptic dopamine autoreceptor agonist (−)-3-hydroxyphenyl)-*N*-propylpiperidine ((−)-3-PPP, **32**) demonstrated significant accumulation of (−)-3-PPP in the central nervous system of mice following intravenous administration [45]. However, (−)-3-PPP exhibited low oral bioavailability in all species examined, i.e. in the rat, 89% of the administered dose was recovered in the urine as (−)-3-PPP glucuronide. These observations suggest that while (−)-3-PPP can be significantly transported across the blood–brain barrier following

intravenous administration, (−)-3-PPP undergoes extensive first-pass metabolism
in the intestinal mucosa and/or liver following oral administration thereby reducing
its systematic availability.

In an attempt to identify potential prodrugs of (−)-3-PPP that would be resistant
to this first-pass metabolism and be capable of delivering significant plasma and
tissue levels of the parent drug following oral administration, a number of derivatives
bearing substituents on the phenolic hydroxyl of (−)-3-PPP were prepared and
evaluated. Urethane derivatives were found to be the most suitable prodrugs. In
particular, the N-arylcarbamates exhibited the most desirable pharmacologic profile. The substituent on the phenyl ring of the N-arylcarbamate significantly
influences the plasma concentration of (−)-3-PPP following oral administration of
the prodrug. For example, the p-chlorosubstituted analog gave lower plasma
concentrations of the parent drug relative to the unsubstituted phenyl carbamate,
while the presence of electron-donating substituents in the phenyl ring enhanced
levels of (−)-3-PPP in the plasma, e.g. $4-CH_3CH_2O-$, $4-(CH_3)_2CH-$ and $3,4-CH_3O-$.
The p-isopropylphenyl carbamate congener (**33**) was identified as the best prodrug if
a low oral bioavailability is the only limiting factor precluding development of
(−)-3-PPP as a useful antipsychotic agent in humans. The general utility of
derivatizing other phenols with this moiety to improve oral availability remains to be
demonstrated.

32   R = H , (-)-3-PPP

33   R = $p-(CH_3)_2CHC_6H_4NHCO-$

The action of specific neuropeptidases on 'peptide-based' prodrugs to selectively
deliver drugs to the brain has been investigated with peptide derivatives of
γ-aminobutyric acid (GABA) [46]. N^α-acylaminoacid-releasing enzyme (NAARE),
purified from the brain of rats, has been shown to cleave $CH_3CO-Met-Ala$ at the
'Met−Ala' bond. $CH_3O_2C-Met-Ala$ (**34**) and $CH_3O_2C-Met-GABA$ (**35**) were
prepared and investigated as potential substrates for NAARE *in vitro*. While Ala
was formed from $CH_3O_2C-Met-Ala$ at a rate of $0.27\,\mu mol\,h^{-1}\,mg^{-1}$ protein
compared to a rate of $0.14\,\mu mol\,h^{-1}\,mg^{-1}$ protein when $CH_3CO-Met-Ala$ was the
substrate, GABA was released from $CH_3O_2C-Met-GABA$ at a substantially
slower rate, $0.62\,nmol\,h^{-1}\,mg^{-1}$ protein. Alternative 'peptide-based' prodrugs of
GABA designed as substrates for chymotrypsin-like activity in the brain were also
resistant to enzymatic hydrolysis.

A series of tertiary 3- and 4-haloalkyl amines (**36**) were prepared and investigated as potential prodrugs related to the muscarinic agent oxotremorine (**38**) [47]. The compounds cyclized in neutral aqueous solution to quaternary ammonium salts (**37**) which were potent muscarinic agonists *in vitro*, in contrast to the parent haloalkylamines which were devoid of this activity. When administered systemically to mice, the haloalkylamines produced central and peripheral muscarinic effects. Central potency was dependent upon the rate of cyclization and the route of administration. The *N*-methyl-*N*-(4-chloropropyl)amine (**36a**) derivative cyclized rapidly and elicited tremors on intravenous, but not on intraperitoneal, injection, whereas the *N*-methyl-(3-chloropropyl)amine (**36b**) derivative cyclized slowly and was not tremorigenic by either route of administration. The *N*-methyl-*N*-(3-bromopropyl)amine (**36c**) and its iodo analog (**36d**) were both potent in eliciting central muscarinic effects on both intravenous and intraperitoneal administration in mice.

In vivo, these tertiary 3- and 4-haloalkylamine derivatives may serve as prodrugs for potent quaternary ammonium salts related to oxotremorine, that are not capable of transport across the blood–brain barrier.

	n =	X =		n =	X =
36a	4	Cl	37a	4	Cl
36b	3	Cl	37b	3	Cl
36c	3	Br	37c	3	Br
36d	3	I	37d	3	I

38   *oxotremorine*

4.4.7 Ophthalmic agents

Sequentially labile diester prodrugs of pilocarpine (**39**) were synthesized recently to improve the ocular delivery characteristics of pilocarpine (**41**) [48,49]. The 'pro-

prodrug' requires enzymatic hydrolysis at the O−acyl bond followed by spontaneous lactonization of the intermediate pilocarpine monoester (**40**)), Fig. 4.6.

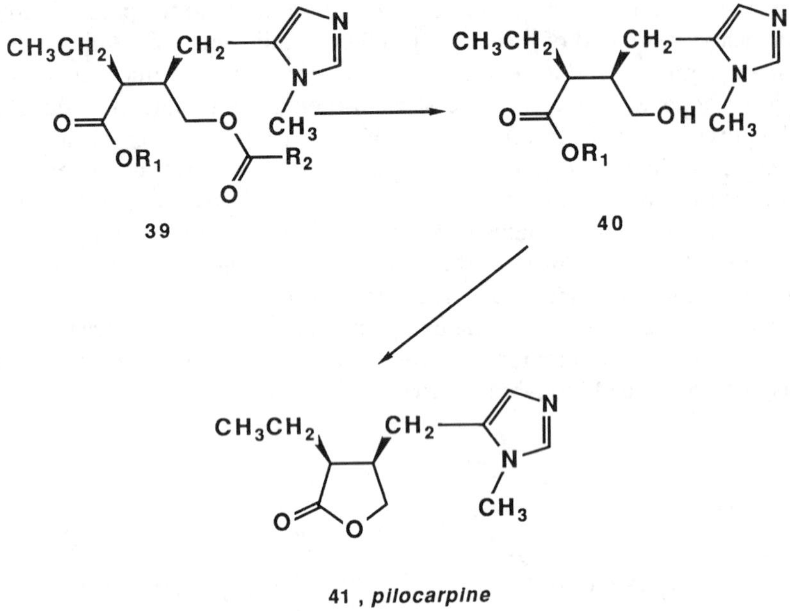

Fig. 4.6 — Sequentially labile diester prodrugs of pilocarpine .

Although the monoesters of pilocarpine (**40**) exhibited enhanced corneal permeability relative to pilocarpine itself, in general, the monoesters exhibited poor solution stability. The diester prodrugs of pilocarpine were more lipophilic than either their corresponding monoester or pilocarpine itself. More importantly, the diester prodrugs exhibited a high solution stability and under simulated *in vivo* conditions converted to pilocarpine at an adequate rate. That is, the rates of enzymatic conversion to the monoesters were such that intraocular elimination pathways for the diester were negligible in determining their overall bioavailability.

A major problem in the use of β-adrenergic receptor antagonists in glaucoma therapy is the relatively high incidence of cardiovascular and respiratory side-effects caused by the systemic absorption of the topically applied β-blocker to the eye. A number of O-acyl derivatives (**42**) of the β-blocker, timolol, were synthesized and evaluated as prodrugs [50,51]. In theory, the increased lipophilicity of the prodrug could improve the corneal penetration of the drug and allow a reduction in the administered dose required to lower intraocular pressure. The reduction in the applied dose could minimize the amount of drug available for systematic absorption and lower the incidence of the cardiovascular and respiratory side-effects.

In vitro hydrolysis studies indicate that the O-acetyl, -propionyl, -butyryl and -pivalyl ester prodrugs of timolol are rapidly cleaved virtually *in toto* in the presence of plasma, aqueous humor and ocular tissue homogenates of pigmented rabbits. Moreover, *in vitro* corneal penetration of all but the O-pivalyl prodrug was two to three times higher than timolol. These observations suggest that at least a two-fold reduction in the topically applied dose of timolol may be possible using the prodrug approach.

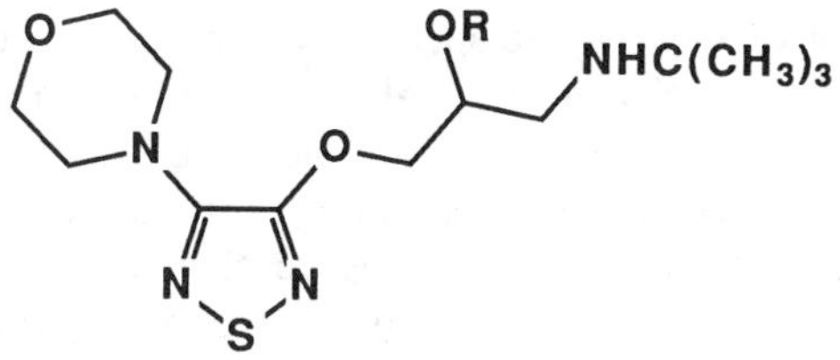

R =

42a	CH_3CO-
42b	CH_3CH_2CO-
42c	$CH_3(CH_2)_2CO-$
42d	$(CH_3)_3CCO-$
	H , *timolol*

4.5   CHEMICAL DELIVERY SYSTEMS

A truly remarkable targeted drug delivery by a site-specific enzyme-activated chemical delivery system was reported recently [52]. In this study, a ketoxime precursor of a β-adrenergic receptor blocking agent (**43**) is effectively converted to the active β-aminoalcohol derivative (**45**) in the iris-cilliary body of the eye, via the ketone intermediate (**44**), Fig. 4.7.

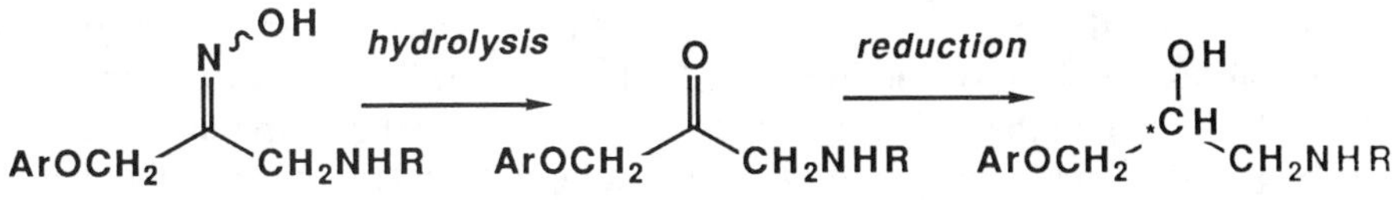

Fig. 4.7 — Site-specific enzyme-activated chemical delivery system for β-adrenergic blocking agents.

The appearance and prolonged presence of the β-aminoalcohol derivative (**45**) was demonstrated and was concomitant with a very significant reduction in the intraocular pressure (IOP) in the eyes of rabbits. A number of analogs containing a variety of Ar and R groups were investigated, and it appears that the efficiency of the two enzyme-mediated conversion steps, hydrolysis and reduction, respectively, critically depends on the lipophilicity of the ketoxime precursor (**43**) and intermediate ketone (**44**). Both the *Z*- and the *E*- ketoxime isomers are substrates for hydrolysis, and the reduction of the ketone intermediate (**44**) is *stereospecific*, yielding the *S*-(−)-isomer of **45** exclusively [53]. Since the *S*-(−)-isomer is the biologically active form, this is the first example of a *stereospecific*, as well as site-specific, drug delivery. The site-specificity is emphasized further by the lack of systemic β-blocking activity of **43**. Oral, intravenous or topical administration of **43** to rats or rabbits did not produce any β-blocking activity [54], consistent with the observation that **43** is cleared from the blood very rapidly. In addition, the presence of **45** in the blood could not be detected. Recently, comprehensive electrophysiological studies in dogs [55] support further the lack of any systemic β-blocking activity of **43**.

The use of macromolecular carriers for the specific delivery of peptides was further pursued by Pardridge [56]. It was proposed that cationized albumin could transport peptides like endorphin through the blood brain barrier. *In vitro* studies using isolated bovine brain capillaries clearly indicated uptake of the endorphin–albumin conjugate. However, the extent to which the macromolecule is endocytosed and transported through the blood brain barrier could not be ascertained from these studies. *In vivo* studies using radiolabeled endorphin–albumin conjugate indicated that some radioactivity reached the brain parenchyma, but it is not clear from these studies to what extent the active entity is released from the transport conjugate. It is recommended that quantitative evaluation of this system be done using the mono-layer model [16] prior to advocating this method as an approach for brain delivery.

4.6 CONCLUSIONS — *QUO VADIS!*

Drug targeting or *site-specific drug delivery* are terms usually associated with carriers such as liposomes or antibodies by a majority of pharmaceutical scientists. Most of the efforts in drug delivery attempting to use these approaches have experienced relatively few successes. The reason for the lack of success using these methods is complex, but relates essentially to inefficient targeting of the drug by the carrier. That is, the carrier is not capable of achieving the sharp distributional differences required between the target site and the rest of the body in order to be effective. In many instances, the lack of success may also be attributed to a poor design of the chemical bond chosen to link the drug to the carrier. Under these circumstances, it is the strength of this chemical bond, which must be broken, that ultimately dictates efficient release of the active moiety at the target site and in pharmacologically relevant concentration. Equally important in these failures is the lack of consideration to problems related to simple stoichiometry. Large molecular carriers are usually incapable of delivering sufficient amounts of the active entity practically, regardless of the presumed potency of the active species. While people do recognize that most of these macromolecular carriers are actually prodrugs, the term 'prodrug' is generally reserved for drug-conjugates with much smaller carrier moieties. In these instances, the protective function is considered to be a perturbation of the drug molecule rather than the drug molecule being considered a perturbation of the larger carrier as in the case of these macromolecular-conjugates.

In the past 20 years or so, a vast number of publications have appeared on 'potential' prodrugs of a wide variety of compounds. Unfortunately, these investigations did not completely recognize what are the major objectives of prodrug design and more importantly, what are its limitations. Despite the large number of 'potential' prodrugs synthesized, the actual number of prodrugs used in clinical therapy is limited to relatively few. Even among this small number of clinically useful prodrugs, the majority were identified as prodrugs in hindsight and were not designed as such. It is imperative to recognize that site-specificity can seldom be achieved simply by the prodrug approach. Prodrugs can be successful when the objectives are to modify general, overall distribution and pharmacokinetic parameters. The success of a number of more sophisticated chemical targeting methods called *site-specific chemical drug delivery systems* illustrates the need to invoke more complex chemical processes that take advantage of the specific enzyme systems in the body. Prodrug design based solely on the trivial chemistry associated with nonspecific esterases or nonspecific peptidases will not accomplish targeting. The *site-specific chemical delivery systems* represent a novel approach based on enzymatic reactions. Successive enzymatic reactions can specifically optimize the presence and activity of the active species at the site of action. Unfortunately, only seldom can one find specific-enzyme activity at the site of required drug action. Therefore, rather than attempting to locate organ-specific and/or site-specific enzyme systems which will potentially activate certain precursors only at the site of action, the examples presented strongly suggest that integration of fundamental principles of physical chemistry, of enzyme activity and kinetics, of receptor-based pharmacologic studies and a knowledge of the metabolic disposition of the system will assist in the design and successful achievement of site-specific drug delivery.

In our opinion, all of the points discussed above suggest one extremely important conclusion: for most drugs already developed and in use today, the *potential to benefit* from combination with a drug carrier is very low. Thus, we recommend that the modification of the physical–chemical properties of any new entity via chemical methods, as well as incorporating site-specific targeting modalities into its chemical structure, should be an integral part of the discovery process. Implementation of these concepts early in the design includes taking into consideration important changes in enzymatic reactions, metabolism and transport–distribution–activity phenomena that may be significantly altered from the norm as a result of the disease state.

The increasing number of patients suffering from a variety of degenerative neurological diseases and psychiatric disorders such as Alzheimer's disease, AIDS dementia, amyotrophic lateral sclerosis (Lou Gehrig's disease), brain infections and brain cancer suggest to us that the next decade will see an increased emphasis in the technology available to effectively deliver therapeutic and imaging agents across the blood brain barrier. Improvements in the specific targeting of these agents to the brain will ensure better diagnoses and more effective treatments than currently available using conventional therapy.

REFERENCES

[1] Widder, K. J., Senyei, A. E., & Ranney, D. F. (1979). Magnetically responsive microspheres and other carriers for the biophysical targeting of antitumor agents. *Adv. Pharmacol. Chemother.* **16**, 213.

[2] Poste, G., Kirsh, R., & Koestler, T. (1984). Targeted drug delivery and biological interaction, in: G. Gregoriadis (ed.) *Liposome Technology*. Volume III, CRC Press, Boca Raton, p. 1.

[3] Poznansky, M. J. & Juliano, K. L. (1984). Biological approaches to the controlled delivery of drugs: a critical review. *Pharmacol. Rev.* **36**, 277.

[4] Tomlinson, E. & Davis, S. S. (eds) (1987). *Site-specific Drug Delivery*. Wiley, New York.

[5] Friend, D. R. & Pangburn, S. (1987). Site-specific drug delivery. *Med. Res. Rev.* **7**, 53.

[6] Tomlinson, E. (1987). Theory and practice of site-specific drug delivery. *Adv. Drug Del. Rev.* **1**, 87.

[7] Ihler, G. M., Glenn, R. H., & Schnure, F. W. (1973). Enzyme loading of erythrocytes. *Proc. Natl. Acad. Sci. USA* **70**, 2663.

[8] Harris, G. (1979). Lymphoid cells and transport of macromolecules, in: G. Gregoriadis (ed.) *Drug Carriers in Biology and Medicine*. Academic Press, New York, p. 167.

[9] Bodor, N. (1984). Novel approaches to the design of safer drugs: soft drugs and site-specifc chemical delivery systems. In: B. Testa (ed.) *Advances in Drug Research*. Volume 13, Academic Press, London, p. 255.

[10] Bodor, N. & Brewster, M. (1983). Problems of delivery of drugs to the brain. *Pharm. Ther.* **19**, 337.

[11] Bodor, N. & Kaminski, J. J. (1987). Prodrugs and site-specific chemical delivery systems. *Annu. Rep. Med. Chem.* **33**, 303.

[12] Bodor, N. & Farag, H. H. (1983). Improved delivery through biological membranes. II. A redox chemical drug delivery system and its use for brain-specific delivery of phenylethylamine. *J. Med. Chem.* **26**, 313.

[13] Bodor, N. (1987). Redox drug delivery system for targeting drugs to the brain. In: R. L. Juliano (ed.) *Biological Approaches to the Controlled Delivery of Drugs. Ann. N. Y. Acad. Sci.* **507**, 289.

[14] Bodor, N., Kaminski, J. J. & Selk, S. (1980). Soft drugs I. Labile quaternary ammonium salts as soft antimicrobials. *J. Med. Chem.* **23**, 469.

[15] Bodor, N. (1984). The soft drug approach. *Chemtech.* **14**, 28.

[16] Audus, K. L., Hidalgo, I. J., & Borchardt, R. T. (1987). Biological barrier to efficient delivery of peptides. In: D. D. Breimer & P. Speiser (eds) *Topics in Pharmaceutical Sciences*. Elsevier, Amsterdam, p. 325 and references quoted therein.

[17] Osiecka, I., Cortese, M., Porter, P. A., Borchardt, R. T., Fix, J., & Gardner, C. R. (1987). Intestinal absorption of α-methyldopa. *In vitro* mechanistic studies in rat small intestinal segments. *J. Pharmacol. Exp. Ther.* **242**, 443.

[18] Debault, L. E., Henriquez, E., Hart, M. N., & Cancilla, P. (1981). Cerebral microvessels and derived cells in tissue culture: II establishment, identification and preliminary characterization of an endothelial cell line. *In Vitro* **17**, 480.

[19] Audus, K. L. & Borchardt, R. T. (1986). Characterization of an *in vitro* blood brain barrier model system for studying drug transport and metabolism. *Pharm. Res.* **3**, 81.

[20] Pardridge, W. (1986). Receptor-mediated peptide transport through the blood brain barrier. *Endocrine Rev.* **7**, 314.

[21] Hunt, C. A., MacGregor, R. D., & Siegel, R. A. (1986). Engineering targeted *in vivo Drug Delivery*. I. The physiological and physicochemical principles governing opportunities and limitations. *Pharm. Res.* **3**, 333.

[22] Levy, G. (1987). Targeted drug delivery — some pharmacokinetic considerations. *Pharm. Res.* **4**, 3.

[23] Anderson, W. R., Simpkins, J. W., Brewster, M. E., & Bodor, N. (1987). Evidence for the restablishment of copulatory behavior in castrated male rats with a brain-enhanced estradiol–chemical delivery system. *Pharmacol. Biochem. Behav.* **27**, 265.

[24] Walker, S. B., Kradjan, W. A., & Bierman, C. W. (1985). Bitolterol mesylate: a β-adrenergic agent, chemistry, pharmacokinetics, pharmacodynamics, adverse effects and clinical efficiacy in asthma. *Pharmacotherapy* **5**, 127.

[25] Svensson, L. (1987). Development of β_2-adrenoreceptor agonist bronchodilator prodrugs. *Curr. Top. Pulm. Pharmacol. Toxicol.* **3**, 1.

[26] Bilski, A. J., Evans, J. R., Harrison, M. P., Jones, G., Marten, T. R., Milburn, G. T., Thomson, D. S., & White, D. F. (1986). Lipoidal antiinflammatory prodrugs as local targeting agents. *Biochem. Soc. Trans.* **14**, 338.

[27] Svensson, L. (1987). Bambuterol — a prodrug-prodrug with built-in hydrolysis brake. *Pharm. Suec.* **24**, 333.

[28] Matsuda, K., Tanaka, Y., Ushiyama, S., Ohnishi, K., & Yamazaki, M. (1984). Inhibition of prostaglandin synthesis by sodium 2-[4-(2-oxocyclopentylmethyl)-phenyl]propionate dihydrate (CS-600), a new antiinflammatory drug and its active metabolite *in vitro* and *in vivo*. *Biochem. Pharmacol.* **33**, 2473.

[29] Mizushima, Y. (1987). Recent advances in non-steroid antiinflammatory drugs. *Drugs Exptl. Clin. Res.* **XIII**, 689.

[30] Gillard, J. W. & Belanger, P. (1987). Metabolic synthesis of arylacetic acid antiinflammatory drugs from arylhexenoic acids. 2. Indomethacin. *J. Med. Chem.* **30**, 2051.

[31] Bundgaard, H. & Nielsen, N. M. (1988). Glycolamide esters as a novel biolabile prodrug type for non-steroidal antiinflammatory carboxylic acid drugs. *Int. J. Pharmaceutics* **43**, 101.

[32] Nielsen, N. M. & Bundgaard, H. (1988). Glycolamide esters as novel biolabile prodrugs of carboxylic acid agents: synthesis, stability, bioconversion and physicochemical properties. *J. Pharm. Sci.* **77**, 285.

[33] Bundgaard, H. & Nielsen, N. M. (1987). Esters of *N,N*-disubstituted 2-hydroxyacetamides as a novel highly biolabile prodrug type for carboxylic acid agents. *J. Med. Chem.* **330**, 451.

[34] Nielsen, N. M. & Bundgaard, H. (1987). Prodrugs as drug delivery systems. 68. Chemical and plasma-catalyzed hydrolysis of various esters of benzoic acid: a reference system for designing prodrug esters of carboxylic agents. *Int. J. Pharmaceutics* **39**, 75.

[35] Bundgaard, H., Nielsen, N. M., & Buur, A. (1988). Aspirin prodrugs: synthesis and hydrolysis of 2-acetoxybenzoate esters of various *N*-(hydroxyalkyl)amides. *Int. J. Pharmaceutics* **44**, 151.

[36] Loftsson, T., Kaminski, J. J., & Bodor, N. (1981). Improved delivery through biological membranes VIII. Design, synthesis and *in vivo* testing of true prodrugs of aspirin. *J. Pharm. Sci.* **70**, 743.

[37] Hansen, A. B. & Senning, A. (1983). Chemical feasibility studies concerning potential prodrugs of acetylsalicylic acid. *Acta Chem. Scand. Ser. B* **37**, 351.

[38] Bohnenkamp, W., Eltze, M., Heintze, K., Kromer, W., Riedel, R., & Schudt, C. (1987). Specificity of the substituted benzimidazole B 823-08: a prodrug for gastric proton pump inhibition. *Pharmacology* **34**, 269.

[39] Yoshimura, Y., Hamagichi, N., & Yashiki, T. (1987). Synthesis and oral absorption of acyloxymethyl esters of (7-β-(2-(2-aminothiazol-4-yl)acetamido)-3-(((1-(2-dimethylaminoethyl)-1-H-tetrazol-5-yl)thio)methyl)ceph-3-em-4-carboxylic acid (Cefotiam). *Int. J. Pharmaceutics* **38**, 179.

[40] Kondo, H., Sakamoto, F., Kawakami, K., & Tsukamoto, G. (1988). Studies on prodrugs. Synthesis and antimicrobial activity of 3-formylquinolone derivatives. *J. Med. Chem.* **31**, 221.

[41] Philip, A., Kepler, J. A., Johnson, B. H., & Carroll, F. I. (1988). Peptide derivatives of primaquine as potential antimalarial agents. *J. Med. Chem.* **31**, 870.

[42] Krasny, H. C. & Petty, B. G. (1987), Metabolism of desciclovir, a prodrug of acyclovir, in humans after multiple oral dosing, *J. Clin. Pharmacol.* **27**, 74.

[43] Petty, B. G., Whitely, R. J., Liao, S., Krasny, H. C., Rocco, L. E., Davis, L. G., & Lietman, P. S. (1987). Pharmacokinetics and tolerance of desciclovir, a prodrug of acyclovir, in healthy human volunteers. *Antimicrob. Agents Chemother.* **31**, 1317.

[44] Buur, A. & Bundgaard, H. (1987). Prodrugs of 5-fluorouracil. VIII. Improved rectal and oral delivery of 5-fluorouracil via various prodrugs. Structure–rectal absorption relationships. *Int. J. Pharmaceutics* **36**, 41.

[45] Thorberg, S. O., Berg, S., Lundstrum, J., Pettersson, B., Wijkstrom, A., Sanchez, D. Linberg, P., & Nilsson, J. L. G. (1987). Carbamate ester derivatives as potential prodrugs of the presynaptic dopamine autoreceptor agonist (−)-3-(3-hydroxyphenyl)-N-propylpiperidine. *J. Med. Chem.* **30**, 2008.

[46] Backwell, F. R. C., Elmore, D. T., & Williams, C. H. (1988). The use of neuropeptidases to release drug from peptide-based prodrugs. *Biochem. Soc. Trans.* **16**, 214.

[47] Ringdahl, B., Roch, M., & Jenden, D. J. (1988). Tertiary 3- and 4-haloalkylamine analogues of oxotremorine as prodrugs of potent muscarinic agonists. *J. Med. Chem.* **31**, 160.

[48] Mosher, G. L., Bundgaard, H., Falch, E., Larsen, C., & Mikkelson, T. J. (1987). Ocular bioavailability of pilocarpic acid mono- and diester prodrugs as assessed by miotic activity in the rabbit. *Int. J. Pharmaceutics* **39**, 113.

[49] Bundgaard, H., Falch, E., Larsen, C., Mosher, G. L., & Mikkelson, T. J. (1986). Pilocarpine prodrugs II. Synthesis, stability, bioconversion and physicochemical properties of sequentially labile pilocarpine diesters. *J. Pharm. Sci.* **75**, 775.

[50] Chang, S. C., Bundgaard, H., Buur, A., & Lee, V. H. L. (1987). Improved corneal penetration of timolol by prodrugs as a means to reduce systemic drug load. *Invest. Ophthamol. Visual Sci.* **28**, 487.

[51] Bundgaard, H., Buur, A., Chang, S. C., & Lee, V. H. L. (1986). Prodrugs of timolol for improved ocular delivery: synthesis, hydrolysis, kinetics and lipophilicity of various timolol esters. *Int. J. Pharmaceutics* **33**, 15.

[52] Bodor, N., El Koussi, A., Kano, M., & Nakamura, T. (1988). Improved delivery through biological membranes 26. Design, synthesis and pharmacologic activity of a novel chemical delivery system for β-adrenergic blocking agents. *J. Med. Chem.* **31**, 100.

[53] Bodor, N. & Prokai, L. (1989). Site and stereospecific drug delivery. Submitted for publication.

[54] Bodor, N. (1988). Designing safe ophthalmic drugs, in: *Proc. Xth Int. Symp. Med. Chem.*, Budapest, Hungary, 15–19 August.

[55] Bodor, N., Polgar, P., Prokai, L., & Somogyi, G. Unpublished results.

[56] Kumagai, A. K., Eisenberg, J. B., & Pardridge, W. M. (1987). Absorptive mediated endocytosis of cationized albumin and a β-endorphin-cationized albumin chimeric peptide by isolated brain capillaries. *J. Biol. Chem.* **262**, 15214.

5

Obstacles to drug development from peptide leads

Jacob J. Plattner and **Daniel W. Norbeck**
Abbott Laboratories, Abbott Park, Illinois, USA

5.1 INTRODUCTION

Over the past decade, the field of biomedical research has witnessed dramatic advances in the understanding, diagnosis, and treatment of human disease. In large measure, these developments have been fueled by an increased awareness of the essential role played by endogenous peptides and proteins in the regulation and integration of life processes [1]. At least three reasons can be identified for the increasing importance of peptides and proteins. Firstly, improved analytical methodology has fostered the discovery of numerous hormonal and neuropeptides. Secondly, progress in synthetic methodology has provided ready access to oligopeptides by enzymatic, solid-phase, or classical solution techniques. Lastly, molecular biology and genetic engineering have enabled the production of polypeptides heretofore unavailable. In turn, these factors have led to the elucidation of biochemical processes and the identification of strategic targets for therapeutic intervention.

Thus equipped with a greater understanding of the role of regulatory peptides in the pathophysiology of human disease, pharmaceutical scientists are routinely using specific peptide sequences as lead structures for drug development. This strategy is exemplified by the recent discovery and successful commercialization of angiotensin-converting enzyme (ACE) inhibitors in cardiovascular therapy. Despite the high level of activity in peptide-based drug research, several serious obstacles hinder the facile development of peptide leads into therapeutically useful agents. Most notable of these obstacles is that of imparting good bioavailability into a peptide-derived drug while maintaining pharmacologic efficacy [2]. Clearly, this problem stems from the unique structural features of peptides, features which are directly linked to their high instability in biological milieu, rapid elimination from plasma, and poor transportability across membranes. In this chapter, recent developments in the field of peptide-based drug discovery are reviewed, with particular emphasis given to the biological barriers which impede efficient bioavailability.

5.2 INTESTINAL ABSORPTION

With an estimated surface area of 200 m^2, the human intestinal tract represents an enormous interface between the organism and its environment. While this surface provides amply for the absorption of food, it also exposes the organism to a range of poisons and pathogens. Thus, the intestinal tract must function as a highly selective barrier. In order to understand the basis of this selectivity, and ultimately, to predict which drug candidates will be orally absorbed, one must attempt to consider the functional morphology of the intestine at a molecular level.

5.2.1 Functional morphology of the intestinal mucosa

The physiology of the intestinal tract has been frequently reviewed, and the following discussion is a synoptic version drawn from previous accounts [3–7]. As a tube approximately 4 m in length and 25 mm in diameter, the small intestine has a nominal surface area of 0.3 m^2; this is amplified by several orders of folding. At the macroscopic level, about 650 helical folds known as Keckring folds or plicae circulares around 1 cm in height and 5 cm in length triple the surface area. At the microscopic level, 10 million villi, ranging in height from 0.5 to 0.8 mm and with a typical thickness of 0.16 mm, increase the absorptive surface by a factor of 7–14. Finally, at the electron-microscopic level, 300×10^{12} microvilli with a diameter of 0.1 μm and height of 1.0 μm, extend like tiny fingers from individual epithelial cells into the intestinal lumen. This striated border enlarges the surface area 14- to 40-fold.

The physical barriers to drug absorption may be considered in terms of a structural unit consisting of several adjacent villi. In a scanning electron micrograph of the lumenal surface of the human jejunum, the villi appear as a serpentine labyrinth of deep mucosal folds. In cross-section, the villi appear as a continuous surface arranged into closely packed, irregular columns resting on a thin base. This continuous sheet of tissue, known as the *muscularis mucosa,* consists of smooth muscle 3–10 cells thick. The core of the villous column, known as the lamina propria, contains extracellular connective tissue, nerve and muscle cells, abundant mononuclear immune cells, and the blood and lymph vessels which transport compounds absorbed by the outermost layer of the villi, the epithelium. Just one cell thick, this layer is bathed in the lumenal contents. Of chief interest here is the structure and function of the major cell type in the epithelial layer, the absorptive cell.

As noted above, the lumenal surface of a single absorptive cell exhibits numerous (ca. 3700) tightly packed microvilli. At a magnification of 50 000×, these microvilli are seen to be coated by a fine fibrous mat. Composed of carbohydrate and glycoprotein, this glycocalyx extends 0.1 μm from the tip of the microvilli, fills the intermicrovillous space, and appears to be anchored to the outer leaflet of the microvillous membrane. Although this membrane has the trilaminar appearance typical of a eukaryotic cell, it is substantially thicker. Furthermore, the microvillous membrane is unusually rich in intramembrane protein particles, cholesterol, and glycolipids. These features are believed to contribute to the low fluidity of the microvillous membrane. As importantly, many of the proteins found in this complex membrane have a digestive function. Because the lateral membranes of neighboring epithelial cells are fused together near the cellular apex to form a tight seal, passage through the microvilli is usually necessary for absorption.

In order to enter the circulation, an absorbed compound must then move through the cytoplasm of an epithelial cell and diffuse through the basolateral portion of its plasma membrane. Unlike the microvillous membrane, the thickness of this membrane, 7 to 9 nm, is typical of a eukaryotic cell. Underlying the basal membrane is a continuous, 30 nm thick layer of fine, fibrillar material which is in close proximity to a network of blood capillaries. The permeability of these capillaries is enhanced by numerous fenestrations 500–1000 Å in diameter. The lymphatic channels, on the other hand, tend to be located in the villous core. Although they lack fenestrations, occasional breaches between cells allow some macromolecules and chylomicrons to pass into the lymphatic system.

5.2.2 Intestinal absorption of metabolically stable drugs

This rudimentary picture of the functional morphology of the small intestine correlates with mathematical models of oral bioavailability. If lumenal degradation and first-pass metabolism are neglected, Dressman *et al.* have proposed [8] that the fraction of a compound absorbed (F_{abs}) is a function of the permeability of the gut wall to the drug (P_w), the aqueous permeability of the drug (P_{aq}), the aqueous solubility of the nonionized species (S_o), the drug dosage (X_o), the fraction of the drug in nonionized form at pH 6.5 (F_{non}), and the volume of the lumenal contents (V_L). Dimensional analysis implied a correlation of the form

$$F_{abs} \propto \left[\left(\frac{P_w}{P_{aq}} \right) (F_{non}) \left(\frac{S_o V_L}{X_o} \right) \right]$$

Noting that the permeability ratio is in many cases proportional to the membrane–water partition coefficient estimated experimentally by the 1-octanol–water partition coefficient, P, these authors defined the absorption potential (AP) as

$$AP = \log \left(PF_{non} \frac{S_o V_L}{X_o} \right)$$

With the lumenal volume set at 250 mL, AP values of -1.5 and 0.7 corresponded to 17 and 67% absorption respectively. AP values greater than one corresponded to virtually complete absorption. Because the passive flux of a compound across any barrier should be proportional to the concentration differential across the interface [9], a compound obviously must be in solution for absorption to occur. In fact, compounds must diffuse through an unstirred water layer approximately 300 nm thick before they reach the microvillous surface [9,10]. In order to proceed further and pass through the apical membrane, a compound must also exhibit lipid solubility. In general, only compounds which are not ionized will meet this criteria. Finally, to enter the circulation, the compound must diffuse through the aqueous cytoplasm and across the basolateral membrane. Thus, good absorption is dependent on maintaining a delicate balance between aqueous and lipid solubility.

5.2.3 Intestinal absorption of peptides

This simple picture is considerably more complicated for peptide-based drugs. As noted above, the chief function of the intestine is the digestion and absorption of foodstuffs, notably protein [11]. Thus, a peptide faces an onslaught of degradative enzymes [12]. Within the intestinal lumen, pancreatic endopeptidases, chiefly trypsin, elastase, and chymotrypsin, together with the exopeptidases carboxypeptidase A and B, produce amino acids and peptides typically 2–6 residues in length. A host of brush border peptidases, such as aminopeptidase A and N, endopeptidase 24.11, dipeptidyl amino peptidase IV, glutamyl dipeptidase, and membrane Gly–Leu peptidase, continue the hydrolysis to produce more amino acids and di- and tripeptides. Specific transport systems then deliver these moieties into the enterocyte cytoplasm [13,14]. Although instances of tetrapeptide transport are known [15], di- and tripeptides with large side chains and the natural L-configuration are preferred. Furthermore, although the transport of peptides is faster than that of amino acids, the action of cytosolic or lysosomal peptidases, such as amino tripeptidase, amino dipeptidase, and prodipeptidase, allows relatively few intact peptides to enter the portal blood.

With this background, it should not be surprising that the efficient absorption of an intact peptide is the exception rather than the rule. As pointed out by Gardner [16], most of these peptides are biologically inactive and contain amino acids which are unusually resistant to peptidases, such as glycine in Gly–Gly, proline in Pro–Pro or Gly–Pro, and rare amino acids such as sarcosine (N-methylglycine) in Sar–Gly, or Gly–Sar, and β-amino acids such as β-alanine in carnosine (β-Ala–His). Examples of orally absorbed, biologically active peptides are rare. Both thyroptropin-releasing hormone (TRH, 1) [17] and the luteinizing hormone-releasing hormone analog, leuprolide (3) [18,19] exert biological activity when given orally in rat and man. It is interesting to note that a pyroglutamic acid residue protects the N-terminus and an amide protects the C-terminus of both peptides from amino peptidases and carboxypeptidases, respectively. Moreover, both leuprolide and TRH contain a proline. The C-amidated N-terminal tripeptide fragment of leuprolide, pGlu–His–Trp–NH$_2$, was also active on oral administration [20]; it is thus conceivable that leuprolide may undergo some degradation and still retain bioactivity. It is important to point out that the oral activity of leuprolide and TRH is a reflection of their extreme potency. In fact, only a small percentage of TRH is actually absorbed in the rat and man [17]. In the rat, absorption is limited to the upper region of the intestine and is mediated by a Na$^+$ dependent, peptide transport system [21]. Remarkably, absorption of DN-1417 (2), a close structural analog of TRH, is not active, but occurs by passive diffusion in all parts of the intestine. However, only 1% is absorbed in the rat and 10% in the dog [22]. This example illustrates the sensitivity of transport proteins to structural modifications in their substrates.

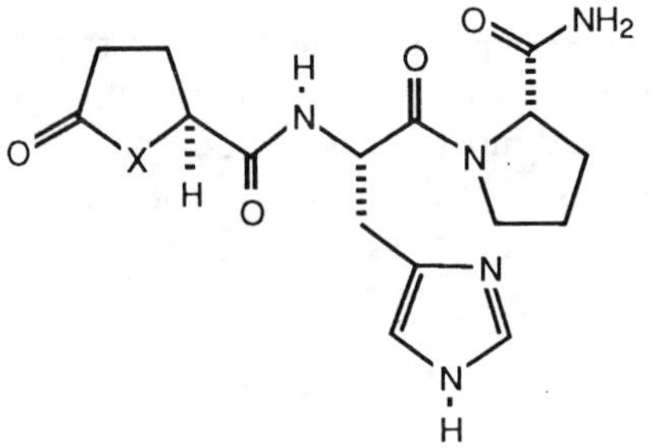

pyro-Glu-His-Trp-Ser-Tyr-
D-Leu-Arg-Pro-NHCH$_2$CH$_3$

3

1 (X = NH), TRH, pyro-Glu-His-Pro-NH$_2$

2 (X = O), DN-1417

Cys-Tyr-Phe-Gln-Asn-Cys-Pro-Lys-Gly-NH$_2$

4

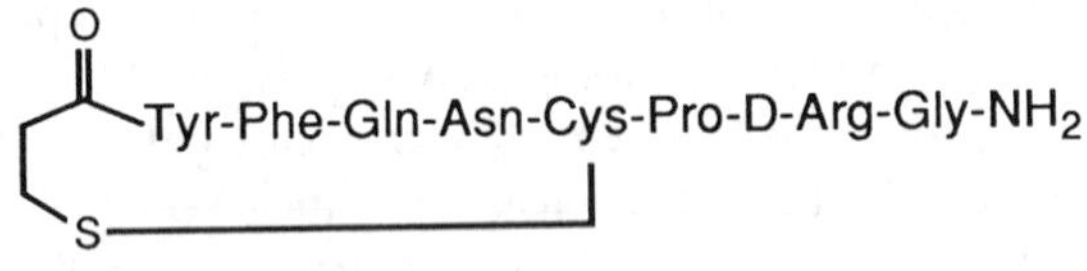

Tyr-Phe-Gln-Asn-Cys-Pro-D-Arg-Gly-NH$_2$

5

5.2.4 Protection of peptides from proteases

Attempts to suppress the degradation of peptides by the co-administration of protease inhibitors have met with limited success. Early experiments in rats indicated that a pancreatic trypsin inhibitor allowed no more than 3% of insulin to cross the intestinal barrier [23]. More recently, FK-448, a potent and specific inhibitor of chymotrypsin, was found to enhance the intestinal absorption of insulin in rats and dogs, whereas FOY-305, a potent trypsin inhibitor, neither inhibited insulin degradation nor influenced its intestinal absorption [24]. Saffran and co-workers have investigated vasopressin as a model for the study of oral administration of peptide drugs [25,26]. In large doses (700 × the i.v. ED$_{50}$ for lysine vasopressin), oral arginine or lysine vasopressin (**4**) caused antidiuresis in the rat, and this activity was enhanced 32.5-fold by co-administration of aprotinin, a natural inhibitor of trypsin. Oral delivery in an impermeable, azoaromatic cross-linked polymer allowed lysine vasopressin to pass unscathed through the small intestine to the upper colon, where the polymer is degraded by bacteria, thereby releasing the peptides for absorption. Despite its ingenuity, this polymer delivery system still requires 105 × the effective i.v. dose. Notably, the most effective strategy for improving the oral efficacy of vasopressin was shown to be chemical modification of the peptide itself. The synthetic analog, 1-deamino-8-D-arginine vasopressin (DDAVP, **5**) [27], is relatively resistant to proteolytic degradation, and, when administered orally, is only 4 × less potent than i.v. lysine vasopressin [26]. Thus, while co-administration of a protease inhibitor may prove to be effective in specific instances, the great variety of proteolytic enzymes constitutes a persuasive argument for the design and synthesis of proteolytically stable peptide analogs.

5.2.5   Orally active peptidomimetics
The rational design of the ideal orally available peptide drug — biologically potent, proteolytically stable, and actively transported — is an extremely difficult objective. Although the problem is greatly simplified by relying on passive diffusion for intestinal absorption, in general, peptides must still undergo considerable structural modification in order to be clinically useful agents. As illustrated below by asperlicin and morphine, these structural changes can be so profound that the resulting molecule is devoid of recognizable peptide character. More commonly, as exemplified by the β-lactam antibiotics, vestiges of peptide ancestry remain. Placed beside these natural products, the efforts of the medicinal chemist at peptide modification, typified here by synthetic angiotensin-converting enzyme and renin inhibitors, appear unsophisticated.

Cholecystokinin (CCK), a regulator of pancreatic enzyme secretion, gall bladder contractility, and gut motility, is typically found in the gut and brain as the octapeptide H–Asp–Tyr(SO_3H)–Met–Gly–Trp–Met–Asp–Phe–NH_2 (CCK-8) [28]. Isolation of asperlicin (**6**) from the extensive screening of fermentation broths for CCK antagonists provided the conceptual breakthrough which ultimately led to the synthesis of a potent, orally effective compound [29]. Asperlicin itself suffers from the same problems associated with many peptide analogs: low water solubility, negligible oral bioavailability, and modest *in vitro* potency. As such, asperlicin is not a particularly attractive lead compound. However, two key elements were recongized in its structure. L-Tryptophan, one of the key amino acids in the carboxyl-terminal sequence of CCK, is represented in the right-hand portion of asperlicin. Embedded in the left-hand portion is a structure reminiscent of the 1,4-benzodiazepine ring found in diazepam (**7**), an anti-anxiety agent. Intriguingly, the endogenous ligand for the benzodiazepine receptor may be a peptide. These considerations led to the synthesis of the composite structure **8**. Although considerably simpler than asperlicin, compound **8** bound to pancreatic CCK receptors almost as strongly as asperlicin itself. Unlike asperlicin, compound **8** was well absorbed after oral administration. Extensive structure–activity studies on **8** led to the amide **9**, which was found to bind to the CCK receptor nearly as strongly as CCK(8) ($K_i = 0.1$ nM) and to antagonize CCK(8)-induced gastric blockade of emptying when administered orally in mice. As noted by Evans *et al.* [29], this seminal work raises the possibility that other nonpeptidal peptidomimetics may be discovered and used:

6

7

8

9

'Whether the benzodiazepine ring in [7 and 9] serves as a conventional structural mimic for key portions of the respective natural ligands or whether it exploits some as yet unidentified feature common to peptide receptors remains unclear. What is clear is that this ring system has now provided very effective ligands for two different peptide receptors, suggesting a generality that could be of much use in the design of ligands for still other such receptors.'

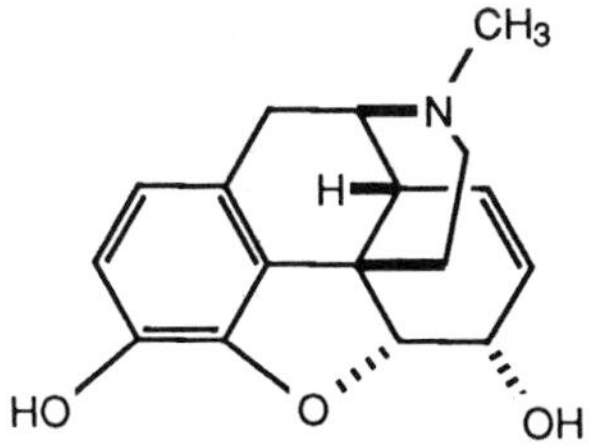

Tyr-Gly-Gly-Phe-X

1 1 (X = Met), Met-enkephalin

1 2 (X = Leu), Leu-enkephalin

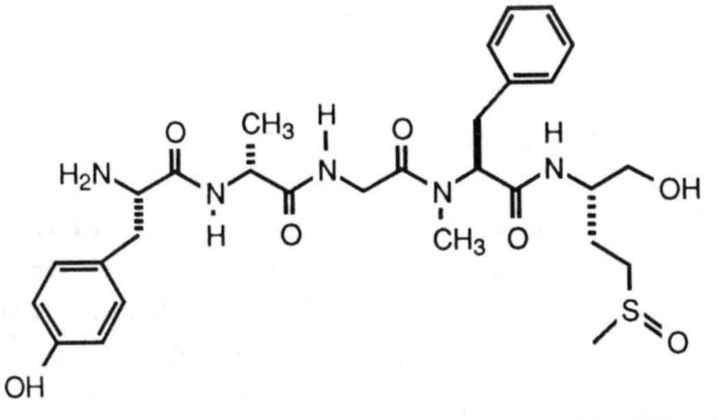

1 0

Tyr----D-Ala----Gly----N-MePhe----Met(O)-ol

1 3

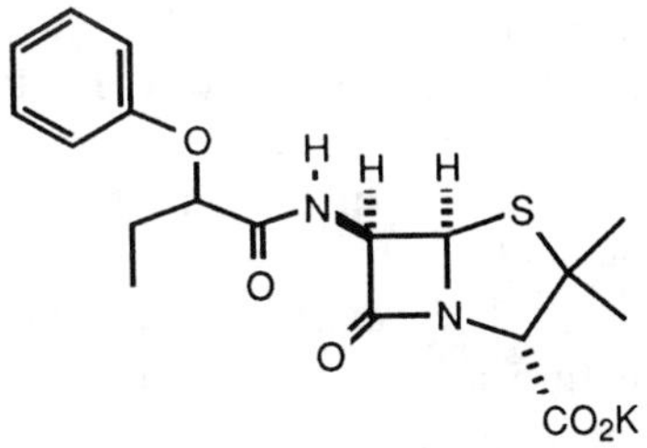

1 4

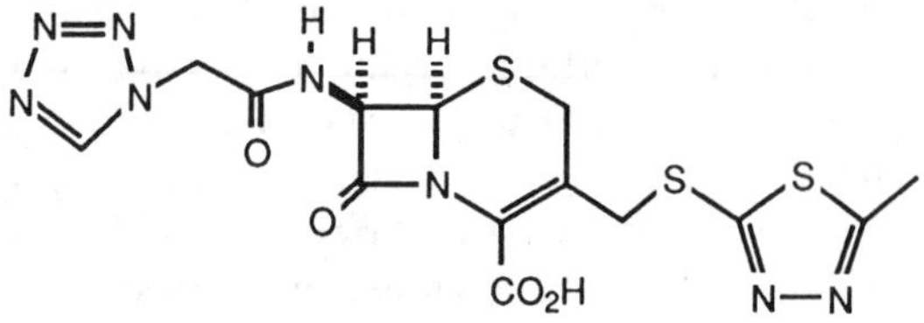

15

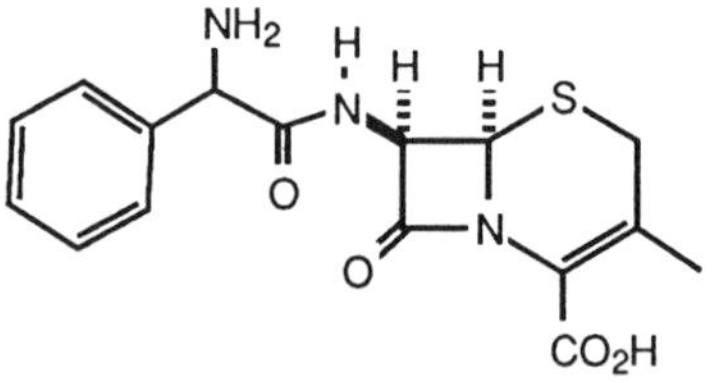

16

Although the structure of morphine (**10**) was fully elucidated in 1953 [30], it was recognized only recently that the natural ligand for the morphine receptor is a peptide, thus identifying morphine as a peptidomimetic [31]. Ironically, the endogenous peptides, methionine and leucine enkephalin (**11** and **12**, respectively), were termed morphinomimetics. In retrospect, several models have been proposed to account for the fact that such dissimilar structures bind competitively to the same receptor [32]. Unfortunately, no paradigm has been developed for comparable prospective rationalizations. It was possible, however, to produce a synthetic analog of methionine enkephalin with prolonged parenteral and oral analgesic activity [33]. As depicted in structure **13**, this required several modifications: replacement of glycine with the unnatural D-alanine, N-methylation of the Gly–Phe amide bond, oxidation of methionine to the sulfoxide, and reduction of the C-terminus to the alcohol.

A classic example of a peptidomimetic, the β-lactam antibiotic, was provided by nature as an ingenious structural analog of acyl-D-alanyl–D-alanine, an intermediate in the biosynthesis of the bacterial cell wall [34]. The molecular basis for the oral efficacy of these antibiotics varies with specific structural features. Monobasic β-lactam antibiotics, such as propicillin (**14**), are absorbed chiefly in the duodenum, a region of relatively low pH. Absorption occurs via passive diffusion of the uncharged species, and is largely dependent on their relative lipophilicity. The poor oral absorption of cefazolin (**15**), a cephalosporin, is attributable to an octanol–water partition coefficient of around 3 for the unionized form, a value about $170 \times$ less than that for propicillin [35]. In contrast, amino-β-lactam antibiotics like cephalexin (**16**) are efficiently absorbed from the small intestine, even though they have low lipid solubility and are ionic at physiological pH. Several groups have demonstrated that their absorption is mediated by a proton-driven dipeptide transport system [36]. Remarkably, this structural recognition as a dipeptide does not extend to intestinal peptidases. In the rat small intestine perfused with 95 µg/ml of cyclacillin (**17**), only

3% of the drug is degraded to the penicilloic acid after 2 h; 85% of the drug is absorbed during this period [37].

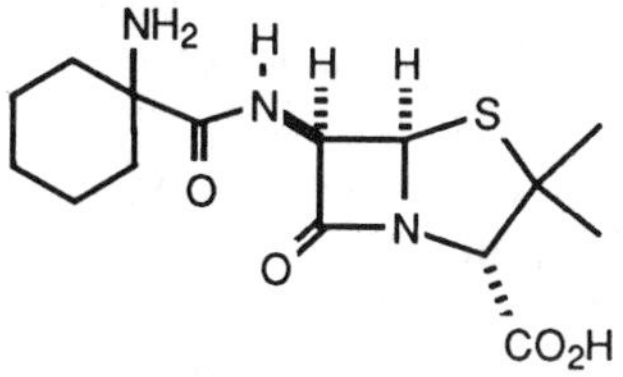

17

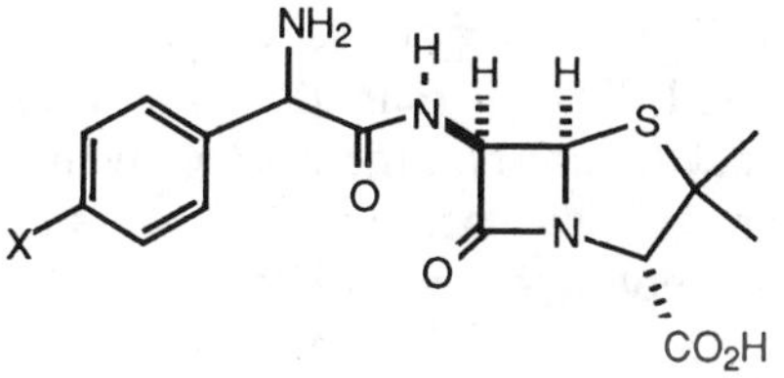

18 (X = H), ampicillin

19 (X = OH), amoxicillin

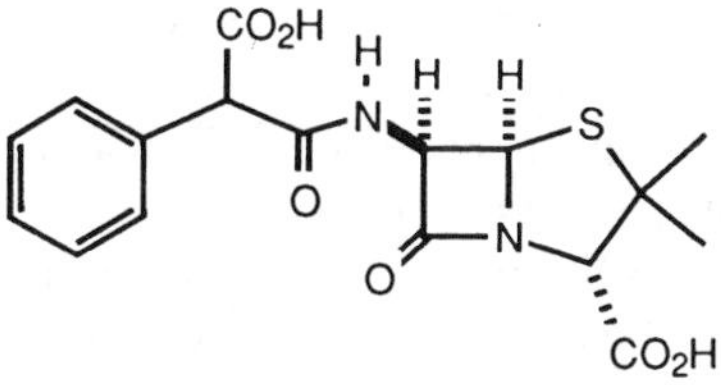

20

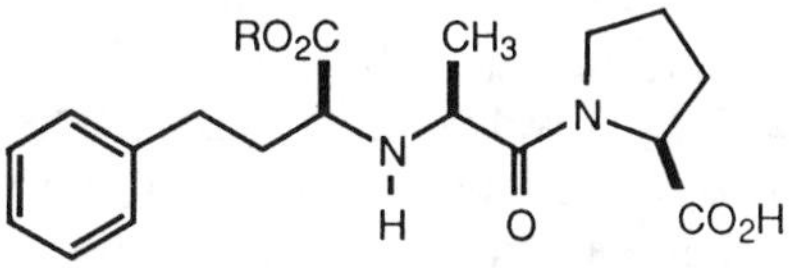

21a (R = H), MK-422

21b (R = Et), MK-421, enalapril

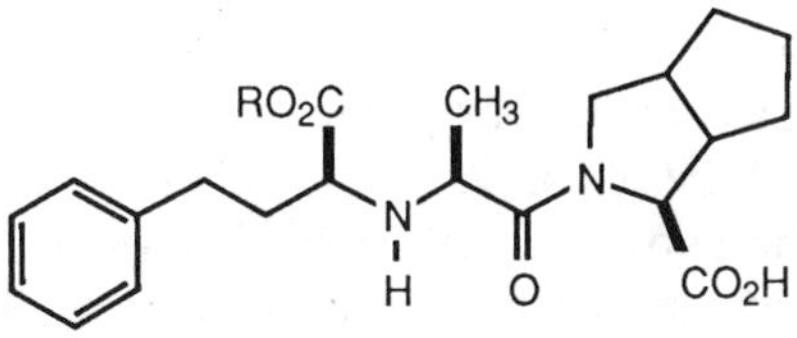

22a (R = H)

22b (R = Et), Hoe 498

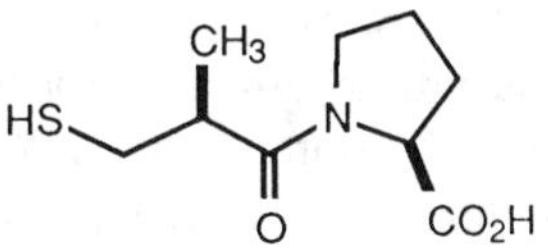

23

In theory, peptidomimetics in any drug category could be designed to exploit the endogenous peptide transport systems. Realistically, in the absence of a detailed knowledge of the specificity of these carriers, the peptidases, and the eventual biological targets, the probability that the structure of an actively transported compound will be determined solely by rational design is slight. Some of the difficulties are illustrated by L-1-aminoethylphosphonic acid, a potent, synthetic inhibitor of bacterial alanine racemase. Although L-1-aminoethylphosphonic acid has no antibacterial activity, derivatization with L-alanine produced L-analyl-L-1-aminoethylphosphonic acid (alafosfalin) [38], which is able to use a bacterial transport system. Once inside the cell, the prodrug is cleaved by bacterial peptidases. Similarly, in the animal host, alafosfalin is actively transported across the intestinal epithelium but largely cleaved in the process, reducing the bioavailability to 14% in rats and 47% in man [22,38]. Modifications which improved the antibacterial potency diminished the oral bioavailability. Thus while Sar–Nva–Nva–Ala(P) had superior *in vitro* activity and *in vivo* metabolic stability, the oral absorption of this larger peptide was poor [39,40].

More consistent success has been realized in the discovery of drugs which traverse the intestinal epithelium by passive diffusion. Although one might expect both ampicillin (**18**) and amoxicillin (**19**) to use the same dipeptide transport system as cyclacillin (**17**), neither does in the rat. In fact, both amoxicillin and cyclacillin can be transported by a common facilitated diffusion process, but ampicillin, which differs from amoxicillin by just a single hydroxyl group, cannot [41]. Nonetheless, ampicillin is sufficiently lipophilic to allow for at least 54% oral absorption in man [42], presumably via a passive mechanism. In contrast, the absorption of the structurally related carbenicillin (**20**), in which the amino group of ampicillin is replaced by a carboxyl residue, is negligible. However, esterification of this group with phenol increases the oral bioavailability to 33% [43], and conversion of ampicillin to its phthalidyl ester results in nearly complete oral bioavailability [44]. This prodrug strategy for increasing the oral absorption of carboxylic acids appears to have some generality. Esterification of the ACE inhibitors MU-422 (**21a**) and Hoe-498-diacid (**22a**) raised their oral absorption from about 10 to 65% [45] and 5 to 56% [46], respectively. The relatively high (60–75%) oral absorption of the structurally related free acid, captopril (**23**), is quite probably due to the involvement of a proton-driven dipeptide carrier in addition to a passive component [47]. Although the transport of captopril is inhibited by Gly–Pro and cephradine (a β-lactam antibiotic), curiously, acetyl-Pro, which, like captopril lacks a free amino group, is not an inhibitor.

The clinical success of ACE inhibitors in the control of hypertension has spurred a continuing effort in the development of inhibitors of renin [48]. This enzyme cleaves angiotensinogen to angiotensin I, the substrate for ACE. Although the fundamental research strategies for the two classes of inhibitor are analogous, the clinical development of renin inhibitors has been hampered by their poor oral bioavailability. Thus, while several research groups have identified compounds with IC_{50}s in the nanomolar range, most of these compounds are not very active orally, even when they are stabilized toward proteolytic degradation. For example, the proline amide linkage present in enalapril has also been used by Thaisrivongs [49] to stabilize the N-terminus of the renin inhibitors **24** and **25** against aminopeptidases. Additional stabilization was imparted by the *tert*-butyloxycarbonyl group and the 2-pyridylmethylamide. Administered intravenously, both 0.28 mg/kg of **24** and 7.1 mg/kg of **25** depressed the blood pressure of hog renin infused rats for about 1.5 h. These doses were judged to be equipotent on the basis of their *in vitro* IC_{50}s and induced nearly identical hypotensive responses. Surprisingly, compound **24** proved to be much less efficacious than **25** when administered orally. While 71 mg/kg of **25** given orally produced an effect comparable to that produced by a 7.1 mg/kg i.v. dose of **25**,

2.8 mg/kg of **24** given orally elicited only a weak hypotensive response relative to the 0.28 mg/kg i.v. dose. This unexplained disparity between two nearly identical structures underscores the obscure nature of the factors underlying peptide absorption. These results, as well as those obtained in sodium-depleted monkeys [50], imply that at least 10% of the orally administered dose of **25** is absorbed. By the same criteria, the oral absorption of the renin inhibitor **26** (CGP-29287) appears to be markedly less [51]. Intravenously, 0.1 mg/kg of CGP-29287 induces a 16 mmHg drop in marmoset blood pressure; orally 100 mg/kg is required to exert a similar effect. While first-pass metabolism (see below) cannot be ruled out as the cause of poor bioavailability, CGP-29287 is basically peptidic in nature, and the diffusion of such a large, positively charged molecule through a lipid bilayer is expected to be poor. Structurally, the most obvious difference between the renin and well absorbed ACE inhibitors is the former's greater size. Yet even the smaller renin inhibitors, such as the 'tetrapeptide' **27** [52], have oral bioavailability of only 2–3% [53]. Because further size reductions have invariably compromised inhibitory potency, future research efforts must focus on modulating the physicochemical properties of existing inhibitors.

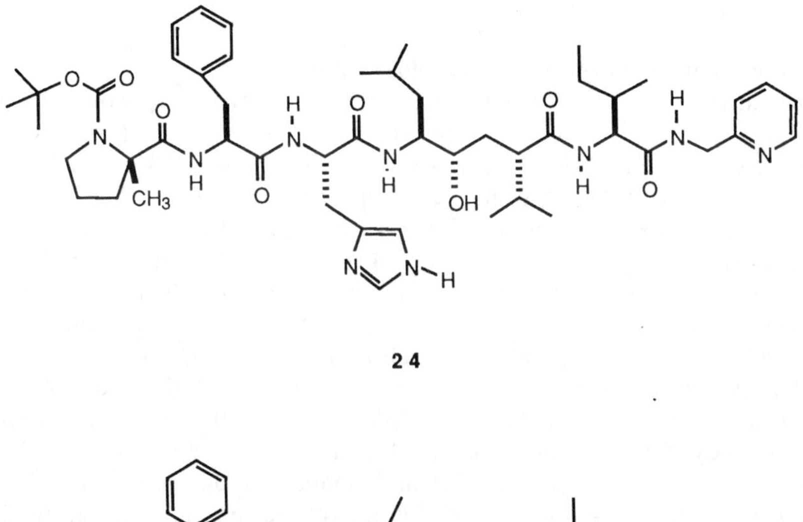

24

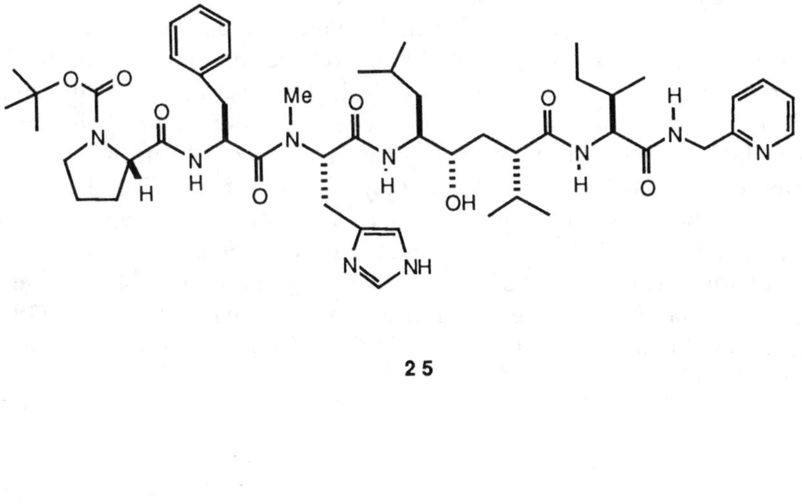

25

Z-Arg-Arg-Pro-Phe-His-Sta-Ile-Lys(Boc)-OMe

2 6

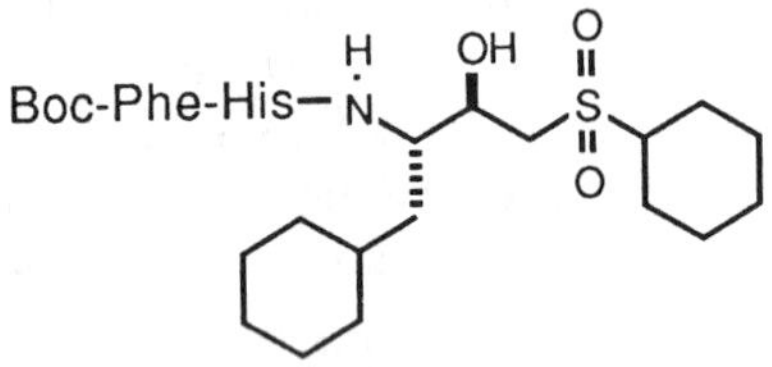

2 7

5.2.6   Formulation approaches to oral bioavailability

An alternative strategy to chemical modification for enhancing peptide uptake is exemplified by the potent immunosuppressive agent, cyclosporin (**28**). As a cyclic peptide, cyclosporin is unusually compact for a compound of its molecular weight and is intrinsically protected from the action of exopeptidases. The presence of D-amino acids and N-methylated amide linkages confers further resistance toward endopeptidases. Despite the fact that cyclosporin is extremely lipophilic, when administered as a solid it is poorly absorbed because it is nearly insoluble in water. Formulation in an olive oil solution, however, results in oral bioavailability as high as 21% in rats [54]. In analogy to other highly lipophilic compounds, such as chloesterol, fatty acids, and the fat-soluble vitamins, it was thought that the absorption of cyclosporin might be mediated by a transport system of the intestinal lymphatics. However, study of thoracic duct cannulated rats demonstrated that less than 2.0% of the absorbed cyclosporin was derived from chylomicrons collected from the lymphatic drainage [54]. Alternatively, the olive oil vehicle may provide an emulsified reservoir of cyclosporin which, by virtue of its high surface area, would facilitate a rapid equilibrium of cyclosporin with the aqueous environment of the intestinal microvilli [55]. Permeabilization of the intestinal mucosa by fatty acid-induced disruption of the enterocyte membrane may also play a role [56]. The safety of absorption promoters which act by this mechanism depends on the rapid reversibility of the disruptive effect. Palmitoyl carnitine, for instance, enhances the absorption of a variety of drugs at doses which do not cause histologically observable damage to the intestinal mucosa. In the case of the somatostatin analog L-363586 (**29**), co-adminstration of palmitoyl carnitine in the rat duodenum raised the bioavailability from 1 to 11% [57].

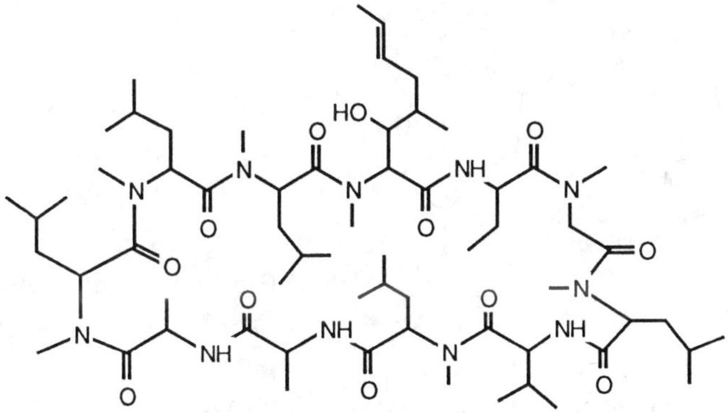

2 8

MeAla-Tyr-D-Trp

Phe-Val-Lys

2 9

H-Ala-Gly-Cys-Lys-Asn-Phe-Phe-Trp

HO-Cys-Ser-Thr-Phe-Thr-Lys

3 0

Asn-Phe-Phe-D-Trp

GABA-Phe-Thr-Lys

3 1

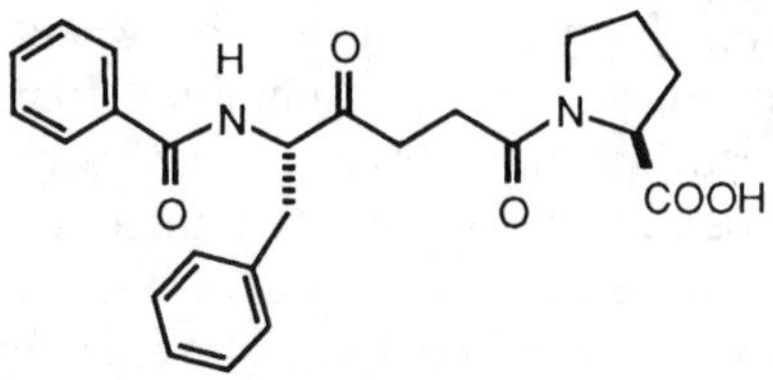

3 2

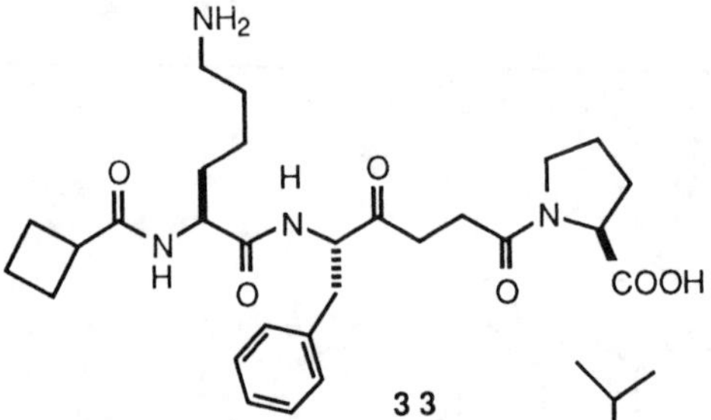

33

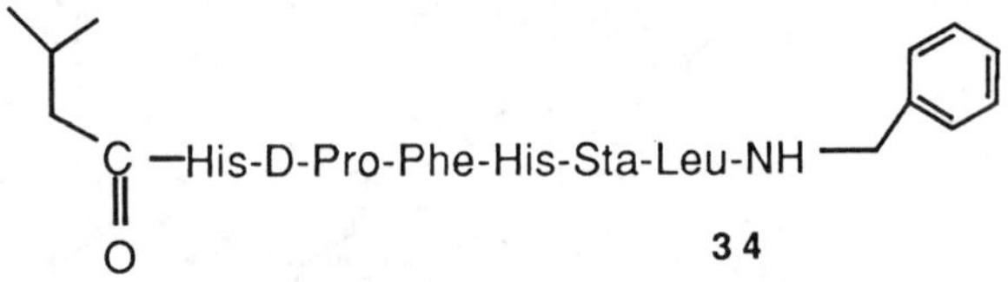

34

5.3 ALTERNATIVE ROUTES OF ADMINISTRATION

Like cyclosporin and somatostatin, many peptides are not easily amenable to chemical modification aimed at improving oral absorption. Although the discovery of intestinal absorption promoters like palmitoyl carnitine offers hope in this situation, so far, alternative modes of administration have received more attention. In theory, the parenteral route is applicable to the majority of agents; but for most conditions, with the notable exception of insulin-dependent diabetes, patient compliance with a regimen of self-injection would be understandably low. Consequently, less invasive routes of administration, such as nasal, rectal, buccal, ocular, pulmonary, transdermal, and surgical implants, have been investigated [58]. Usually, these 'unnatural' delivery routes require the use of adjuvants.

5.3.1 Penetration enhancers

Lee has classified penetration enhancers into four major types: chelators, surfactants, bile salts, and fatty acids [59]. Chelators, such as EDTA, citric acid, salicylates, and enaminones, allow paracellular transport to occur by collapsing the intercellular space. Surfactants, such as polyoxyethylene alkyl ethers and sodium lauryl sulfate, tend to increase membrane fluidity by the leaching of protein. Bile salts, such as sodium deoxycholate, sodium glycocholate, and sodium taurocholate, while less effective than surfactants at releasing protein from the membrane, facilitate diffusion toward the membrane surface by reducing the viscosity of the adherent mucus layer. Fatty acids, such as oleic acid and monoolein, increase membrane fluidity by disordering the phospholipid domain. Because all penetration enhancers must perturb the membrane in some way, their safety and acceptance for general use will depend on the minimal extent and rapid reversibility of the disruptive effect. So far, the nonsurfactant types of enhancers come the closest to meeting the criteria. According to Lee, the preferred enhancer appears to be sodium glycocholate for the nasal route, citric acid for the vaginal route, and salicylates for the rectal route.

5.3.2 Transnasal delivery

The most promising and extensively investigated of these is the intranasal route [60]. This mucosal surface has a high surface area and is extensively vascularized. The rate of absorption through the single layer of epithelial cells is rapid, and first-pass metabolism in the liver is avoided. While a growing number of peptidic compounds have been found to be nasally absorbed, for example, cephalosporins, thyrotropin-releasing hormone, metkephamid, somatostatin analogs, buserelin, nafarelin, secretin, luteinizing hormone-releasing hormone, oxytocin, and various vasopressin analogs, only the last three are actually administered in the clinic by the nasal route. The degree of absorption appears to decrease with increasing molecular weight, and in general, compounds with molecular weights less than 1000 are well absorbed [61]. This trend is illustrated in the human by TRH (MW 362, 40% absorbed), oxytocin (MW 1007, 10% absorbed), and growth hormone-releasing factor (MW 4800, 2% absorbed). Such a dependence on molecular weight is consistent with a nonspecific diffusion through size-restrictive, aqueous channels between the adjacent epithelial cells. To overcome the limit on molecular weight, recent work has focused on the development of nonirritating, nontoxic permeation enhancers. In one study, intranasal aerosolized insulin containing laureth-9 as a surfactant showed promise as an adjunct to subcutaneous insulin in patients with type I diabetes. This formulation was tolerated by some patients for as long as three months [62]. An alternative formulation with sodium deoxycholate has also been shown to deliver insulin intranasally with highly reproducible kinetics and about 10 to 20% efficiency [63,64]. Another bile acid, sodium glycocholate, increases the nasal absorption of leuprolide from 0.11 to 3% [65] and the absorption of insulin from 5 to 30% [66] in the rat. Despite these recent successes, the intranasal delivery of peptides is not without liabilities. Irritation of the nasal mucosa is common, and some dosage forms inhibit mucociliary function. Significant peptidase activity in the nasal mucosa may also hinder the absorption of intact peptides [60]. Finally, patient compliance with a nasal delivery regimen would almost certainly be lower than with a comparable oral formulation.

5.4 METABOLISM AND EXCRETION

After a peptidic drug has been translocated across the epithelial cells of the intestinal tract, it is collected by the splanchnic circulation and enters the portal vein. At this point the substance is in the general circulation and faces a hostile environment and several major obstacles. The first deterrent encountered by the absorbed drug is the liver, through which the portal blood supply must pass before wide-scale distribution throughout the body. Approximately 40% of the cardiac output is delivered to the liver. Removal of substances from the blood by the liver after absorption from the gastrointestinal tract can prevent distribution to other parts of the body. This phenomenon, known as the 'first-pass effect' or presystemic hepatic elimination, is usually undesirable during oral drug treatment. First-pass clearance or metabolism can cause poor drug availability to the systemic circulation despite the fact that the drug may be efficiently absorbed from the gastrointestinal tract.

5.4.1 Biliary excretion

Briefly, the liver consists of a labyrinth of sinusoidal spaces formed by endothelial cell syncytia. The sinusoids are the vasculature of the liver and receive blood from branches of the portal vein and hepatic artery. In addition to the sinusoidal labyrinth, the biliary system also courses throughout the liver. The bile canaliculi are the structural unit of the biliary tree, and are formed by the contact of two adjoining liver cells which fit together to form a cylindrical lumen. After entering the liver, a drug which is excreted in the bile must pass through two cellular membranes, first at the entry into the liver cell itself and then when crossing the canalicular membrane into the bile. For those compounds which are concentrated in bile (i.e. bile-to-plasma ratio > 1.0), carrier-mediated transport systems appear to be operative. The sites for these transport systems are most likely located in the hepatic plasma membrane and/or the canalicular membrane [67]. In rats, at least three transport systems are known to exist for excretion of organic compounds in the bile: one for organic acids, one for ammonium compounds, and another for neutral organic compounds [68]. A drug's susceptibility to excretion in bile is related to its physicochemical properties [69, 70]. The minimum molecular weight necessary for a compound to be excreted in the bile is species dependent. For example, the rat has a relatively low molecular weight threshold, approximately 200 for biliary excretion of quaternary ammonium compounds and about 300 for aromatic anions. For humans this threshold is shifted upward to 500 for most other compounds. Based upon observations for a wide range of xenobiotics in humans, it has been suggested that lower molecular weight compounds (200–400) are eliminated via a renal pathway, whereas substances excreted into the bile are generally larger molecules with molecular weights greater than 400 [71].

Generalizations relating the polarity of a compound to biliary excretion have also been noted [71]. Larger molecules containing strongly polar groups capable of ionizing at physiological pH are thought to promote extensive biliary excretion. Clear exceptions exist, however, as exemplified by neutral molecules such as the cardiac glycosides which show substantial biliary excretion.

In recent years, rapid biliary excretion of peptide-derived substances has proven to be a major problem for the drug-discovery scientist. Somatostatin (**30**), for instance, is a hypothalamic peptide which exhibits a range of biological activities. Due to its effects on insulin, glucagon and gastric acid secretions, the potential utility of synthetic analogs in the therapy for diabetes [72] and ulcers [73] has been suggested. Toward these objectives, a large number of somatostatin analogs have been prepared to overcome the negligible oral absorption and short duration of action of the parent compound. Workers at Merck approached the problem by establishing a working model for the biologically active conformation of somatostatin [74]. This was accomplished by synthesizing conformationally constrained analogs, and then conducting detailed evaluations of their physical and biological properties. Further refinement of the model was aided by the use of computer graphic methods and the synthesis of additional analogs, leading to the identification of the cylic hexapeptide **29**. Noteworthy structural features of **29** include the D-Trp, the *N*-methyl-Ala and the conformational rigidity of the cyclic hexapeptide. These features resulted in extreme resistance to enzymic degradation and increased potency over somatostatin in eliciting certain physiological responses. Unfortunately, radiolabeling experiments with **29** in rats and dogs indicated a rapid uptake by the liver and subsequent rapid excretion of the intact peptide in bile [75]. The rapid elimination of **29** resulted in low bioavailability and prevented the attainment of pharmacologically useful concentrations in the blood, thus precluding further development of this agent. Using a somewhat different chemical strategy, the cyclic octapeptide **31** (CGP-15425) was synthesized by Peters and co-workers and shown to display a longer plasma half-life than somatostatin owing to its greater stability to enzymatic attack in the tissues [76]. The primary route of elimination of this compound in rats is by biliary excretion with only limited enterohepatic circulation.

As noted above, peptide inhibitors of angiotensin-converting enzyme are being used therapeutically in cardiovascular therapy, and these compounds have shown different levels of biliary excretion, depending on their structural characteristics. KetoACE (**32**) is a ketomethylene tripeptide which shows potent inhibition of angiotensin-converting enzyme *in vitro*, but which is not efficacious *in vivo* [77]. This compound has been stabilized to proteolytic degradation by replacement of the Phe–Gly amide bond with a ketomethylene group. The poor antihypertensive activity of **32** in renal hypertensive rats has been attributed to a short half-life in blood, as a result of rapid biliary excretion of unchanged drug. Modification of **32** to the pentapeptide analog **33** increased *in vitro* potency by a factor of 10 but did not substantially increase *in vivo* efficacy. Metabolism studies with radiolabeled **33** demonstrated that this compound is better absorbed than **32**, but is still rapidly excreted into the bile and urine [78].

In contrast to the ketomethylene ACE inhibitors described above, the class of *N*-carboxyalkyl dipeptide ACE inhibitors shows therapeutically useful antihypertensive activity in animals and in man, and does not show prohibitive biliary excretion problems [2]. Enalapril (**21b**) and ramapril (**22b**) are representative examples of the *N*-carboxyalkyl dipeptides. Although these compounds possess molecular weights not too different from **32,** they possess substantially different physicochemical properties, and this may account for their more favorable biliary excretion patterns.

As pointed out earlier, inhibition of the enzyme renin represents an alternative approach to modulate the renin–angiotensin system. By virtue of a large active site cleft for this enzyme, almost all peptidic renin inhibitors have displayed higher molecular weights than inhibitors of ACE. This feature has tended to both reduce absorption and cause rapid biliary excretion, and consequently has significantly slowed the commercial development of these agents [48]. Documented examples of peptidic renin inhibitors that are rapidly excreted into the bile include the pepstatin derivative **34**. This compound, although stabilized against proteolytic degradation, is nevertheless excreted to the extent of 63% into the bile within 2 h following injection to dogs [79]. Likewise, pepstatin A-[^{14}C]glycine was rapidly excreted intact in the bile (and urine) after intravenous administration to rats [80]. Facile liver uptake of peptidic renin inhibitors is not limited to analogs of pepstatin. The dipeptide analogs of angiotensinogen, **35** [81] and **36** [82], both stable to chymotrypsin, are rapidly excreted in the bile following intraduodenal administration to rats and i.v. administration to monkeys, respectively. As mentioned above, biliary excretion in humans is favored as molecular weight increases over 500. One explanation for the rapid biliary excretion of renin inhibitory peptides may be their lipophilic character and high molecular weights, ranging from 670 to 980 for the compounds described above. However, the *in vivo* effectiveness of drugs such as erythromycin (MW = 734), reserpine (MW = 609) and cyclosporin (MW = 1202) suggests that molecular weight is not the sole factor promoting rapid biliary excretion.

3 5	X = N₃
3 6	X = iPr

3 7	X = NH
3 8	X = CH₂
3 9	X = O

Increasing the molecular weight of peptidic agents can sometimes diminish the amount of liver uptake. A good example is illustrated by the report of Gores *et al.* where they evaluated the hepatic extraction of the naturally occurring cholecystokinin (CCK) peptides [83]. In this study, cholecystokinin octapeptide (CCK-8) was extensively extracted in a single pass through the liver, whereas CCK-33 was extracted minimally. This difference in hepatic extraction contrasts with the similar binding affinities and similar potencies for these two peptides in all other classical target organs. Further examination of CCK fragments has shown that the carboxyl-terminal tetrapeptide of CCK-8 is extracted more than the amino terminal tetrapeptide fragment. The authors of this study conclude that the hepatocyte is the cell type involved in hepatic extraction.

As illustrated by the examples cited above, hepatic extraction of peptides or peptide-derived agents is a very poorly understood process. Clearly, physical properties such as molecular weight, lipophilicity, solubility, and ionic charge play an important role in the recognition by the liver. However, the individual and collective effects of the physicochemical properties on hepatic cell uptake are not well defined.

Thus, the chemist is limited in his ability to rationally design compounds that maintain biological efficacy while resisting rapid hepatic elimination. Further research efforts directed towards delineating the relationships of peptide structure to liver recognition and uptake may greatly facilitate the development of peptides as therapeutically useful drugs.

5.4.2   Renal metabolism and excretion

The ability of the kidney to clear compounds from the plasma represents a major barrier to drug development. Approximately 25% of the cardiac output is delivered to the kidneys. Blood enters via the renal arteries from the abdominal aorta, and leaves the kidneys from the renal veins to return to the general circulation via the inferior vena cava. The functional unit of the kidney is the nephron, which occurs to the extent of a million or more in each kidney. A discrete component of the nephron, the proximal tubule, is the site where reabsorption and/or degradation of peptides and proteins takes place. Morphologically, the epithelial cells of the lumenal brush border of the proximal tubule share many of the transporting properties with their sister cells in the small intestine [84]. Thus, both the intestinal cells (described earlier) and the proximal tubule cells contain a host of degradative enzymes capable of hydrolyzing peptidic substances. Substantial evidence has now accumulated that small peptides filtered at the glomerulus are hydrolyzed at the lumenal membrane of the proximal tubule, with reabsorption of metabolites [84]. Alternatively, oligopeptides may be absorbed in the proximal tubule by the process of endocytosis [85,86]. This pathway is dependent on metabolic energy and inhibited by cytochalasin B which interferes with microfilament function. Since the proximal tubule epithelium has a high capacity for the reabsorption of solutes and small molecules [84], the renal 'barrier' can be overcome largely by developing enzymatically stable peptides with suitable physicochemical properties. Compounds designed in this way will be filtered at the glomerulus and then enter the proximal tubule. While passing through the proximal tubule, reabsorption of the compound can occur without proteolysis if both enzymatic stability and proper lipophilicity have been achieved. The compound will then re-enter into systemic circulation and most likely be metabolized in the liver. If proteolytic stability has been imparted but the lipophilicity is insufficient to promote translocation across the proximal tubule epithelium, the peptide will continue its passage through the nephron and ultimately be excreted into the urine. Thus, the key attributes of a peptidal compound for survival in the kidney and re-entry into circulation are enzymatically stability and properly adjusted lipophilicity.

5.5   ENHANCEMENT OF PROTEOLYTIC STABILITY

If a peptidic drug is able to clear the liver and kidney without suffering major extraction and/or proteolysis, it will then enter the systemic circulation and will be widely disseminated throughout the body. The peptide will initially be distributed to rapidly perfused tissues such as heart, lung, kidneys and brain, and then more slowly to fat, skin and muscle. In order to exert a useful pharmacologic effect, the peptidic agent must present a sustained concentration at the target receptors. For peptides, in particular, this presents a problem owing to the large number of peptidases that are prevalent in the blood and throughout various tissues. Enzymatic cleavage of amide bonds in the peptide chain by these peptidases represents a major degradative pathway for peptides in the body. A significant challenge facing chemists involved in peptide drug discovery is to prevent the undesired proteolytic degradation.

The amide bond is the focal point when one considers enzymatic stability of a peptide substance. This structural unit of peptides and/or peptidomimetics serves a number of important functions. It can function as a spacer connecting distal pharmacophoric elements; it can provide a specific spatial disposition of the attached side chains (i.e. *S-cis* versus *S-trans* rotational isomers); or it can be intimately involved in binding of a peptide to a receptor or an enzyme through hydrogen bonding interactions. In reality, not all amide bonds are proteolytically labile. The susceptibility of an amide bond to enzymatic attack depends on its local environment (i.e. 3-dimensional orientation) and on the adjacent amino acid side chains. Certain peptidases require a charged group in their peptide substrate for recognition. For example, amino peptidases cleave from the N-terminal position of a peptide chain and require the presence of a free α-amino group. The simple expedient of *N*-acylation or *N*-alkylation is often sufficient to block the action of this enzyme. Likewise, carboxy peptidases cleave from the C-terminal end of a peptide and require the presence of a free carboxyl group, while trypsin-like enzymes cleave after an arginine or lysine in a peptide chain. Cleavage by other endopeptidases is dependent on their ability to recognize and bind specific structural elements present in the peptide or peptidomimetic or peptoid.

A general strategy that has evolved in developing peptide leads into useful drugs has involved identifying the cleavage sites in the peptide and then characterizing the degrading enzyme(s). With this knowledge, the chemist can then proceed to modify the structure of the peptide so that recognition by the peptidase is reduced or eliminated while affinity for the target bioreceptor is maintained. Preserving biological activity in a peptide lead while imparting enzymatic stability represents a difficult task for the peptide chemist. Experience has taught that structure–function studies focusing on potency and selectivity of action should be conducted in parallel or nearly parallel with structural modifications probing proteolytic stability. This convergent strategy allows for the simultaneous assessment of several variables and may prevent having to re-optimize potency on a compound after it has previously been stabilized against proteolytic degradation.

Over the past several decades, peptide chemists have developed a large number of modified amino acid residues and bioisosteric replacements that resist proteolytic degradation when incorporated into peptides or peptidomimetics [2,87]. A partial list of the most commonly used amide isosteres is depicted in Fig. 5.1. In many cases, synthetic replacement of labile portions of a peptidic substance by derivatives which are not recognized by the natural proteases represents the first tactic employed by the peptide chemist. *N*-Methylation, α-*C*-methylation, and the use of D-amino acids are examples of alterations that have shown particular utility in imparting proteolytic stability. Carbonyl reduction to a reduced amide function has also been used in those cases where the incorporation of a basic amino group is not deleterious. Alternatively, the hydroxy ethylene and thiomethylene isosteres are examples of non-charged replacements for the amide bond. When an amide bond serves predominantly a

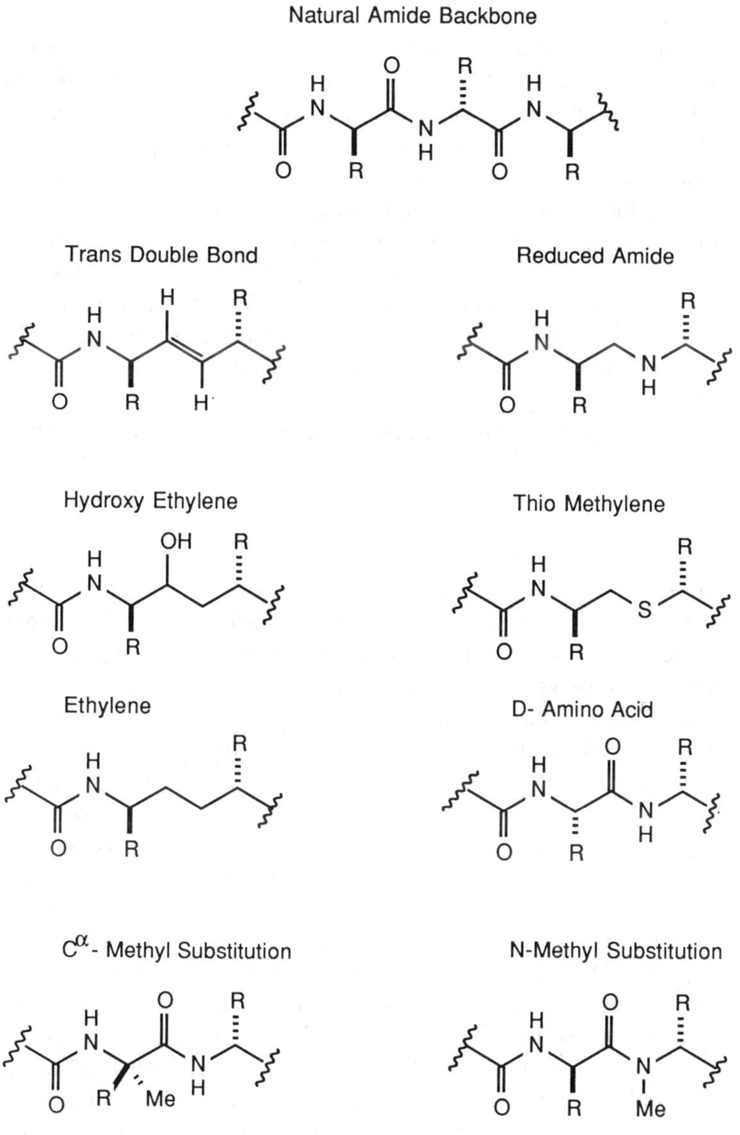

Natural Amide Backbone

Trans Double Bond

Reduced Amide

Hydroxy Ethylene

Thio Methylene

Ethylene

D- Amino Acid

C^α- Methyl Substitution

N-Methyl Substitution

Fig. 5.1 — Amide bond isosteres and structural modifications which reduce proteolysis.

structural role of orienting the receptor recognition elements, then replacement with a trans olefin has proven useful. This isosteric moiety provides useful replication of bond angles and rigidity but lacks the hydrogen bonding capability. Retroinverso amide bonds are yet another stabilization technique which has shown particular merit in certain specific instances [88].

In some cases, amide bond stabilization effected by using a modified amino acid or an amide bond isostere exerts an influence not only at the site of introduction but also at distal positions of the peptide chain. This enhanced stability at positions removed from the site of modification has been ascribed to an alteration of peptide conformation such that recognition by degrading enzymes is no longer favorable. Peptide chemists frequently use this concept, known as conformational constraint, to enhance biological activity while removing proteolytic liability [89]. Conformational constraints that are quite easily introduced into peptide analogs include D-amino acids, N-methylamino acids and α-methylamino acids. Synthetically more challenging constraints consist of covalent modifications leading to the formation of cyclic or polycyclic peptides. Strategic incorporation of proline or five- or six-membered lactams [90] has proven successful, as have cyclizations through amide bonds or disulfide bridges [91]. In general, the use of conformational constraints to identify the bioactive conformation of a peptide lead has produced novel analogs with significant metabolic stability.

To illustrate an approach that chemists have used in developing enzymatically stable peptides, a recent example from the literature will be described [82]. The case considered involves the design of renin inhibitory peptides as antihypertensive agents. Following a systematic structure–activity search, compound **37** was identified as a potent inhibitor of human plasma renin with an IC_{50} of 0.9 nM. When **37** was incubated with a battery of standard enzymes and tissue homogenates to probe for enzymatic stability, the pancreatic enzyme chymotrypsin was found to effect a rapid cleavage between the Phe and His residues, yielding the corresponding inactive fragments. Since chymotrypsin is known to be present in the gastrointestinal tract, stability to this enzyme was thought to be necessary for good oral absorption of the intact molecule. At this point, the task focused on introducing subtle structural changes into **37** so that affinity towards renin was maintained while recognition by chymotrypsin was reduced or eliminated. Molecular modeling proved useful in identifying important hydrogen bonding interactions of **37** with both enzymes in their active site regions. The key structural element of **37** simplified to the α-NH of Phe. With chymotrypsin, a serine protease, this NH of **37** corresponds to the P_1 subsite and is involved in an energetically important hydrogen bond with Ser-214; consequently, disruption of this interaction prevents recognition and productive binding. With the aspartic protease renin, on the other hand, the same NH in **37** occurs in the P_3 position and is not essential for productive binding. Replacement of the NH in compound **37** with either a methylene (**38**) or an oxygen (**39**) was found to preserve potent renin inhibitory activity while leading to substantially enhanced stability against chymotrypsin. As can happen in many cases in drug development, the successful solution of one particular problem does not always result in a therapeutically useful agent. Neither **38** nor **39** demonstrated good oral bioavailability in rats and monkeys. The problem was ultimately traced to low absorption and/or rapid biliary excretion. Thus for peptides, proteolytic degradation as a principal limiting factor in drug discovery can now be overcome by a variety of rational strategies; however, transportability and excretion remain as serious obstacles and challenges.

From the above discussion, it is clear that enzymatic stability of a peptide, while very important, represents only one of several factors affecting *in vivo* efficacy. An interesting report demonstrating how imparting proteolytic stability can have different effects *in vitro* versus *in vivo* is illustrated by a study with leucine enkephalin analogs [92]. The pentapeptide, H–Tyr–Ala–Gly–Phe–Leu–NH$_2$, exhibited potent opiate-like activity when evaluated in isolated tissue preparations. However, in whole animal experiments, including direct introduction into the brain, no antinociceptive activity was observed. The problem was finally traced to the degradation by aminopeptidase enzymes present in plasma and brain tissue. As mentioned earlier in this chapter, N-methylation and D-amino acid replacement both inhibit this degradative process. Thus, substitutions of this type produced an analog (H–Tyr–D–Ala–Gly–Phe–Leu–NH$_2$), which showed potent antinociceptive- activity following direct injection into the brain. This compound still lacked activity when administered intravenously, however. By incubation with various tissue homogenates, the instability was identified as a sensitivity of the peptide to degradation by liver and kidney enzymes. A solution to this newly identified barrier was explored with a subseries of descarboxy–leucine analogs (H–Tyr–D–Ala–Gly–Phe–NHCH$_2$CH$_2$CHMe$_2$). A series of five analogs with their corresponding biological data are depicted in Table 5.1. The parent compound, **I**, is a rather weak

Table 1 — Stabilized enkephalin analogs [92]

	Analog	Kidney $t_{1/2}$ (min)	G. pig ileum (potency rel. to [Met-5] Enk = 1.0)	Mouse writing ED$_{50}$ (mg/kg), i.v.
I	Tyr–D–Ala–Gly–Phe–NH–CH$_2$CH$_2$CHMe$_2$	2	9.4	> 100
II	NMe–Tyr–D–Ala–Gly–Phe–NHCH$_2$CH$_2$CHMe$_2$	5	5.2	0.2
III	Tyr–D–Ala–Gly–NMe–Phe–NHCH$_2$CH$_2$CHMe$_2$	6	5.0	0.2
IV	NMe–Tyr–D–Ala–Gly–NMe–Phe–NHCH$_2$CH$_2$CHMe$_2$	> 120	2.35	0.3
V	NMe–Tyr–D–Ala–Gly–NMe–Phe–NMe–CH$_2$CH$_2$CHMe$_2$	> 60	0.710	3.0

analgesic *in vivo* as evidenced by the high value in the mouse-writhing assay. This analog is also rapidly degraded by kidney enzymes. N-Methylation of the Tyr residue in **I** gave **II** which shows roughly the same activity in the guinea pig ileum assay but which demonstrates enhanced *in vivo* efficacy. Analog **III**, containing an N-methyl Phe, is quite similar in activity to **II**, whereas double N-methylation (**IV**) greatly improves enzymatic stability. Triple methylation (**V**) improves enzymatic stability still further but results in lowered activity. It is interesting to note that analogs **II** and **III** exhibit reduced receptor affinity for the guinea pig ileum, but show potent *in vivo* activity. The higher plasma concentrations for these compounds, presumably arising from their enhanced proteolytic stability to kidney enzymes, apparently override their lower *in vitro* potency and produce potent effects in the mouse-writhing test.

5.6 THE BLOOD–BRAIN BARRIER

The pre-eminence of the brain in biological regulation establishes this organ as a primary target for drug therapy. Moreover, peptides which mediate cerebral function continue to be discovered at a rapid pace. Unfortunately, the well known 'blood–brain barrier' (BBB) [93,94] constitutes a formidable obstacle to the development of centrally acting, peptide-based drugs. Morphologically, the BBB consists of a specialized capillary endothelium in which the adjacent cells form extremely tight, impermeable junctions. Thus, if a molecule is unable to use a specific transport system (e.g. for glucose, amino acids, or nucleosides), its entry into the cerebral interstitial space will depend on its ability to passively diffuse through the phospholipid membrane. This ability is, in turn, determined by molecular size and lipophilicity. Although a more circuitous route of entry is possible from the fluid through the circumventricular organs, the cerebrospinal surface area of this barrier is only 0.02% of the BBB itself. Given their array of polar amide bonds and other ionic functionality, one would expect most peptides to be excluded from the brain. This expectation has been confirmed experimentally. Whole-body autoradiography shows little penetration of the TRH analog (**40**) [95] or the somatostatin analog (**31**) [96] into the central nervous system, and less than 2.5% of radiolabeled cholecystokinin, somatostatin, or Leu-enkephalin is retained in the brain following arterial injection in the rat [97]. However, in some instances, even this low degree of penetration may be sufficient to elicit a central response. In humans, for example, peripherally administered MIF-I, a tripeptide (**41**), has been shown to reduce the symptoms of Parkinsonism and improve the mood of depressed patients [98,99]. β-Endorphin (**42**) has been used to alleviate pain in cancer patients [100], and delta sleep-inducing peptide (**43**) has been used to treat insomnia [101]. The mechanism by which these central effects are exerted is controversial [102,103]. These peptides, rather than actually gaining access to the brain, may interact with other receptors located in the periphery or on the lumenal side of the brain capillary. Alternatively, some peptides may exert a central effect by altering the permeability of the BBB to other substances [104].

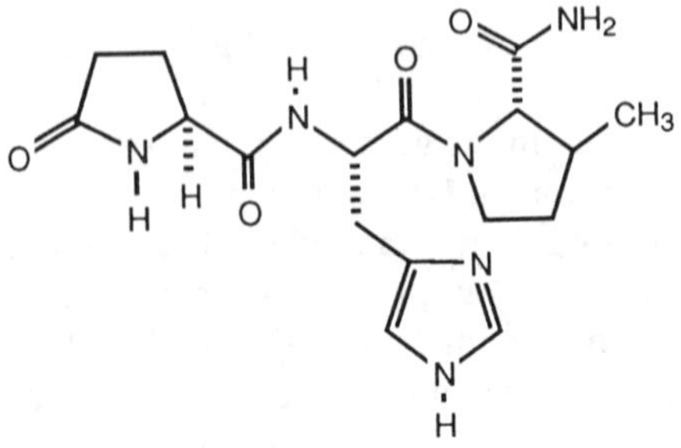

4 0

Pro-Leu-Gly-NH$_2$

4 1

Tyr-Gly-Gly-Phe-Met-Thr-Ser-Glu-Lys-Ser-Gln-Thr-Pro-Leu-Val-Thr-
Leu-Phe-Lys-Asn-Ala-Ile-Ile-Lys-Asn-Ala-Tyr-Lys-Lys-Gly-Glu

4 2

Trp-Ala-Gly-Gly-Asp-Ala-Ser-Gly-Glu

4 3

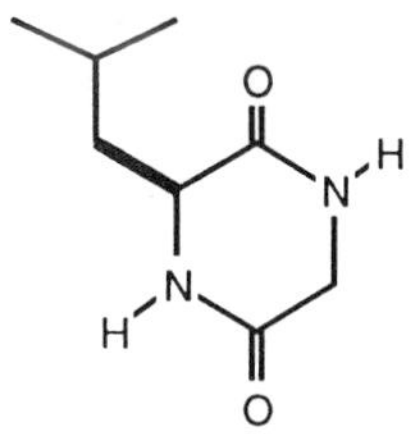

4 4

The basic chemical strategies for enhancing penetration through the BBB are similiar to those employed for improving absorption through the small intestine: stabilization to proteolysis, reduced molecular weight, and optimized lipophilicity. A study of the permeability of the rat brain capillary to 27 structurally diverse compounds established a correlation of the form $\log P_c = -4.605 + 0.4115 \log [P(M_r) - 1/2]$, where P_c is the permeability coefficient, P is the octanol–water partition coefficient, and M_r is the molecular weight [105]. The permeability coefficients of compounds with molecular weights greater than 400 were at least an order of magnitude less than the value predicted by this equation. Another study of 18 peptides found lipophilicity to be more important than size or charge in determining BBB penetration [106]. The entry of delta sleep-inducing peptide and its analogs into the rat brain and dog CSF also appears to correlate with lipophilicity [107]. Although there is evidence for brain-to-blood transport systems for some peptides, a blood-to-brain transport system has not yet been found [102]. Thus, while phenylalanine and leucine enter the rat brain by a carrier system, the entry of glycyl-L-phenylalanine and glycyl-L-leucine is negligible [108]. In contrast, the diketopiperazine cyclo (Leu–Gly) (**44**), which represents a metabolically stable version of the C-terminal dipeptide of oxytocin and MIF, has been shown to penetrate into the brain [109]. Cyclization removes two highly polar functional groups from the dipeptide and reduces its size. Lipophilic prodrugs may also be used to increase the rate of passive diffusion for small, polar compounds [93,110]. The Schiff-base amide (**45**) [110], for example, crosses the BBB and releases gamma-aminobutyric acid (GABA), a neutotransmitter. An especially ingenious approach for brain-specific delivery involving the dihydropyridine–pyridinium salt redox system is illustrated by the dopamine prodrug **46** [112]. After diffusing into the brain, **46** is oxidized to the pyridinium form **47**. Now charged, the prodrug is locked in the brain tissue and hydrolyzed to release dopamine.

4 5

4 6   **4 7**

5.7 CONCLUSION

Although no class of drugs is exempt from the problems of oral bioavailability, tissue distribution, metabolism and excretion, these difficulties are particularly acute for peptide-based drugs. Nonetheless, the enormous benefits promised by new therapies based on peptide function will continue to serve as a powerful incentive to continue research in this area. For example, endothelin, a 21-residue peptide produced by vascular endothelial cells, was recently isolated and shown to be one of the most potent vasoconstrictors known [113]. Derived from a preproendothelin polypeptide by a series of proteolytic cleavages, endothelin may be important in the control of systemic blood pressure. If so, inhibition of the putative endothelin-converting enzyme by peptidic substrate analogs might constitute the basis of a novel antihypertensive therapy. The dependence of even the simplest lifeforms on peptide function for their survival is illustrated by the human immunodeficiency virus (HIV), the causative agent of AIDS. The HIV genome codes for a protease which processes a large viral polyprotein into smaller functional units. Elimination of the proteolytic activity by a site-directed mutation in the protease gene led to the production of non-infectious virions [114]. Several groups are currently synthesizing inhibitors of the HIV protease as the first step in the development of an urgently needed therapy for AIDS. In analogy with previous efforts to inhibit renin and angiotensin-converting enzyme, most of these compounds will be transition state analogs with substantial peptide character. As with any peptide-based drug, bridging the gap between *in vitro* inhibitors and a therapeutic agent will be achieved most quickly by confronting the biological liabilities of peptides from the outset. As discussed above, this will require the medicinal chemist to consider structure–activity relationships within the human host as well as in the test tube.

REFERENCES

[1] Samanen, J. (1985). Biomedical polypeptides — a wellspring of pharmaceuticals. In C. G. Gebelein & C. E. Carraher (eds) *Bioactive Polymeric Systems: An Overview*. Plenum Press, New York, p. 279.

[2] Humphrey, M. J. & Ringrose, P. S. (1986)., Peptides and related drugs: a review of their absorption, metabolism, and excretion. *Drug Metab. Rev.* **17,** 283.

[3] Madara, J. L. & Trier, J. S. (1987). Functional morphology of the mucosa of the small intestine. In: L. R. Johnson (ed.) *Physiology of the Gastrointestinal Tract*. 2nd edn, Vol. II. Raven Press, New York, p. 1209.

[4] Carr, K. E. & Toner, P. G. (1984). Morphology of the intestinal mucosa. In: T. Z. Csaky (ed.) *Handbook of Experimental Pharmacology. Vol. 70/I: Pharmacology of Intestinal Permeation I*. Springer-Verlag, New York, p. 1.

[5] Kulenkampff, H. (1975). The structural basis of intestinal absorption. In: W. Forth & W. Rummel (eds) *International Encyclopedia of Pharmacology and Therapeutics, Section 39B, Pharmacology of Intestinal Absorption: Gastrointestinal Absorption of Drugs*, Vol. I. Pergamon Press, New York, p. 1.

[6] Esposito, G. (1984). Polarity of intestinal epithelial cells: permeability of the brush border and basolateral membranes. In: T.Z Csaky (ed.) *Handbook of Experimental Pharmacology, Vol. 70/I: Pharmacology of Intestinal Permeation I*. Springer-Verlag, New York, p. 283.

[7] Csaky, T. Z. (1984). Intestinal permeation and permeability: an overview. In: T. Z. Csaky (ed.) *Handbook of Experimental Pharmacology, Vol. 70\I: Pharmacology of Intestinal Permeation I*. Springer-Verlag, New York, p. 51.

[8] Dressman, J. B., Amidon, G. L., & Fleisher, D. (1985). Absorption potential: estimating the fraction absorbed for orally administered compounds. *J. Pharm. Sci.* **74,** 588.

[9] Csaky, T. Z. (1984). Intestinal absorption of xenobiotics. In: T. Z. Csaky (ed.) *Handbook of Experimental Pharmacology, Vol. 70/II: Pharmacology of Intestinal Permeation II*. Springer-Verlag, New York, p. 1.

[10] Thomson, A. B. R. & Dietschy, J. M. (1984). The role of the unstirred water layer in intestinal permeation. In: T. Z. Csaky (ed.) *Handbook of Experimen-*

tal Pharmacology, Vol. 70\II: Pharmacology of Intestinal Permeation II.
Springer-Verlag, New York, p. 165.

[11] Alpers, D. H. (1987). Digestion and absorption of carbohydrates and proteins. In: L. R. Johnson (ed.) *Physiology of the Gastrointestinal Tract,* 2nd edn, Vol. II. Raven Press, New York, p. 1469.

[12] Agolev, A. M., Iezuitova, N. N., & Smirnova, L. F. (1984). Role of digestive enzymes in the permeability of the enterocyte. In: T. Z. Csaky (ed.) *Handbook of Experimental Pharmacology, Vol. 70/II: Pharmacology of Intestinal Permeation II.* Springer-Verlag, New York, p. 31.

[13] Esposito, G. (1984). Intestinal permeability of water-soluble nonelectrolytes: sugars, amino acids, peptides. In: T. Z. Csaky (ed.) *Handbook of Experimental Pharmacology, Vol. 70/I: Pharmacology of Intestinal Permeation I.* Springer-Verlag, New York, p. 567.

[14] Silk, D. B. A. (1981). Peptide transport. *Clin. Sci.* **60,** 607.

[15] Chung, Y. C., Silk, D. B. A., & Kim, Y. S. (1979). Intestinal transport of a tetrapeptide, L-leucylglyclyglyclylglycine, in rat small intestine *in vivo. Clin. Sci.* **57,** 1.

[16] Gardner, M. L. G. (1984). Intestinal assimilation of intact peptides and proteins from the diet — a neglected field? *Biol. Rev.* **59,** 289.

[17] Yokohama, S., Yamashita, K., Toguchi, H., Takeuchi, J., & Kitamori, N. (1984). Absorption of thyrotropin-releasing hormone after oral administration of TRH tartrate monohydrate in the rat, dog, and human. *J. Pharm. Dyn.* **7,** 101.

[18] Gonzalez-Barcena, D., Kastin, A. J., Miller, M.C., Schalch, D. S., Coy, D. H., Schally, A. V., & Escalante-Herrera, A. (1975). Stimulation of luteinizing hormone (LH) release after oral administration of an analogue of LH releasing hormone. *Lancet* **2,** 1126.

[19] Okada, H., Yamazaki, I., Ogawa, Y., Hirai, S., Yashiki, T., & Mima, H. J. (1982). Vaginal absorption of a potent luteinizing hormone-releasing hormone analog (leuprolide) in rats. I. Absorption by various routes and absorption enhancement. *J. Pharm. Sci.* **71,** 1367.

[20] Amoss, M., Rivier, J., & Guillemin, R., (1972). Release of gonadotropins by oral administration of LRF or a tripeptide fragment of LRF. *J. Clin. Endocrinol. Metab.* **35,** 175.

[21] Yokohama, S., Yoshioka, T., Yamashita, K., & Kitamori, N. (1984). Intestinal absorption mechanisms of thyrotropin-releasing hormone. *J. Pharm. Dyn.* **7,** 445.

[22] Kimura, T. (1984). Transmucosal absorption of small peptide drugs. *Pharm. Int.* **5,** 75.

[23] Laskowski, M., Jr., Haessler, H. A., Miech, R. P., Peanasky, R. J., & Laskowski, M. (1958). Effect of trypsin inhibitor on passage of insulin across the intestinal barrier. *Science* **127,** 1115.

[24] Fujii, S., Yokoyama, T., Ikegaya, K., Sato, F., & Yokoo, N. (1985). Promoting effect of the new chymotrypsin inhibitor FK-448 on the intestinal absorption of insulin in rats and dogs. *J. Pharm. Pharmacol.* **37,** 545.

[25] Saffran, M., Franco-Saenz, R., Kong, A., Papahadjopoulos, P., & Szoka, F.

(1979). A model for the study of the oral administration of peptide hormones. *Can. J. Biochem.* **57,** 548.

[26] Saffran, M., Bedra, C., Kumar, G. S., & Neckers, D. C. (1988). Vasopressin: a model for the study of effects of additives on the oral and rectal administration of peptide drugs. *J. Pharm. Sci.* **77,** 33.

[27] Zaoral, M., Kole, J., & Sorm, F. (1967). Amino acids and peptides. LXXI. Synthesis of 1-deamino-8-D-γ-aminobutyrine-vasopressin, 1-deamino-8-D-lysine-vasopressin, and 1-deamino-8-D-arginine vasopressin. *Collect. Czech. Chem. Commun.* **32,** 1250.

[28] Williams, J.A. (1982). Cholecystokinin: a hormone and a neurotransmitter. *Biomed. Res.* **3,** 107.

[29] Evans, B. E.,.Bock, M. G., Rittle, K. E., Dipardo, R. M., Whitter, W. L., Veber, D. F., Anderson, P. S., & Freidinger, R. M. (1986). Design of potent, orally effective, non-peptidal antagonists of the peptide hormone cholecystokinin. *Proc. Natl. Acad. Sci. USA* **83,** 4918.

[30] Rapoport, H. & Lavigne, J. B. (1953). Stereochemical studies in the morphine series. The relative configuration at carbons thirteen and fourteen. *J. Amer. Chem. Soc.* **75,** 5329.

[31] Hughes, J., Smith, T.W., Kosterlitz, H. W., Fothergill, L. A., Morgan, B. A., & Morris, H. R. (1975). Identification of two related pentapeptides from the brain with potent opiate agonist activity. *Nature* **258,** 577.

[32] Farmer, P. S. (1980). Bridging the gap between bioactive peptides and nonpeptides: some perspectives in design. In: E. J. Ariens (ed.) *Drug Design,* Vol. X. Academic Press, New York, p. 119.

[33] Roemer, D., Beuescher, H. H., Hill, R. C., Pless, J., Bauer, W., Cardinaux, F., Closse, A., Hauser, D., & Huguenin, R. (1977). A synthetic enkephalin analogue with prolonged parenteral and oral analgesic activity. *Nature* **268,** 547.

[34] Gale, E. F., Cundliffe, E., Reynolds, P. E., Richmond, M. H., & Waring, M. J. (1981). *The Molecular Basis of Antibiotic Action,* 2nd edn. Wiley, New York, p. 79.

[35] Tsuji, A., Miyamoto, E., Kubo, O., & Yamana, T. (1979). GI absorption of β-lactam antibiotics III: kinetic evidence for *in situ* absorption of ionized species of monobasic penicillins and cefazolin from the rat small intestine and structure–absorption rate relationships. *J. Pharm. Sci.* **68,** 812.

[36] Hori, R., Okano, T., Kato, M., Maegawa, H., & Inui, I.-I. (1988). Intestinal absorption of cephalosporin antibiotics: correlation between intestinal absorption and brush-border membrane transport. *J. Pharm. Pharmacol.* **40,** 646.

[37] Tsuji, A., Nakashima, E., Kagami, I., & Yamana, T. (1981). Intestinal absorption mechanism of amphoteric β-lactam antibiotics II: Michaelis–Menten kinetics of cyclacillin absorption and its pharmacokinetic analysis in rats. *J. Pharm. Sci.* **70,** 772.

[38] Allen, J. G., Havas, L., Leicht, E., Lenox-Smith, I., & Nisbet, L. J. (1979). Phosphonopeptides as antibacterial agents: metabolism and pharmacokinetics of alafosfalin in animal and humans. *Antimicrob. Agents Chemother.* **16,** 306.

[39] Atherton, F. R., Hall, M. J., Hassall, C. H., Holmes, S. W., Lambert, R. W.,

Lloyd, W. J., & Ringrose, P. S. (1980). Phosphonopeptide antibacterial agents related to alafosfalin: design, synthesis, and structure–activity relationships. *Antimicrob. Agents Chemother.* **18**, 897.

[40] Ringrose, P. S. (1985). Warhead delivery and suicide as concepts in antimicrobial drug design. *Symp. Soc. Gen. Microbiol.* **38**, 219.

[41] Kimura, T., Endo, H., Yoshikawa, M., Muranishi, S., & Sezaki, H. (1978). Carrier-mediated transport sytems for aminopenicillins in rat small intestine. *J. Pharm. Dyn.* **1**, 262.

[42] Cole, M., Kenig, M. D., & Hewitt, V. A. (1973). Metabolism of penicillins to penicilloic acids and 6-aminopenicillanic acid in man and its significance in assessing penicillin absorption. *Antimicrob. Agents Chemother.* **3**, 463.

[43] Clayton, J. P., Cole, M., Elson, S. W., Hardy, K. P., Mizen, L. W., & Sutherland, R. (1975). Preparation, hydrolysis, and oral absorption of α-carboxy esters of carbenicillin. *J. Med. Chem.* **18**, 172.

[44] Clayton, J. P., Cole, M., Elson, S. W., & Ferres, H. (1974). BRL. 8988 (talampicillin), a well-absorbed oral form of ampicillin. *Antimicrob. Agents Chemother.* **5**, 670.

[45] Ulm, E. H. (1983). Enalapril maleate (MK-421), a potent, nonsulfhydryl angiotensin-converting enzyme inhibitor: absorption, disposition, and metabolism in man. *Drug Metab. Rev.* **14**, 99.

[46] Eckert, H. G., Badian, M. J. Gantz, D., Kellner, H.-M., & Volz, M. (1984). Pharmacokinetics and biotransformation of 2-[N-[(S)-1-ethoxycarbonyl-3-phenylpropyl]-L-alanyl]-(1S,3S,5S)-2-azabicyclo [3.3.0] octane-3-carboxylic acid (HOE 498) in rat, dog, and man. *Arzneim. Forsch./Drug Res.* **34**(II), 1435.

[47] Amidon, G. L. & Hu, M. (1988). Passive and carrier-mediated intestinal absorption components of captopril. *J. Pharm. Sci.* **77**, 1007.

[48] Greenlee, W. J. (1987). Renin inhibitors. *Pharm. Res.* **4**, 364.

[49] Thaisrivongs, S., Pals, D. T., Lawson, J. A., Turner, S. R., & Harris, D. W. (1987). α-Methylproline-containing renin inhibitory peptides: *in vivo* evaluation in an anesthetized, ganglion-blocked, hog renin infused rat model. *J. Med. Chem.* **30**, 536.

[50] Pals, D. T., Thaisrivongs, S., Lawson, J. A., Kati, W. M., Turner, S. R., DeGraff, G. L., Harris, D. W., & Johnson, G. A. (1986). An orally active inhibitor of renin. *Hypertension* **8**, 1105.

[51] Wood, J. M., Gulati, N., Forgiarini, P., Fuhrer, W., & Hofbauer, K. G. (1985). Effects of a specific and long acting renin inhibitor in the marmoset. *Hypertension* **7**, 797.

[52] Dellaria, J. F., Maki, R. G., Bopp, B. A., Cohen, J., Kleinert, H. D., Luly, J. R., Merits, I., Plattner, J. J., & Stein, H. H. (1987). Optimization and *in vivo* evaluations of a series of small, potent, and specific renin inhibitors containing a novel leu-val replacement. *J. Med. Chem.* **30**, 2137.

[53] Dellaria, J. F. Personal communication, Abbott Laboratories, 1988.

[54] Veda, C. T., Lemaire, M., Gsell, G., & Nussbaumer, K. (1983). Intestinal lymphatic absorption of cyclosporin A following oral administration in an olive oil solution in rats. *Biopharm. Drug Disp.* **4**, 113.

[55] Serajuddin, A. T. M., Sheen, P. C., Mufson, D., Bernstein, D. F., &

Augustine, M. A. (1988). Physicochemical basis of increased bioavailability of a poorly water-soluble drug following oral administration as organic solutions. *J. Pharm. Sci.* **77**, 325.

[56] Reymond, J.-P., Sucker, H., & Vonderscher, J. (1988). *In vivo* model for cyclosporin intestinal absorption in lipid vehicles. *Pharm. Res.* **5**, 677.

[57] Fix, J. A., Engle, K., Porter, P. A., Leppert, P. S., Selk, S. J., Gardner, C. R., & Alexander, J. (1986). Acylcarnitines: drug absorption-enhancing agents in the gastrointestinal tract. *Am. J. Physiol.* **25**, G332.

[58] Davis, S. S. (1986). Advanced delivery systems for peptides and proteins — pharmaceutical considerations. In: S. S. Davis, L. Illum & E. Tomlinson (eds) *Delivery Systems for Peptide Drugs*. Plenum Press, New York, p. 1.

[59] Lee, V. H. L. (1986). Enzymatic barriers to peptide absorption and the use of penetration enhancers to modify absorption. In: S. S. Davis, L. Illum & E. Tomlinson (eds) *Delivery Systems for Peptide Drugs*. Plenum Press, New York, p. 87.

[60] Su, K. S. E. (1986). Intranasal delivery of peptides and proteins. *Pharm. Int.* **7**, 8.

[61] McMartin, C., Hutchinson, L. E. F., Hyde, R., & Peters, G. E. (1987). Analysis of structural requirements for the absorption of drugs and macromolecules from the nasal cavity. *J. Pharm. Sci.* **76**, 535.

[62] Salzman, R., Manson, J. E., Griffing, G. T., Kimmerle, R., Ruderman, N., McCall, A., Stoltz, E. I., Mullin, C., Small, D., Armstrong, J., & Melby, J. C. (1985). Intranasal aerosolized insulin: mixed-meal studies and long-term use in type I diabetes. *N. Engl. J. Med.* **312**, 1078.

[63] Flier, J. S., Moses, A. C., Gordon, G. S., & Silver, R. S. (1985). Intranasal administration of insulin: efficacy and mechanism. In: Y. W. Chein (ed.) *Transnasal Systemic Medications*. Elsevier, Amsterdam, p. 217.

[64] Moses, A. C., Gordon, G. S., Carey, M. C., & Flier, J. S. (1983). Insulin administered intranasally as an insulin–bile salt aerosol: effectiveness and reproducibility in normal and diabetic subjects. *Diabetes* **32**, 1040.

[65] Okada, H., Yamazaki, I., Ogawa, Y., Hirai, S., Yashiki, T., & Mima, H. J., (1982). Vaginal absorption of a potent luteinizing hormone-releasing hormone analog (leuprolide) in rats. I. Absorption by various routes and absorption enhancement. *J. Pharm. Sci.* **71**, 1367.

[66] Hirai, S., Yashiki, T., & Mima, H. (1981). Effect of surfactants on the nasal absorption of insulin in rats. *Int. J. Pharm.* **9**, 165.

[67] Rollins, D. E., Woodbury, D. W., & Freston, J. W. (1973). Active transport of organic anions into hepatic cells and bile. *Gastroenterology* **65**, 567.

[68] Klaassen, C. D. & Watkins II, J. B. (1984). Mechanisms of bile formation, hepatic uptake, and biliary excretion. *Pharmacol. Rev.* **36**, 1.

[69] Levine, W. G. (1978). Biliary excretion of drugs and other xenobiotics. *Annu. Rev. Pharmacol. Toxicol.* **18**, 81.

[70] Rollins, D. E. & Klaassen, C. D. (1979). Biliary excretion of drugs in man. *Clin. Pharmacokinetics* **4**, 368.

[71] Klaassen, C. D., Eaton, D. L., & Cagen, S. Z. (1981). Hepatobiliary disposition of xenobiotics. In: J. W. Bridges and L. F. Chasseaud (eds) *Progress in Drug Metabolism*. Vol. 6, Wiley, New York, p. 1.

[72] Lundback, K. (1978). Somatostatin: clinical importance and outlook. *Metabolism* (Suppl. 1) **27**, 1463.

[73] Veber, D. F. & Saperstein, R. (1979). Somatostatin. *Annu. Rep. Med. Chem.* **14**, 209.

[74] Freidinger, R. M. & Veber, D. F. (1984). Design of novel cyclic hexapeptide somatostatin analogs from a model of the bioactive conformation. In: J. A. Vida & M. Gordon (eds) *Conformationally Directed Drug Design*. American Chemical Society, Washington, D. C., p. 170.

[75] Caldwell, L. J., Parr, A., Beihn, R. M., Agha, B. J., Mlodozeniec, A. R., Jay, M., & Digenis, G. A. (1985). Drug disposition and biliary excretion pattern of a cyclic somatostatin analog: a comparison of ^{14}C labeled drug and a ^{131}I iodinated drug analog. *Pharm. Res.* 80.

[76] Baker, J. R. J., Kemmenoe, B. H., McMartin, C., & Peters, G. E. (1984). Pharmacokinetics, distribution, and elimination of a synthetic octapeptide analogue of somatostatin in the rat. *Regul. Pept.* **9**, 213.

[77] Almquist, R. G., Steeger, T., Jackson, S., & Mitoma, C. (1985). Absorption, metabolism, and excretion studies of carbon 14- and tritium-labeled derivatives of a ketomethylene containing tripeptide. *Life Sci.* **37**, 299.

[78] Almquist, R. G., Jennings-White, C., Chao, W.-R., Steeger, T., Wheeler, T., Rogers, J., & Mitoma, C. (1985). Synthesis and biological activity of pentapeptide analogues of the potent angiotensin converting enzyme inhibitor 5(*S*)-benzamido-4-oxo-6-phenylhexanoyl-L-proline. *J. Med. Chem.* **28**, 1062.

[79] Boger, J., Bennett, C. D., Payne, L. S., Ulm, E. H., Blaine, E. H., Homnick, C. F., Schorn, T. W., Lamont, B. I., & Veber, D. F. (1985). Design of proteolytically-stable, peptidal renin inhibitors and determination of their fate *in vivo. Regul. Pept.* (Suppl. 4), 8.

[80] Grant, D. A. W., Ford, T. F., & McCulloch, R. J. (1982). Distribution of pepstatin and statine following oral and intravenous administration in rats. Tissue localization by whole body autoradiography. *Biochem. Pharm.* **31**, 2302.

[81] Rosenberg, S. H., Woods, K. W., Kleinert, H. D., Stein, H., Nellans, H. N., Hoffman, D. K., Spanton, S. G., Pyter, R. A., Cohen, J., Egan, D., Plattner, J. J., & Perun, T. J. (1989). Azido-glycols: potent, low molecular weight renin inhibitors containing an unusual post scissile site residue. *J. Med. Chem.* in press.

[82] Plattner, J. J., Marcotte, P. A., Kleinert, H. D., Stein, H. H., Greer, J., Bolis, G., Fung, A. K. L., Bopp, B. A., Luly, J. R., Sham, H. L., Kempf, D. J., Rosenberg, S. H., Dellaria, J. F., De, B., Merits, I., & Perun, T. J. (1988). Renin inhibitors. Dipeptide analogues of angiotensinogen utilizing a structurally modified phenylalanine residue to impart proteolytic stability. *J. Med. Chem.* **31**, 2277.

[83] Gores, G. J., LaRusso, N. F., & Miller, L. J. (1986). Hepatic processing of cholecystokinin peptides. I. Structural specificity and mechanism of hepatic extraction. *Am. J. Physiol.* **250**, G344.

[84] Carone, F. A., Peterson, P. R., & Flouret, G. (1982). Renal tubular processing of small peptide hormones. *J. Lab. Clin. Med.* **100**, 1.

[85] Wall, D. A. & Maack, T. (1985). Endocytic uptake, transport, and catabolism of proteins by epithelial cells. *Am. J. Physiol.* **248**, C12.

[86] Maack, T., Johnson, V., Kau, S. T., Figueiredo, J., & Sigulem, D. (1979). Renal filtration, transport, and metabolism of low molecular weight proteins: a review. *Kidney Int.* **16,** 251.

[87] Roberts, D. C. & Vellaccio, F. (1983). Unusual amino acids in peptide synthesis. In: E. Gross & J. Meienhofer (eds) *The Peptides: Analysis, Synthesis, Biology.* Vol. 5. Academic Press, New York, Chapter 6.

[88] Goodman, M. & Chorev, M. (1979). On the concept of linear modifed retro-peptide structures. *Accts. Chem. Res.* **12,** 1.

[89] Veber, D. F. & Friedinger, R. M. (1985). The design of metabolically-stable peptide analogs. *Trends Neurosci.* **8,** 392.

[90] Freidinger, R. M., Perlow, D. S., & Veber, D. F. (1982). Protected lactam-bridged dipeptides for use as conformational constraints in peptides. *J. Org. Chem.* **47,** 104.

[91] Boger, J. (1986). Renin inhibitors: drug design and molecular modelling. *Spec. Publ. — R. Soc. Chem.* **55,** 271.

[92] Metcalf, G. (1979). Some therapeutic prospects for enkephalin analogues. *Pharm. J.* 356.

[93] Pardridge, W. M. (1985). Strategies for delivery of drugs through the blood-brain barrier. *Annu. Rep. Med. Chem.* **20,** 305.

[94] Bodor, N. & Brewster, M. E. (1983). Problems of delivery of drugs to the brain. *Pharm. Ther.* **19,** 337.

[95] Metcalf, G., Dettmar, P. W., Lynn, A. G., Brewster, D., & Havler, M. E. (1981). Thyrotropin-releasing hormone (TRH) analogs show enhanced CNS selectivity because of increased biological stability. *Regul. Pept.* **2,** 277.

[96] Baker, J. R. J., Kemmenoe, B. H., McMartin, C., & Peters, G. E. (1984). Pharmacokinetics, distribution, and elimination of a synthetic octapeptide analogue of somatostatin in the rat. *Regul. Pept.* **9,** 213.

[97] Oldendorf, W. H. (1981). Blood-brain barrier permeability to peptides: pitfalls in measurement. *Peptides* 2 (Suppl. 2), 109.

[98] Ehrensing, R. H. & Kastin, A. J. (1978). Dose related biphasic effect of prolyl-leucyl-glycinamide (MIF-I) in depression. *Am. J. Psych.* **135,** 562.

[99] Ehrensing, R. H., Kastin, A. J., Larsens, P.F., & Bishop, G. A. (1977). Melanocyte-stimulating-hormone release-inhibiting factor I and tardive dsykinesia. *Dis. Nervous Syst.* **38,** 303.

[100] Oyama, T., Fukushi, S., & Jin, T. (1982). Epidural β-endorphin in treatment of pain. *Can. Anesth. Soc.* **29,** 24.

[101] Schneider-Helmut, D., Gnivss, F., Monniev, M., Schenker, J., & Schonenberger, G. A. (1981). Acute and delayed effects of DSIP (delta sleep-inducing peptide) on human sleep behavior. *Int. J. Clin. Pharmacol. Ther. Toxicol.* **19,** 341.

[102] Banks, W. A. & Kastin, A. J. (1987). Minireview: saturable transport of peptides across the blood–brain barrier. *Life Sci.* **41,** 1319.

[103] Kastin, A. J., Olson, R. D., Schally, A. V., & Coy, D. H. (1979). Minireview: CNS effects of peripherally administered brain peptides. *Life Sci.* **25,** 401.

[104] Sankar, R., Domer, F. R., & Kastin, A. J. (1981). Selective effects of α-MSH and MIF-I on the blood brain barrier. *Peptides* **2,** 345.

[105] Levin, V. A. (1980). Relationship of octanol/water partition coefficient and

molecular weight to rat brain capillary permeability. *J. Med. Chem.* **23,** 682.

[106] Banks, W. A. & Kastin, A. J. (1985). Peptides and the blood–brain barrier: lipophilicity as a predictor of permeability. *Brain Res. Bull.* **15,** 287.

[107] Banks, W. A., Kastin, A. J., Coy, D. H., & Angulo, E. (1986). Entry of DSIP peptides into dog CSF: role of physicochemical and pharmacokinetic parameters. *Brain Res. Bull.* **17,** 155.

[108] Zlokovic, B. V., Begley, D. J., & Chain, D. G. (1983). Blood–brain barrier permeability to dipeptides and their constituent amino acids. *Brain Res.* **271,** 65.

[109] Hoffman, P. L., Walter, R., & Bulat, M. (1977). An enzymatically stable peptide with activity in the central nervous system: its penetration through the blood–CSF barrier. *Brain Res.* **122,** 87.

[110] Bodor, N. (1987). Prodrugs and site-specific chemical delivery systems. *Annu. Rep. Med. Chem.* **22,** 303.

[111] Worms, P., Depoortere, H., Durand, A., Morselli, P. L., Lloyd, K. G., & Bartholini, G. (1982). γ-Aminobutyric acid (GABA) receptor stimulation. I. Neuropharmacological profiles of progabide (SL76002) and SL75102, with emphasis on their anticonvulsant spectra. *J. Pharmacol. Exp. Ther.* **220,** 660.

[112] Simpkins, J. W., Bodor, N., & Enz, A. (1985). Direct evidence for brain-specific release of dopamine from a redox delivery system. *J. Pharm. Sci.* **74,** 1033.

[113] Yanagisawa, M., Kurihara, H., Kimua, S., Tombe, Y., Kobayashi, M., Mitsui, Y., Yazaki, Y., Goto, K., & Masaki, T. (1988). A novel potent vasoconstrictor peptide produced by vascular endothelial cells. *Nature* **332,** 411.

[114] Kohl, N. E., Emino, E. A., Schleif, W. A., Davis, L. J., Heimbach, J. C., Dixon, R. A. F., Scolnick, E. M., & Sigal, I. S. (1988). Active human immunodeficiency virus protease is required for viral infectivity. *Proc. Natl. Acad. Sci. USA* **85,** 4686.

Part III
Biochemistry/molecular biology

6

Biochemical approaches to drug discovery and characterization

Michael Williams and **Michael F. Jarvis**[*]
Pharmaceutical Products Division, Abbott Laboratories, Abbott Park, Illinois, USA
[*]Research Department, Pharmaceutical Division, CIBA-GEIGY Corporation, Summit, New Jersey, USA

6.1 INTRODUCTION

The scientific elements comprising the identification and accreditation of a new (or novel) chemical entity (NCE) arise from many different disciplines working in concert to determine the profile of the compound and its relationship to the goals of the research project.

There are many different criteria for the inception of a drug research project and as many different criteria cited in deciding that the goals of a project have been achieved. These are discussed to some extent by Spilker [1]. Very often, the criteria of a project are molded by the progress that is made within the project and also by advances in basic knowledge related to the area of science being exploited. Two approaches to drug discovery can, however, be defined, based on historical criteria and current theoretical approaches. These are termed the classical approach, which can be described as semi-empirical and serendipitous in nature and the more intellectual, mechanistic approach.

Many drugs currently in use have been found more or less accidentally, However, it is important to bear in mind that it was hardly accidental that these compounds were evaluated preclinically and found to be of sufficient interest to be introduced into man where serendipity could then occur. Compounds such as chlorpromazine [2] initially evaluated by Laborit for use in the treatment of surgical shock and 'potentiation' of anesthesia, and chlordiazepoxide [3], initially tested as part of a 'psychosedative' program at Roche, proved to be seminal (and still widely used drugs) in the areas of psychosis and anxiety, respectively. Haefley has noted [3] that the Roche program was hampered by the fact that 'nothing was known about the molecular mechanisms of action' of psychosedatives when the benzodiazepines were initially tested. Indeed, it was not until some 17 years after their first clinical use that the central benzodiazepine receptor was discovered [4,5]. Serendipity is not restricted to CNS drugs, with a recent example being the finding that granulocyte–macrophage colony stimulating factor (GM–CSF) during clinical trials for treatment of anemia was found to be especially efficacious in lowering plasma cholesterol [6a].

The mechanistic approach that has evolved in the past decade has occurred as the result of major advances in technology as well as a philosophical shift in approaches to the initiation of drug discovery programs. The philosophy of the molecular approach to drug discovery can be traced back to the pioneering work of the fathers of modern pharmacology, Langley, Ehrlich and Clarke, who developed the receptor concept [7]. While this concept is close to a century old and represents the cornerstone of all modern pharmacological science, it was not until the discovery of propanolol and cimetidine by research groups headed by Sir James Black [6b], and the development, by David Cushman and Miguel Ondetti, of the angiotensin-converting enzyme inhibitor, captopril, that the value of using the mechanistic approach in the drug discovery environment was demonstrated beyond doubt.

Given the success of this latter approach, both in terms of the fulfilling of unmet medical need by providing superior medications and in terms of the increased revenues for the companies involved (and certainly such successes in terms of revenues have exceeded those for many other classes of drugs [8]), it would appear that the recipe for a successful drug discovery program is to choose a protein target — enzyme or receptor — thought to be involved in the etiology of a given pathophysiological state or in the regulation of physiological function and find active, selective entities that are agonists or antagonists for the chosen target.

From a strategic viewpoint, mechanistic-based approaches have been of two types: the first where the molecular target is known to be involved in the disease under study, and the second where little is known about the target other than there is good reason to suspect that it is involved in the etiology of a given condition. An example of the former instance is the central benzodiazepine receptor. This entity is known to be intimately involved in the clinically observed effects of the benzodiazepines [9,10]. Because of the side-effect profile of this class of anxiolytics, there is a need for newer compounds that have the same antianxiety effects as diazepam but lack the side-effect profile. The mechanistic approach has thus focussed on screening NCEs against the benzodiazepine receptor with the resultant discovery of compounds like tracazolate [11], CGS 9896 [12] and the β-carbolines [13]. In the second type of approach, the need is for a selective ligand to subsequently evaluate the target in the disease state chosen. As noted, a large element of serendipity is involved in this approach since the therapeutic endpoint is often vague based on limited knowledge related to the observed function of the natural ligand in disease models and pathophysiological states. The latter approach may be appropriately termed 'targeted screening' in that random screening is directed toward a defined molecular target. This approach is increasing in popularity in the drug discovery process [14]. The cause-and-effect relationship involved often remains unknown until the selective ligand is available and in several instances the initial premise is proved incorrect by subsequent testing of the new ligand. A time-honored variation on this 'novel' mechanistic approach is the identification of a molecular target following identified activity of an NCE *in vivo*, thus determining the mechanism of action of a new compound. The novel anticonvulsant/non-competitive *N*-methyl-D-aspartate (NMDA) antagonist, MK 801 [15], is an additional representative of this type of approach.

A major element in the mechanistic screening approach, whether the target is one with which a known compound interacts or is one which may have some causal disease relationship, is that there are many unknowns that require delineation. In the case of the benzodiazepines, what are the factors contributing to their side-effect profile? Are there receptor subtypes or regional differences in effect? The ability to evaluate a series of novel compounds, both *in vitro* and *in vivo*, can extend knowledge of the structure–activity requirements and hopefully separate out advantageous and deleterious characteristics. A crucial factor in pursuing these approaches is that the initial evaluation should be high throughput, rapid, robust and economical to run. In addition, it should form part of a sequential flow chart to identify intrinsic efficacy (agonist or antagonist), selectivity, bioavailability and systemic versus oral activity in an appropriate animal model [8].

In recent years, biochemical screens, including receptor–enzyme binding and various types of second messenger generation, have been increasingly amenable to the screening approach as well as to automation. The newest area of biochemistry, molecular biology, as it becomes recognized as a tool for drug discovery rather than a panacea to bolster lackluster research projects (and departments) will add considerably to the ability of the receptor-oriented pharmacologist to study efficacy and receptor heterogeneity in *in vitro* models.

6.2 PROTEIN–LIGAND INTERACTIONS

Nearly all aspects of NCE testing revolve around the concept of the receptor–ligand interaction first developed by Langley and Ehrlich, refined by Clarke, Hill, Schild and others (see [7,16–19] for reviews).

In many respects, receptors have been treated from a theoretical viewpoint much the same as enzymes, many of the analytical techniques being derived from the quantitative use of the Law of Mass Action by the Michaelis–Menten derivation [7]. It is important to note, however, that the process of receptor ligand interaction differs from that of enzyme catalysis. Thus for an enzyme:

$$E + S \underset{k_{-2}}{\overset{k_{+1}}{\rightleftharpoons}} ES \overset{k_{+2}}{\rightarrow} E + P$$

whereas for a receptor:

$$R + L \underset{k_{-2}}{\overset{k_{+1}}{\rightleftharpoons}} RL \overset{k_{+2}}{\rightarrow} R + L + \text{transduction event}$$

While an enzyme (E) reaction results in the transformation of substrate (S) to product (P), the process of receptor (R) activation leaves the ligand (L) unchanged as a result of the protein–ligand interaction with the initiation of a thermodynamically driven transducing event. The R–L complex once formed is a dynamic intermediate, the energy change occurring as the result of agonist binding, enthalpic or entropic, contributing to the intrinsic efficacy of the ligand and subsequent changes in intramembrane protein and glycolipid elements.

A priori, therefore, R–L interactions occur independently of ligand transformation. Since, in addition, the mass action law is not synonymous with the Langmuir isotherm, as the former situation is not an equilibrium condition *per se*, but rather the achievement of equilibrium [20], receptor-mediated events are rarely stoichiometric, the efficacy or intrinsic activity that is responsible for the transduction step, usually one of amplification, being somewhat qualitative in concept [7,19]. This situation is further compounded by the discovery of receptor complexes [21] which differ from enzyme multimers in being composed of different functional units in varying proportions.

6.2.1 Receptor concepts
Receptors are classified in terms of their pharmacology, their tissue and cellular localization and their function. Ligands, on the other hand, are described in terms of their efficacy, affinity and selectivity. Efficacy is the ability of a ligand to induce a physiological or pharmacological response in a tissue (i.e. relaxation) or animal (i.e. increase in heart rate). Affinity relates to the ability of a ligand to bind to a recognition site, or receptor. A ligand with high intrinsic efficacy and low affinity that does not bind especially tightly to its recognition site may be able to induce a response of a given magnitude in an appropriate test system and may be equivalent to another ligand that binds with high affinity yet has low intrinsic efficacy and a corresponding reduced ability to induce the given response. In the first instance, the response evoked is limited by the affinity of the ligand whereas in the second, the response is finite owing to a lack of intrinsic efficacy, which may be a property of either the ligand or the tissue. A full agonist in one tissue may only be a partial agonist in another tissue because of the degree of coupling between the receptor and the functional components to which it is linked. Because of the possibility of tissue differences, caution is required in extrapolating findings on a receptor from one tissue to another [7].

Selectivity reflects the ability of a ligand to elicit a defined response through its ability to bind with greater preference and corresponding efficacy to one recognition site as opposed to another. In many instances the resultant pharmacological activity of a compound may be the result of its ability to interact with several types of receptors. A case in point is the new antipsychotic, risperidone [22], which has evidenced no clinical signs of tardive dyskinesias. This NCE has potent affinity for dopamine-2, serotonin-2 and histamine-1 receptors which may in combination be contributory to the observed *in vivo* profile of the compound. Conversely, such heterologous interaction can be responsible for the side-effect profile of a compound.

A receptor can be conceptualized as a transductional entity on the external surface of the cell membrane which also has the ability to recognize a substance, termed the ligand. Thus in the classical 'lock' and 'key' concept of Ehrlich [7], the recognition portion of the receptor is the 'lock', with the ligand, agonist or antagonist representing the 'key'. A receptor–agonist ligand interaction leads to a modification of cell function, and ultimately a change in tissue and organ function. The receptor *per se* can thus be divided into three major conceptual elements: the protein portion situated on the external membrane surface that recognizes ligands and is responsible for linking the thermodynamics of ligand binding to intramembrane transducing elements, the G proteins, and the enzymes or ion channels linked to the G proteins (Fig. 6.1). Alterations in enzyme activity or ion channel gating can

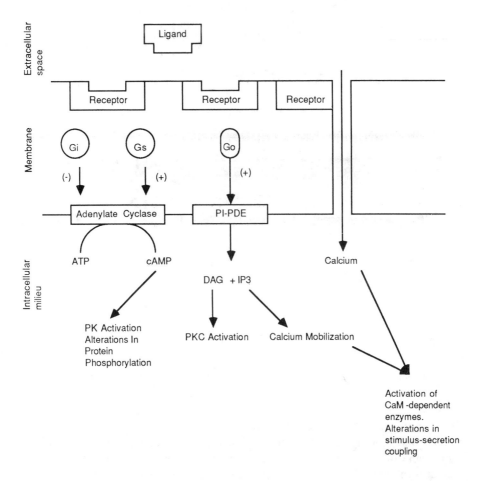

Fig. 6.1 — Schematic of a receptor and transduction elements: G=G proteins (i=inhibitory, s=stimulatory, o= a G protein); PKC=protein kinase C; DAG=diacylglycerol; CaM=calmodulin.

then lead to altered levels of intracellular second messenegers, enzyme products or ions, which then alter the activities of other enzymes within the cell.

Major advances in receptor isolation and cloning have led to sequencing of several receptor types including rhodopsin, muscarinic cholinergic, α and β adrenergic, glycine, $GABA_A$, insulin, calcium channel and dopamine D-2 receptors [23–31]. Receptor isolation and cloning have led to the identification of receptor superfamilies originating from common genomic elements. Site-directed mutagenesis studies on cloned adrenoceptors [32] have resulted in the production of a series of chimeric adrenoceptors with recognition and coupling elements for both α and β receptors further supporting evolution from a common genomic origin. Members of the receptor family identified to date are composed of seven protein domains (Fig. 6.2).

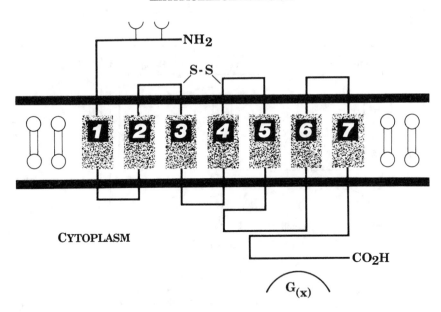

Fig. 6.2 — Schematic of receptor domains of G-protein-linked receptor superfamilies. Transmembrane segments 2, 3, and 7 in this receptor class are responsible for agonist binding.

Somewhat surprisingly, given the presence of extramembrane domains, the recognition (ligand binding) elements of the cloned β-adrenoceptor are located inside the membrane in a hydrophobic pocket [33]. For further discussion of this area the reader is referred to Chapter 9. A receptor superfamily also exists for the intracellular receptors that modulate transcriptional events via ligands such as the various classes of steroids and thyroid hormone [34].

In terms of receptor binding, the structure–activity profile generated using this technology is confined to the recognition portion of the receptor triad. Some ability to determine the agonist or antagonist profile for a ligand can occur with those receptors linked to a G-protein [33]. In the presence of high concentrations of GTP, agonist binding can be decreased whereas that of antagonist ligands is unaffected.

From a drug discovery viewpoint, however, it is often far more practical to measure these latter parameters in a defined tissue system where functionality and intrinsic efficacy can also be measured.

6.2.2 Ligand nomenclature

Two major types of receptor–ligand interactions were originally defined. Agonists were ligands that produced an effect on tissue and organ function by virtue of their ability to initiate the transduction process. Antagonists bound to the receptor and blocked the effects of an agonist. An antagonist, by definition, is a ligand with zero efficacy, i.e. the compound can bind to the receptor but in doing is unable to induce a transduction effect. Experimental variations in response maxima resulting from differences in intrinsic efficacy soon led to the description of partial agonists, ligands that were able to produce only a proportion of the effect seen with a full agonist (Fig. 6.3) [7]. Since antagonism was reflective of zero efficacy, then partial

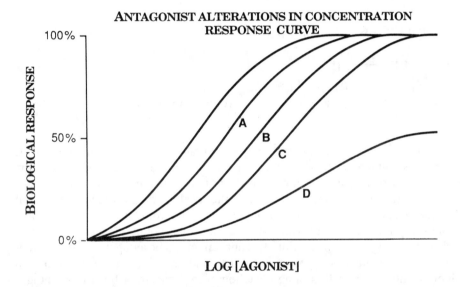

Fig. 6.3 — Dose–concentration response curves. Effects of competitive and non-competitive antagonists on response to full agonist. Unmarked curve =full agonist; A, B and C, full agonist in presence of a competitive antagonist. D=full agonist in presence of non-competitive antagonist.

agonism is by definition also partial antagonism. More recently, however, based on work on the benzodiazepine receptor complex, the concept of inverse agonists has been proposed. While the subject of some controversy, this latter class of ligand is one that has negative efficacy but is capable of producing effects opposite to those of a full agonist. In addition, some inverse agonists are also able to act as antagonists for the agonist ligand at a given receptor.

The way in which a full antagonist can bind to the recognition portion of the receptor and prevent activation by a ligand is not well understood. Various theories relate to binding to the receptor in a conformation similar manner but distinct from an agonist, as in the case of a competitive antagonist, or by binding to a site separate and distinct from that of the agonist by which means the antagonist can restrict agonist access to the receptor active site, or allosterically alter the agonist interaction with the transduction process thereby blocking the effects of the latter. In this case the antagonist would be termed non-competitive. Antagonists have also been termed 'uncompetitive' based on kinetic experiments where both the affinity of the ligand for its receptor and the apparent receptor density are changed by the antagonist. The mechanistic and functional correlates of this effect at the receptor level are not well understood. However, by analogy with similar criteria from enzymology theory [35], a competitive antagonist can interact with the receptor to form a complex distinct from that of the receptor–antagonist interaction:

$$
\begin{array}{lll}
R+L \rightleftharpoons RL \rightarrow \text{Effect} & & \\
R+I \rightleftharpoons RI & & \text{(a) competitive}
\end{array}
$$

$$
\begin{array}{lll}
R+L \rightleftharpoons RL \rightarrow \text{Effect} & & \\
\updownarrow +I \quad\quad +I \updownarrow & & \text{(b) non-competitive} \\
RI \rightleftharpoons RIL & &
\end{array}
$$

$$
\begin{array}{lll}
R+L \rightleftharpoons RL \rightarrow \text{Effect} & & \\
\quad\quad\quad \updownarrow +I & & \text{(c) uncompetitive} \\
\quad\quad\quad RIL & &
\end{array}
$$

where I is the antagonist. Pharmacological antagonism occurs when an R–L interaction is antagonized by another ligand that modulates a given receptor-mediated event by altering receptor activation. Functional antagonism results in a similar end effect except that the readout is the result of the interfacing of several distinct mechanisms. For example, if a dopaminergic neuronal system impinges on a neurotensin system which in turn alters the function of a cholinergic system, which in turn causes a change in CNS function, this final effect can be antagonized pharmaco-logically by a dopamine antagonist and functionally by either a neurotensin or a cholinergic antagonist. A lack of appreciation of the concept of functional antago-nism makes it easy to identify a cholinergic antagonist as a dopamine antagonist because, at face value, both agents produce the same effect. Unfortunately such instances are far from rare.

Receptor–receptor interactions can also modify the effects of receptor activation acting both within the context of receptor complexes and in phenomena such as clustering and internalization which are also receptor mediated [36]. In receptor complexes, ligands can inhibit the binding of a separate ligand to its site or, as in the case of the benzodiazepine and N-methyl-D-aspartate (NMDA) receptor complexes, binding of ligands can be increased. At the benzodiazepine receptor, GABA can enhance diazepam and t-butylbicyclophosphothionate (TBPS) binding to the benzo-diazepine and chloride channel components of the receptor complex, respectively [10]. At the NMDA receptor, binding of dissociative anesthetics to the phencycli-dine-type receptor can be enhanced by L-glutamate [37].

Receptors can be quantitatively described in terms of their dissociation constants, or K_d values, a measure of the affinity of a receptor for a given ligand, and apparent B_{max} values, the density of binding sites on the concentration/weight basis, a measure of the total number of receptors in a tissue. The K_d value has units of concentration whereas the B_{max} value is the number of receptors/mg protein. The tissue and cellular distribution of receptors is also important in their definition. If a receptor is found in a tissue where no response has been previously shown, or if a receptor is enriched in a cellular subfraction uninvolved with cellular communication, the significance of the binding site and the functionality of the presumed receptor must be questioned. For instance, peripheral benzodiazepine receptors have been localized to the outer mitochondrial membrane of mammalian cells where they are associated with a voltage-sensitive anion channel designated porin [38] and the enzyme, pyruvate dehydrogenase [39]. The locale is rather unusual for a receptor thought to be involved in intercellular communication. Yet interestingly, one of the more potent natural products that can displace PK 11195, a selective ligand for the peripheral benzodiazepine receptor, is protoporphyrin IX [40]. The receptor thus appears to be involved in the modulation of cellular metabolism, inhibiting mitochondrial respiratory control [106].

Receptors recognize ligands with different affinities depending on the 'fit' of the ligand to the receptor. Under equilibrium conditions, affinity can be defined in terms of the IC_{50} or ED_{50} value, that concentration of ligand required to inhibit/stimulate a particular measure of receptor function. Stimulation of radioligand binding is recently discovered phenomenon. Its functional relevance has yet to be determined.

6.2.3 Receptor classification

Receptor classification is a topic that has increased in complexity as binding assays continue to provide evidence for receptor subtypes and new receptors. A case in point is that of the CNS serotonin receptor which in 1979 existed in two subtypes, $5HT_1$ and $5HT_2$. In 1989, there are seven and possibly more 5HT receptor subclasses [41]. The criteria used for their classification have caused concern to the extent that an international body has been set up to establish a series of guidelines similar to those for enzymes [42].

At the molecular level, receptor classification can be simply related to the structure–activity profile for a binding site and additionally, kinetic characteristics and tissue and cellular location. This can be further extended to receptor structure and physicochemical characteristics. For instance, muscarinic receptors can be classified pharmacologically into M1, M2, and M3 subtypes [43], but five subtypes (m_1–m_5) have been described based on receptor cloning technology [44]. The relationship between the entities described in the two systems is unclear at this time. It is, however, important to remember that the classification of receptors based on binding is untenable until some other evidence, based on the use of a selective ligand, or by functional correlation in intact tissues, is obtained. Classical pharmacologists use the relative potency of agonists to classify receptors. This parameter is currently being extended to the transducing elements involved in the final tissue response [42].

Receptor classification based on a tissue or on a particular species requires caution. The pharmacological activity of a compound can be defined with reference to its actions in a particular tissue. Very often this compound is then used as a tool to define other receptor-mediated actions in other tissues. Effects ascribed to an interaction with a receptor in a second tissue are then interpreted in terms of the properties of the recognition site characterized in the original tissue, irrespective of the possibility that in the latter tissue, the compound may produce its effects via other receptor types. This approach can lead to erroneous conclusions in describing the type of receptor mediating a given response and has been the subject of comment in regard to Black's analytical pharmacology concept [45]. The existence of tissue-specific transduction systems that contribute to agonist potency presents an additional factor that may contribute to error in classifying receptors [42].

Receptor theory and classification are also complicated by the existence of receptors for endogenous ligands and binding sites for drugs. The prototypical endogenous drug-like ligands from a receptor perspective were the enkephalins and endorphins [46]. The first 'drug receptor' *per se* was that for the benzodiazepine anxiolytics [4,5]. These seminal discoveries have generated a multitude of endogenous ligands, some ephemeral and some still being evaluated as bona fide entities as well as a number of drug receptors that are either artifactual or actually reveal activity of a drug at a known recognition site. An example of this latter phenomenon is the dibenzocycloalkeneimine anticonvulsant, MK 801, which was inactive in a number of receptor binding assays [47]. However, when labeled, it displayed a binding pharmacology consistent with the compound being active at phencyclidine (PCP)-type receptors and acting as a non-competitive antagonist at the NMDA receptor [15].

6.2.4 Receptor theory

Equations describing the response of a tissue to receptor activation (and blockade) are based on the Michaelis–Menten-type kinetics developed for quantifying the interactions of enzymes and their substrates. As already pointed out, receptor-mediated responses are more complex than those involving enzymic catalysis, such that the mathematics of receptor activation may often be approximations. The most commonly accepted theory of receptor agonism is the occupancy theory developed by Clark, who assumed, based on the sigmoidal shape of the classical dose–response curve and the rightward shift seen with competitive antagonists (Fig. 6.3), that the biological or functional response to receptor activation was directly proportional to the number of receptors occupied by a given ligand at equilibrium [48]. The R–L interaction can be outlined as follows for occupancy theory:

- The R–L complex is reversible
- Association is a bimolecular and dissociation a monomolecular process
- All receptors of a given type are equivalent and independent of one another
- Binding of the ligand to the receptor does not alter the free (F) concentration or the affinity of the receptor for the ligand
- The response elicited by receptor occupation is directly proportional to the number of receptors occupied by the ligand
- The biological response is dependent on the attainment of an equilibrium between R and L

From the equation: $R+L \rightleftharpoons R-L \rightarrow$ Effect $+R$, the K_d can be defined by the equation:

$$K_d = \frac{[R][L]}{[R-L]}$$

where $K_d = K_{-1}/K_1$. By analogy with the Michaelis–Menten treatment, K_d becomes the ligand concentration where 50% of the available receptor is occupied. This theory has inherent limitations because of the inability to define the relative concentrations of free receptor and R–L complex. It does, however, provide a useful working basis for delineating receptor theory.

The effects of a competitive antagonist can be overcome by increasing agonist concentration, and from the generation of a series of dose–response curves derived in the presence of fixed, progressive increases in antagonist concentration (Fig. 6.3), a pA_2 value for the antagonist can be determined, which is the negative log of the concentration of antagonist that requires a two-fold increase in agonist concentration to achieve the same effect in a given system [49].

$$-pA_2 = -\log_{10} K_B$$

where K_B = dissociation constant for a competitive antagonist.

The concept of intrinsic activity proposed by Ariens [16] ascribed to full antagonists a value of zero and to full agonists a value of 1.0. Partial agonists and agonist/antagonists then had intermediate values. Accordingly inverse agonists then had intrinsic activity values varying between zero and -1. By analogy to enzyme theory, where the velocity of an enzyme reaction, E, is proportional to the concentration of enzyme–substrate complex, for a receptor, E_R is proportional to [RA]:

$$E_R = \alpha_{r_o} 1 + (K_R/[A])$$

where r_o is the total receptor concentration and K_R is the affinity constant. Drug action is thus a consequence of both K_R and α, the latter being a proportionality constant.

Partial agonists led Stephenson [50] to propose the concept of efficacy. This assumed that a maximal response occurred when only a small proportion of available receptors in a tissue were occupied, indicating that a relationship between tissue response and receptor occupation need not be linear. A response occurred as the result of a stimulus (S) which was defined as the product of the fraction of receptors occupied and the efficacy of the ligand. Efficacy differed from intrinsic activity in that the latter is described as a proportion of the size of the maximal response (effect=α[LR] where α is the intrinsic activity). However, the description of efficacy relies on a relationship between the stimulus given to a tissue, S, where $S=\varepsilon KL$ and where ε=efficacy, K=equilibrium association constant and L=drug concentration. Affinity constants differ when efficacy and intrinsic activity definitions are used under similar experimental conditions. Modification of the intrinsic activity concept has led to the definition of intrinsic efficacy which is more equivalent to Stephenson's efficacy concept [51].

The spare receptor was proposed by Nickerson [52] from studies on histamine-evoked responses in guinea-pig ileal strips. In the presence of an irreversible competitive antagonist that reduced the number of available histamine receptors to 1% of total, a maximal response was still observed. It was concluded that with an efficacious agonist, it was only necessary to occupy a small fraction of the receptors in a tissue to elicit maximal response. This concept was further modified by Furchgott [53] to include the tissue concentration of receptors in the concept of intrinsic efficacy. This resulted in efficacy being a strictly drug- rather than drug/tissue-related term. The concept of 'mobile receptors' has also been used to account for responses that are disproportionate to ligand presence [54]. Spare receptors or 'receptor reserves' have been defined as 'fraction of the total receptor pool not required for a maximal tissue response' [7]. Drug-evoked responses in a given tissue have been considered, therefore, to depend on four factors:

  (i)   receptor density
 (ii)   tissue efficiency in translating ligand binding into a tissue response
(iii)   the equilibrium dissociation constant of the LR complex
 (iv)   the intrinsic efficacy of the drug for the receptor.

Although the spare receptor concept is a convenient rationale for explaining experimental data that deviates significantly from that predicted using occupancy theory, it has yet to be reconciled on a molecular basis. Why should there be changes in receptor number when the agonist input to a given tissue is reduced (supersensitivity) or increased (subsensitivity/tolerance) if spare receptors for a given agonist are present on a tissue? It has been suggested [55] that for a response that is rapid in onset and termination, a receptor excess allows a relatively low affinity agonist concentration to elicit a tissue response. The low affinity also ensures a rapid dissociation of the agonist from the receptor and a corresponding rapid termination of the physiological response. The efficiency of receptor coupling has been compared to a power amplifier [7]. Thus receptor occupancy *per se* can be seen as a function not only of the efficacy of the ligand but also of the coupling system(s). What are the features of a molecule that contribute to efficacy? Is it the ability of an agonist to enhance effector coupling in some manner, by changing a 'loose' coupling state to a 'tight' one? And to what extent does the ability of the tissue to respond affect the classification of its intrinsic efficacy? Spare receptor concepts like those related to intrinsic efficacy/ activity, remain dimensionless terms with limited comprehension in molecular terms, either biochemical or chemical.

Based on the persistence of antagonist-mediated effects, the 'fade' of agonist actions where maximal but transient responses occur followed by longer lasting responses of lesser magnitude and agonist-mediated 'block' of their own actions, Paton [56] modified occupancy theory to a more chemically based rate theory. In this theory, it is not the number of receptors occupied that determines the response but rather the rate of R–L formation; thus the effect E is equal to a proportionality factor

θ and the velocity V of the response, where θ is an efficacy term related to the R–L interaction. Thus:

$$E=\theta V_{eq}$$

The rate of R–L formation is therefore quantal, being measured in terms of discrete 'all-or-none' changes in receptor-related events within the cell or tissue.

Rate theory, as noted, predicts that potency is a function of the affinity of the ligand for the receptor. While rate theory can reasonably explain the experimental data derived by Paton in guinea-pig ileum, numerous other examples exist where rate theory is not applicable. For instance, if the efficiency of coupling is a major rate limiting (or amplifying) step, then the kinetics of the R–L response as defined in rate theory may not reflect the tissue response to receptor activation. Rate theory has been described as a 'provocative conceptualization ... with limited applicability' [17]. The concept of the R–L interaction involving only a single receptor and ligand does not readily accommodate either allosteric receptor modulators that influence receptor function by binding to sites adjacent and proximal to the site under study, or receptor complexes. In fact it has been questioned whether current receptor theory requires significant reanalysis based on such phenomena [19,57].

One such modification to traditional receptor theory is that of inactivation theory. Proposed by Gosselin [58], this accommodates the major elements of both the occupancy and the rate approaches. Receptor inactivation theory is based on the premise that following the formation of the R–L complex, an inactive form of the receptor, R', occurs according to the schema

$$[R]+[L] \underset{k_{-1}}{\overset{k_{+1}}{\rightleftharpoons}} [R][L]$$
$$\overset{k_3}{\nwarrow} \quad \overset{k_2}{\swarrow}$$
$$[R'][L]$$

with k_{+1} being the rate of onset, k_{-1} the rate of offset, k_2 the rate of formation of inactive receptor, and k_3 the rate constant for regeneration of the active entity. The response is proportional to the rate of R' formation, which is equal to $k_3[R'L]$, and is dependent both on the number of receptors occupied and on the rate of R' formation. Efficacy is then a function of the relative magnitudes of k_2 and k_3. Like rate theory, unequivocal experimental evidence to support the theory appears to be difficult to obtain. Indeed, under equilibrium conditions, it is not possible to distinguish between occupancy, rate and receptor inactivation theories [7,19]. This is a point of some interest since it assumes that maximal receptor occupancy due to the rapid 'on/off' predicted for a full agonist under rate theory and, in a finite sense, as predicted from occupancy theory, as well as the rapid regeneration fo R from R' predicted from inactivation theory, all are equally effective in eliciting a maximal response. Spare receptors would appear to have no role in receptor-mediated events under such conditions.

6.2.5 Receptor allosterism

Allosteric modulators differ from classical receptor ligands by acting at sites distinct from the active site of the receptor. Intrinsic to this concept is that binding of the modulator induces a conformational change which then facilitates or prevents further ligand association. The two allosteric models are the concerted model of Monod, Wyman and Changeux [59] and the Koshland, Nemethy and Filmer [60] sequential or induced-fit model. These models are assumed to consist of oligomeric protein units with identical subunits that exist in two states which are in equilibrium in the absence of ligand. Ligand binding induces a conformational change, moving the equilibrium between the two states to favor that with the higher affinity for the ligand. The assumption is that the shift in the state of the oligomers conforms to a difference in the functionality of the receptor. As with the various receptor theories, the extrapolation of enzyme theory to receptor allosterism is not total. In the absence of purified, functional receptors, it is unlikely that the data generated from receptor studies is of sufficient sophistication at the present time to permit the detection of subunit interactions within a kinetic framework. The multimeric nicotinic cholinergic receptor of the *Torpedo electroplax* is probably the most studied of all neurotransmitter receptors, primarily because of its abundance and the simplicity of the system in which it is found [61]. Information derived from the isolation, cloning and sequencing of this receptor [24,44] has yielded little information at this time to increase understanding of the properties related to ligand recognition of the design of new ligands as NCEs although the group from Bell laboratories [107] using two-dimensional NMR has determined the conformation of acetylcholine bound to the nicotinic receptor. Given the apparent wealth of basic information on this receptor, it is surprising that it is probably the least studied from a drug discovery viewpoint, indicating that the large body of molecular data is not being paralleled by functional studies.

6.3 RADIOLIGAND BINDING

6.3.1 Basic concepts

The use of radiolabeled ligands, drugs and natural effector agents to 'tag' receptors arose in the 1950s from significant advances in radiochemistry, resulting in the biological application of these tools in the study of drug metabolism. Early studies were hampered, however, by the fact that the process of labeling reduced the functional activity and specificity of the ligand. The lack of 'hot' ligands (specific activity > 15 Ci/mmol) also made it difficult to differentiate binding to the receptor from that occurring to various environmental and tissue surfaces that were non-specific in relation to the defined receptor, though the process of absorption was also a limiting factor. In the 1970s these technical problems were overcome [62], and radioligands with specific activities in the range of 15–90 Ci/mmol are now in routine use. Isotopes used to label ligands include tritium ($[^3H]$), iodine ($[^{125}I]$) and sulphur ($[^{35}S]$). In the case of $[^{125}I]$, specific activities of 2200 Ci/mmol are theoretically achievable. This can facilitate the study of receptors (i) that are found in very low concentrations in tissues of interest, i.e. adenosine receptors in cardiac tissue and (ii) where the costs of ligands, as in the case of peptides, can be prohibitive. Increasingly,

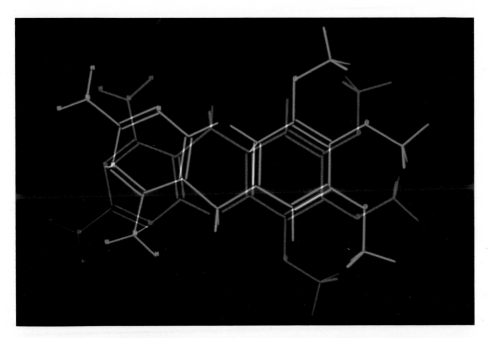

Fig. 1.1 — Superpositioning of trimethoprim on itself in two different orientations.

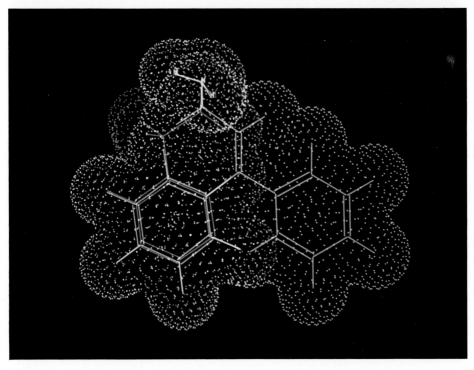

Fig. 1.2 — Superposition of phenylethylamine (shown in red) and 'diphenylethylidine' (shown in blue) matching the respective amine and phenyl groups.

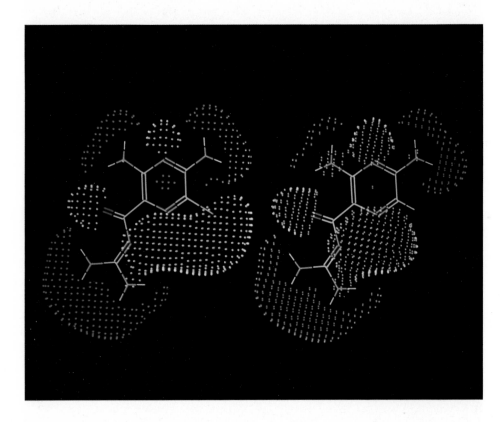

Fig. 1.3 — 15 kcal/mol isopotential surfaces for amiloride and deschloro-amiloride.

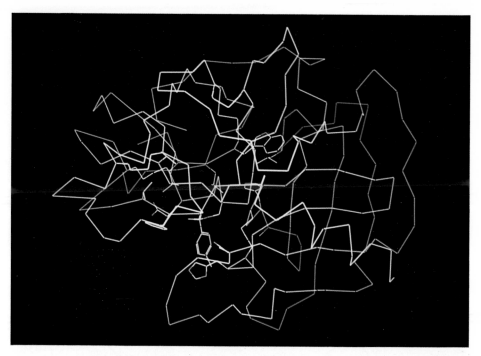

Fig. 1.4 — X-ray crystal structure of tosyl-porcine pancreatic elastase.

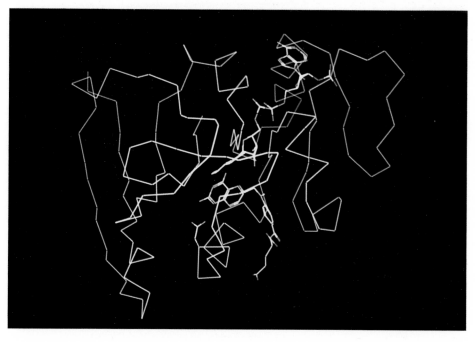

Fig. 1.5 — X-ray crystal structure of methotrexate and NADPH bound to dihydrofolate reductase from *L. casei*.

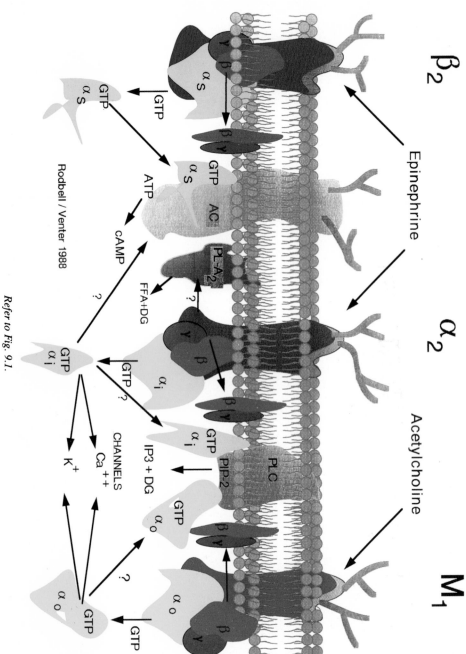

β₂   α₂   M₁

Epinephrine

Acetylcholine

Rodbell / Venter 1988

Refer to Fig. 9.1.

environmental concerns with the use of radiolabeled ligands have directed interest to the evaluation of systems such as ELISA (enzyme-linked immunosorbent assay) which have replaced iodine in many radioimmunoassay systems.

6.3.2 Practical aspects

Receptor–ligand (R–L) complexes are formed by the incubation of receptor-rich tissue together with radioligand of suitable selectivity and radioactivity, usually 15 Ci/mmol or greater [62]. The time required for equilibrium is a function of the receptor being studied, the radioligand used and the incubation conditions. Despite the fact that hypo-osmotic buffers are often used as incubation media, the procedures used to prepare tissues are usually sufficiently non-physiological that the rationale for returning to a physiological buffer system to do binding, except in the case of intact cells [63], is often unclear.

Once the R–L complex is formed, unbound radioactivity must be removed to allow determination of the radioactivity bound. This is usually accomplished by one of two methods: centrifugation or filtration under reduced pressure. Free radioactivity, that unassociated with tissue, is removed by washing. Theoretical considerations indicate that affinity measurements for R–L complexes of ligands with low affinity ($K_d > 20$ nM) and/or a fast dissociation rate cannot be reliably or accurately determined using filtration methodology but rather require the gentler conditions of centrifugation [64]. Filtration requires the active washing of the R–L complex whereas centrifugation results in the removal of the complex from the reaction milieu either by pelleting or by separation of the aqueous phase from tissue by centrifugation through phthalate oils.

The decision of which isolation technique to use is not always clear, reflecting much of the mystique of the technique where the predictable does not always work. Thus, many assays have been documented where filtration methodology has been used relatively successfully with ligands that have K_d values in the micromolar range. Filtration has obvious advantages over centrifugation, in terms of both equipment costs and sample processing. For centrifugation, the number of samples that can be run is limited by the number of spaces available in a centrifuge rotor and the availability of the centrifuge. As the R–L complex is sedimented, it also requires that the complex be dissolved for counting, a tedious and time-consuming process. For filtration, the R–L complex is isolated on a filter, which, after drying, can be directly transferred to a scintillation vial. In typical experiments, many hundreds of samples can be processed using filtration in the same time it takes to do a 70–100 sample experiment using centrifugation. The lack of availability of radioligands with receptor affinity sufficient to allow filtration may, however, preclude the use of this technique which is one of the reasons motivating the development of new ligands. Following isolation of the R–L complex, radioactivity can be determined by conventional β- or γ-spectrometry.

In addition to binding to sites with characteristics of the receptor of interest, radioactivity is also associated, either by absorption or by sequestration, to non-specific sites. Radioactivity can also bind to the filters used for the isolation of tissue, or can bind to the test tube in which the centrifugation or binding reaction is performed, or be trapped in the R–L complex pellet obtained. This binding is the non-specific binding and can be measured by including in parallel, assay tubes with an excess ($> 100 \times$) of an unlabeled ligand specific for a given receptor. Measurement of binding in the absence and presence of this 'specific' agent provides data on total ligand binding and non-specific binding, respectively. This difference is the specific binding of the ligand which is the pharmacologically relevant receptor-associated binding used to measure R–L interactions. Specific binding can vary, between 40 and 98% of total binding, depending on the ligand and tissue source. Working with less than 30% specific binding can severely limit the usefulness of the data derived, but there are often no other alternatives until studies using such a binding assay yield new ligands that give better specific binding characteristics. Obviously the higher the 'signal-to-noise' ratio, the better the data derived. An example of this approach is in the characterization of the NMDA receptor. Initially, L-glutamate was used as a ligand [65]. This agonist ligand required the use of a postsynaptic density membrane preparation that took a day to prepare sufficient tissue for a single experiment and a cold ligand 'cocktail' to block non-NMDA sites to which L-glutamate bound. Data obtained in different laboratories was also very variable. Newer ligands such as the antagonist CPP (2-carboxypiperazin-4-yl)propyl-1-phosphonic acid [66] were discovered that allow direct labeling of NMDA receptors with specific binding in the region of 80% and a K_d value of 200 nM. This affinity still required the use of a centrifugation assay to isolate R–L complexes. CGS 19755 was next identified and found to have a K_d in the low nanomolar range (4–25 nM) allowing R–L complexes to be isolated by filtration [67]. This progression in ligand development for the NMDA receptor now allows larger numbers of NCEs to be evaluated for activity at this receptor.

Non-specific binding in filtration assays can be reduced by the presoaking of filters in polyethylenimine (PEI) which prevents absorption of radioactivity [68]. However, the choice of the non-specific agent used is important in characterizing binding. When the pharmacology of a receptor is known, there are usually many different structural entities that interact specifically with the receptor. It is then possible and preferable to use a non-specific agent that is structurally distinct from the radioligand rather than the corresponding cold ligand. In the case of serotonin$_{1A}$ (5HT$_{1A}$) receptors, the aminotetralin, 8-OH-DPAT, can be used as a radioligand, with 10 μM 5HT being used to determine non-specific binding [69]. The α_1-adrenoceptor ligand, WB 4101, can also be used to label 5HT$_{1A}$ receptors, its predominant α_1-adrenergic component being blocked by the inclusion of 30 nM prazosin, a more selective α_1-adrenergic ligand. The 5HT ligand, lisuride, can then be used to measure non-specific binding [70]. In other binding assays, especially those used for measuring peptide receptors [71], there are rarely any compounds other than modified peptides that can be used to determine non-specific binding. Usually specific binding is measured in an excess of such cold ligands. This causes problems inasmuch as an apparent decrease in total binding can occur, not only due to the blockade of specific binding sites, but also to isotope dilution. The cold-non-specific agent reduces the specific activity of the radioligand such that it is possible to have the same total amount of binding occurring which appears to be reduced based on the number of counts bound. As an example, if total binding of peptide Z is 10 000 cpm, a 100-fold decrease in specific activity due to the presence of a 100-fold excess of unlabeled peptide Z would result in only 100 counts being bound that would be termed non-specific. Thus the decrease of 9900 cpm would be ascribed to specific binding when, in fact, the same final concentration of peptide Z is bound. Even though such assays have serious limitations which must be kept in mind when characterizing these receptors, the assays can be useful in evaluating NCEs. The peripheral CCK receptor can be labeled with [^{125}I]CCK using a large excess of unlabeled CCK to determine non-specific binding. Using such conditions, the non-peptidic CCK antagonist, asperlicin, was identified [72] along with the benzodiaze-pine derivative, L 364 718, was synthesized and found to have subnanomolar affinity at peripheral CCK receptors [73].

Radioligands are not always specific, and it may be necessary, although not preferable, to mask components of specific binding in what are called 'cocktail' assays. The examples of L-glutamate binding to the NMDA receptor and WB 4101 binding to the 5HT$_{1A}$ receptor have already been discussed. Another example is the non-selective adenosine agonist, 5'N-ethylcarboxamidoadenosine (NECA), which binds to both A$_1$ and A$_2$ subtypes of the adenosine receptor in rat striatum. Non-specific binding is determined in the presence of an excess of another adenosine ligand permitting measurement of [^{3}H]NECA binding to both A$_1$ and A$_2$ receptors. However, if a highly selective A$_1$ ligand such as cyclopentyladenosine is included in the assay to selectively block the A$_1$ component of NECA binding, the assay can then be used to selectively measure A$_2$ receptors [73]. In this instance, the signal-to-noise ratio is poor for the A$_2$ receptor. However, the use of this assay permitted the discovery and characterization of the A$_2$ selective agonist, CGS 21680, which directly labels the A$_2$ receptor without the need for another ligand to block the A$_1$ receptor [74].

In evaluating a new ligand, it is now common to derive a binding profile. Thus a compound shown to be of interest as a lead in a drug discovery project is evaluated for activity in 20–30 other assays. From experience, activity in the 10^{-5} M range for a ligand active at another receptor in the low nanomolar range can be considered 'inactive'. Where activity is found at concentrations 5–20-fold less than that at the receptor of interest, this information should be borne in mind as the compound moves through subsequent evaluation as a potential drug candidate.

Specific binding requires validation before it can be equated with receptor binding. Several criteria for such validation are shown in Table 6.1. However, even when such criteria are validated, binding need not always be synonymous with receptor-related proteins. The most famous example of this is the stereoselective binding of the opiate antagonist, naloxone, to talc [75].

6.3.3 Peptide receptors

In addition to the theoretical concerns related to the non-specific agent used for peptide binding assays, the lability of the radioligand as well as the time course to equilibrium binding are problematic [76,77]. Peptide radioligands also tend to avidly bind to surfaces in which they come into contact. This affects the measurement of free and bound ligand concentrations. The inclusion of bovine serum albumin in the assay mixture can block these non-specific absorption sites. Ligand degradation can be prevented by the use of protease inhibitors such as bacitracin, leupeptin, phenanthroline and EDTA that are selected on an *ad hoc* basis, provided they do not affect radioligand binding. The authenticity of the bound ligand should be checked, but this presents analytical problems when the amount bound is on the order of

Table 6.1 — Criteria for identification of binding sites as receptors [75]

---

1. Binding of radioligand to recognition site should be saturable, indicating a finite number of binding sites.
2. Binding affinity should be high (K_d value $\sim 10^{-10}$–10^{-8} M), consistent with a potential role as a neurohumoral agent.
3. Radioligand binding should be easily reversible, consistent with a physiological action for the termination of ligand action.
4. The distribution of binding sites, both between tissues and within the cell/tissue, should be compatible with the proposed physiological role of the natural ligand.
5. The pharmacology of the binding site should have similar agonist/antagonist properties to those observed for the natural ligand or its analogs in functional test procedures.
6. A simultaneous correlation of binding with biological dose–concentration curves in identical tissue preparations should be feasible.

10^{-12} M. Sensitive assay techniques are then necessary to measure such small ligand amounts. An additional factor related to ligand stability is that the association rate constants for peptide radioligands are often three orders of magnitude below those seen for the other types of radioligand [76]. In consequence, at times, 5–8 h incubation times have to be balanced against the instability of the ligand, the stability of the receptor source, possible desensitization of the receptor and pseudo-irreversible binding. In practice, therefore, some assays are not run to equilibrium to circumvent these problems.

6.3.4 Receptor sources
In using receptor binding to study receptor function, the choice of tissue source can affect the interpretation of the data obtained. There is considerable evidence for distinct differences in receptor pharmacology, depending on the species used [78]. For instance, both adenosine receptor subclasses show dramatic species differences [79,80]. This has obvious implications in choosing the appropriate animal receptor source for compounds designed to be used in man or indeed for assembling a flow chart for a drug discovery project [8].

Another issue in regard to the choice of receptor source for binding is that the technique has only recently begun to be extended to tissues other than the CNS. The CNS is enriched in many receptors found in peripheral tissues and, in a large number of cases, these receptors have similar pharmacology to peripheral receptors. This makes the CNS an ideal tissue source since receptor densities in peripheral tissues are usually one-tenth to one-hundredth that found in the brain, reflecting the discrete nature of nerve innervation. As evidenced by the tissue selectivity of many classes of drugs, the understanding of differences in receptor pharmacology and function between tissues is a major challenge in the area of molecular pharmacology for the next decade.

One way to circumvent low receptor densities is to use radioactive ligands with high specific activity. Another is the use of cell lines rich in a given receptor [63]. The

NG 108-15 neuroblastoma cell line and the PC-12 pheochromocytoma cell line can be used to study the characteristics of several neurotransmitter receptors whereas the U-937 and Hl-60 cell lines are useful models for the human monocyte and neutrophil, respectively, with abundant receptor populations. While the data derived is subject to scrutiny because the cell lines are by their very nature atypical, they are useful and allow for the preparation of receptor-enriched membrane tissue sources without the excessive use of animal tissues. One ready application for the technology of molecular biology is the cloning and expression of large quantities of homogeneous receptor populations.

6.3.5   Intracellular receptors

Receptors are normally viewed as extracellular elements. However, the three classes of steroid hormone — the adrenal steroids, the sex steroids and vitamin D_3, as well as thyroid hormone — produce their effects via specific intracellular receptors on DNA [34,81] which are termed ligand-responsive transcription factors (LRTFs). The R–L complex formed by the interaction of these ligands with their receptors leads to changes in gene expression. Hormone response elements on a gene thus act as transcriptional enhancers. The intracellular receptor superfamily has segments that are related to viral oncogenes [29, 34]. The precursors to several of these factors, the proto-oncogenes, are intimately involved in cellular transductional processes in mammalian tissues at the G-protein level [82] especially in the brain [83]. DNA and its associated promoters, while thought of in terms of drug receptor targets in relation to cancer therapy [84], also appear to mediate the immunosuppressant actions of cyclosporine [85]. Antisense RNA and DNA probes, the synthetic 'nonsense' oligonucleotides, may represent new antiviral and anticancer agents [86] although they represent a major challenge to the medicinal chemist in terms of their probable size and three-dimensional structure.

6.3.6   Receptor autoradiography

The ability to characterize receptors anatomically in intact tissues is a natural extension of the homogenate approach [87]. A tissue slice, or cell preparation, can be affixed to a conventional histological slide and, using similar techniques to those used for binding in cell homogenates, specific binding can be measured in discrete tissue regions. When the binding reaction is completed, the labeled slides are juxtaposed to tritium-sensitive film which, following a suitable exposure time (dependent on the radioisotope), can be developed and the film read using computer-assisted densitometry. Color enhancement of the films then permits the striking evaluation of differences in receptor densities. This latter process produces dramatic graphical representations of receptor distribution which, to date, have been used more often in the annual reports of biotechnology companies rather than in deriving information useful to the drug discoverer. More recently, however, the characteristics of binding sites identified via autoradiography have been subjected to the same kinetic and pharmacological analysis for homogenate receptors. The numerical data obtained, while not as visually striking as the color-enhanced photographs, has been used to assess the quantitative regional and tissue differences in receptor pharmacology as well as to evaluate the effect of drug treatments and animal manipulations — surgical or pharmacological — on discrete receptor populations [88]. This is a labor-intensive process since all films need to be read by hand but will become more useful in drug discovery as computer-assisted analysis improves in sophistication. Like other binding techniques, receptor autoradiography has its limitations, primarily in relation to removing excess radioactivity from the incubated tissue sections without destroying their architecture and the problem of quenching when using tritium [87,88].

6.3.7 Data analysis

Before the advent of personal computers and easy access to mainframes, the most common methods used for analysis of data from receptor binding experiments relied on graphical approaches to procedures amenable to the use of calculators. For saturation experiments, where the amount of ligand specifically bound is determined at varying ligand concentrations, untransformed data can be described in terms of a rectangular hyperbola (Fig. 6.4) similar to that observed for dose–response relation-

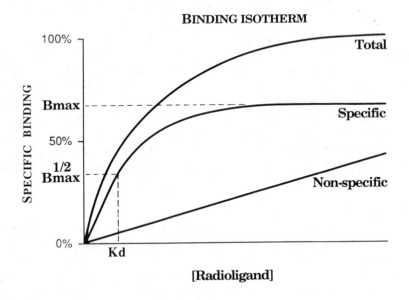

Fig. 6.4 — Ligand saturation curve: total specific and non-specific binding; see section 6.3.7 for further details.

ships (Fig. 6.3). Non-specific binding is a linear function with respect to the concentration of radioligand. The total number of sites, or apparent B_{max}, is the amount of binding observed at saturating concentrations of radioligand, and is represented by an asymptote to the top of the hyperbola. The K_d value is that concentration of ligand at which, by definition, 50% of the total number of receptors can be labeled (Fig. 6.4).

While there are a plethora of computer programs and books devoted to the analysis of binding data, from a drug discovery viewpoint, the information required from a routine binding experiment relates to the derivation of K_d and B_{max} values to define receptor characteristics either in the validation of an assay or as part of the workup for a new ligand. In general, therefore, once the K_d and B_{max} values for a ligand are defined, the remaining information of value relates to the derivation of IC_{50}/K_i values as well as the assessments of state/receptor multiplicity by deriving the Hill coefficient and subsequent nonlinear regression analysis. These topics are covered in detail elsewhere [17–19].

6.3.7.1   The Scatchard/Rosenthal plot

Owing to the non-linearity of saturation curves, both the 'apparent' B_{max} and the K_d values can only be approximated using non-transformed data. It is usual to transform the data and plot it in linear form as a Scatchard or Rosenthal plot. The Scatchard plot was originally used to determine the number of binding sites per unit of protein in a defined milieu, where the total number of binding sites was known. Since in the typical binding experiment, the latter value is often not known, the Rosenthal plot was developed for situations where the receptor concentration was unknown. Although the designation 'Rosenthal plot' is probably more accurate, the Scatchard terminology is used where B/F is plotted as a function of B:

$$\frac{B}{F} = -\frac{1}{K_d}[B] + \frac{B_{max}}{K_d}$$

where B is the amount specifically bound and F represents the amount of free ligand. Using this procedure, the B_{max} value can be obtained from the intercept on the abscissa and the K_d value is obtained from the negative reciprocal of the slope (Fig. 6.5). When the radioligand binds to a single site, a linear Scatchard plot is generated and reasonable estimates of B_{max} and K_d values can be obtained by using linear regression programs. Linear Scatchard plots can also be obtained, however, when a non-selective radioligand binds to more than one site with the same affinity. It is important to use high enough concentrations of radioligand to ensure that simple one-site binding following the mass action law occurs. While, ideally, 90% of binding sites should be occupied requiring radioligand concentrations 9–10 times that of the anticipated K_d value, 70–80% saturation can be sufficient since a second, low affinity binding site may not be detectable if high enough concentrations of ligand are not used. Even though extrapolation of the line generated using low ligand concentrations may indicate the presence of a single site, the lower affinity site may not be detected owing to compression of the data points at high concentrations of radioligand.

Concave-downward Scatchard plots, which are fortunately rarely observed, can indicate the presence of positive cooperativity, where the binding of one molecule of radioligand to the receptor facilitates the subsequent binding of other radioligand molecules. However, a similar shaped plot can be obtained owing to artifactual reasons, e.g. if equilibrium is not adequately achieved, a common problem in the case of peptide radioligands. Non-linear concave-upward Scatchard plots (Fig. 6.6) occur under several conditions; if non-specific binding is imprecisely defined; if the

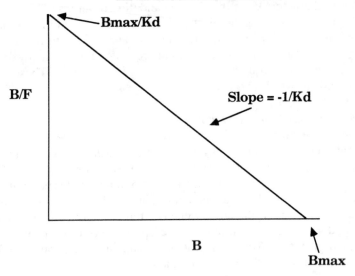

Fig. 6.5 — Scatchard transformation of saturation isotherm.

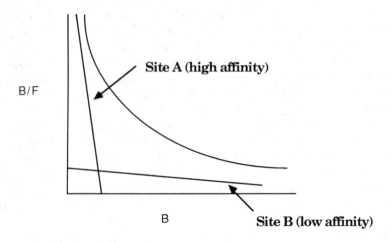

Fig. 6.6 — Non-linear Scatchard plot. Resolution of a curvilinear Scatchard into two components.

receptor recognizes the labeled and unlabeled ligand with different affinities; in the presence of multiple independent receptor sites to which the radioligand binds with different affinities; and when negative cooperativity occurs, i.e. where binding of the radioligand reduces further binding of ligand to the receptor. The presence of multiple states of a single receptor population or the existence of two-step, three-component binding can give similar plots. The use of ternary complex models may assist in data interpretation in this latter instance [89].

Graphical analysis is not sufficiently sophisticated to deal with non-linear Scatchard plots, as considerable subjectivity occurs when asymptotes to the two linear components of the curve are estimated and drawn by hand. Corresponding approximations of the actual values of B_{max} and K_d values for multiple component binding using Scatchard plots are usually inaccurate. Determination of the slopes of the curves such that each point on the actual data curve represents the summation of the two linear components [90] is more accurate than the 'pencil and paper' method but it is quite tedious. And while linear regression analysis can also be used to ensure greater objectivity and accuracy, this method is incorrect since the nature of the Scatchard plot involving free ligand (F) on both ordinate and abscissa is biased towards a regression based on a common variable [78].

The value for F can be determined by subtracting the amount of known radioactivity bound from that added ($F-B$), or F can thus be determined directly by taking an aliquot of the reaction mixture after the termination of the reaction when the tissue has been removed. Under experimental conditions, however, this may not be an accurate measure given that in a typical experiment approximately 10 000 cpm would be added in a volume of 1 mL and only 2–3% would be expected to bind, i.e. 200–300 cpm. The probability of error in taking microliter aliquots is large as is the calculation of the molar free concentration of ligand through a series of dilution corrections. In either instance, relatively small changes in the radioactivity determined can cause differences in the estimated free concentration; such situations require the use of more sophisticated analytical methods which are capable of analyzing untransformed binding data, such as computerized non-linear regression techniques.

6.3.7.2   The Hill plot

Another method of determining the K_d value from saturation experiments is the use of the Hill equation [91]:

$$B = \frac{B_{max}\,[L]^n}{K'_d + [L]^n}$$

where n is the Hill coefficient, [L] is the concentration of free ligand and K'_d is the K_d at $n_H = 1$. When transformed, the data can be plotted linearly as $\log(B/B_{max} - B)$ as a function of $\log[L]$ according to the relationship

$$\log \frac{B}{(B_{max} - B)} = n \log [L] - \log K'_d$$

The K_d value occurs when $\log [B/(B_{max} - B)] = 0$. The Hill plot does not allow the determination of an estimate of the B_{max}.

6.3.7.3 *Competition experiments*

In competition experiments, a fixed concentration of radioligand is incubated in the presence of various concentrations of inhibitor. Those experiments are generally employed to study the pharmacology of the receptor. The ability of compounds to inhibit the specific binding of a radioligand can be quantitatively evaluated by determining the IC_{50} value, which is that concentration of inhibitor at which 50% of specific radioligand binding is inhibited. IC_{50} values can be determined by several methods, including visual inspection of plotted data, log-logit analysis or log-probit transformation. In the latter case, data is transformed and logit B, or $\log (B_i/B_o - B_i)$ is plotted as a function of $\log [I]$ according to the equation

$$\log \frac{B_i}{B_o - B_i} = n \log [I] - n \log IC_{50}$$

where B_i represents the amount of ligand bound in the presence of competitor I, B_o represents the amount of ligand bound in the absence of competitor, and n_H represents the psuedo-Hill coefficient.

In this analysis, $x = IC_{50}$ value when $\log (B_i/B_o - B_i) = 0$. The slope of the line, termed the pseudo-Hill coefficient, or the slope factor n_H, indicates whether binding is simple or complex. Although not a true Hill coefficient, since binding of I is indirectly determined, it is often referred to as the Hill coefficient. Slope factors of one are consistent with binding to one site that follows the mass action law. However, slope factors of one can also be obtained when a non-selective compound inhibits the binding of non-selective ligand that labels more than one receptor. Slope factors greater than unity may reflect positive cooperativity, whereas n_H may be less than unity for several reasons, including the presence of multiple receptor subtypes, negative cooperativity, multiple interconverting receptor states or two-step, three-component binding (e.g. ternary complex formation [89]). When such complex binding occurs, data analysis needs to be equally sophisticated to resolve binding into individual components.

In determining the IC_{50} value for a compound, it is essential that an adequate number of concentration points and a sufficiently broad range of concentrations be used to derive the most accurate information from this experiment. While IC_{50} values can be derived with three-point competition curves covering the region of 50% inhibition, such data is limited since it allows no evaluation of binding behavior at either end of the competition curve. In this manner, important differences in the biological activity of the competitor that would provide information of the molecular interactions and contribute significantly to knowledge of the physiological activity of the compound would be omitted. An IC_{50} should therefore be determined using 7–10 concentration points over a three log unit range.

COMPETITION CURVES

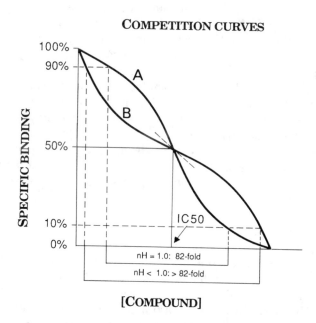

[COMPOUND]

Fig. 6.7 — Competition curves and IC_{50} determination. Plotting data at the 50% midpoint (dotted line) while generating an IC_{50} value can seriously limit the amount of data derived, as indicated by plot A. Curve A, for a competitive inhibitor of specific binding, has a pseudo-Hill coefficient of unity, requiring an 82-fold difference in compound concentration to displace over the range 10–90%. In more complex situations (curve B), where two components of binding appear to exist, the range of compound concentrations required to cause displacement is greater than 82-fold. In addition, as indicated, the compound may be unable to fully displace specific radioligand binding. In all instances the IC_{50} values derived are approximately the same.

The IC_{50} value is a function of the radioligand concentration. The Cheng–Prusoff derivation [92] allows determination of a K_i value that is corrected for the concentration of radioligand. K_i values can then be used to compare the pharmacology of competitive compounds, irrespective of the ligand concentration according to the equation

$$K_i = \frac{IC_{50}}{1 + [L]/K_d}$$

where [L] represents the ligand concentration and K_d is the affinity of receptor, R, for L. Several assumptions are made in the derivation of this formula. The relationship is valid only when the receptor concentration ≪ ligand concentration, i.e. $[R] < 0.1$ $[L]$, and when there is only a single class of receptors present that obeys the mass action law.

Conversion of an IC_{50} value to a K_i value is particularly important when comparing the pharmacology of a given inhibitor across a range of different binding assays where differences in K_d values and the concentrations of ligand used can give rise to misleading information. For example, in considering the situation where the ability of a compound to inhibit binding of muscarinic and bradykinin receptor ligands is compared and the compound has an IC_{50} value of 1 nM for [³H]QNB binding and 2 nM for [³H]bradykinin binding, it could be concluded that the compound was two-fold selective for the muscarinic cholinergic receptor. However, the respective radioligand concentrations are 0.06 and 1.0 nM with corresponding K_d values of 0.06 and 0.01 respectively. At the cholinergic receptor, a K_i value of 0.5 nM $\{1/1 + (0.06/0.06)\}$ would occur and at the bradykinin receptor a value of 0.02 nM $\{2/(1 + (1.0/0.01))\}$ would be generated. Thus, in this example, the compound, rather than being 2-fold selective for muscarinic receptors, is actually 25-fold selective for bradykinin receptors.

6.3.7.4 *Computer analysis*

Computer programs, mostly based on the method of Feldman [93], allow for better, more objective and less time-consuming 'number-crunching' methods for examining untransformed binding data. This limits the measurement error to a single variable, i.e. amount bound. A number of packages using non-linear regression analysis (LIGAND, LUNDON-1, RS/1) provide a graphical representation of the 'best fit' of the mathematical model to the data through the use of successive iterations.

When multiple binding components are indicated by computer analysis of curvilinear Scatchard data, multiple receptor subtypes cannot be assumed to be present. Rather, data consistent with either the presence of multiple sites or states should be generated. If multiple subtypes of the receptor are present, the total number of binding sites would be expected to be the same regardless of whether an agonist or antagonist radioligand is used. This is not always the case if multiple states are present.

While the analysis of radioligand binding data has advanced considerably since the exclusive use of 'pencil and paper' graphics, it is somewhat premature to consider that the present advancements have accomplished all that needs to be done in the analysis of receptor binding data. A judicious assessment of the usefulness of computerized data analysis within the context of the accuracy of biological test procedures being examined can in many cases clarify the extent to which the former can contribute in a logical manner. For instance, while it is of interest to know that multiple receptor states exist, their functional significance within the context of subsequent pharmacological evaluation is often unclear.

From a drug discovery viewpoint, automated 'downloading' of data from a scintillation counter to a buffer box or dedicated PC/MicroVax in a spread-sheet-type format (RS/1, Lotus, Excel) removes a time-consuming and error-prone step: that of manually re-entering data. In addition, subject to editing of data for gross experimental error, IC_{50} values and Hill coefficients can be determined by an integral non-linear regression program, removing yet another tedious step in data processing.

6.3.8   Receptor dynamics

Receptors are dynamic cellular constituents with half-lives that vary between 3 h and several days [94]. Despite evidence for receptor turnover, the use of irreversible and quasi-irreversible ligands as therapeutic agents is not currently accepted, a fact that may also be attributed to a lack of selectivity since many such entities are alkylating agents.

The increased availability of an endogenous ligand either through medication or because of alteration in normal function due to a change in tissue homeostasis resulting from a diseased condition can lead to changes in receptor function when intercellular signaling is too intense for normal cell-to-cell interactions. This may occur either by a change in receptor number, a downregulation or an alteration in the coupling of the receptor to its transduction element. This last-mentioned effect is often very subtle and may not be preserved in *ex vivo* experiments. Mechanisms that can contribute to receptor desensitization include (i) alterations in the phosphorylation state of membrane-associated coupling units, mediated either via cyclic nucleotide, calcium or phospholipid modulation of intracellular protein kinase entities [95]; (ii) trans-synaptic regulation of second messenger formation due to the summation of inputs that both positively and negatively regulate G protein coupling to the effector system [96]; and (iii) receptor internalization or clustering [18].

6.3.8.1   *Receptor downregulation*
Downregulation is a mechanism to reduce receptor functionality that results in altered K_d and apparent B_{max} values. Alterations in receptor affinity can theoretically alter functionality by requiring greater concentrations of agonist to elicit a response. Since excess agonist is the cause of downregulation, affinity changes are unlikely to be an effective means to change receptor function. A decrease in receptor number is a more tangible response to excess ligand and has been noted in response to many drug treatments [96].

6.3.8.2   *Receptor upregulation*
When the amount of endogenous agonist interacting with a receptor is reduced either by decreased availability or in the presence of an antagonist, an opposite effect to downregulation occurs, namely an increase in receptor number to increase the receptor functionality. This can occur by an increase in receptor affinity (decreased K_d) which results in an increased likelihood of agonist interacting with receptor or an increase in receptor number.

6.3.9   Receptor isolation

The ability to isolate and clone receptors using the powerful techniques of molecular biology has resulted in the sequencing of many receptors and the identity of receptor superfamilies [23,24]. Such research has appeared somewhat esoteric from the more applied environment of drug-related research especially in the light of the limited pharmacology that has been used to derive structure–activity profiles for individual ligands and the corresponding amino acid sequences [33]. Extensive work has yet to be done to permit the use of isolated receptors as templates for molecular modeling; it seems probable however that cloned receptors reconstituted in a suitable environment may be useful as homogeneous screening sources. Furthermore, the ability to express receptors in frog oocytes has shown that function can be studied in a defined cellular environment [28,32]. A stellar example of the use of this technique is in the case of the NMDA receptor which when expressed in a frog oocyte shows an absolute dependence on the presence of glycine for function [96] providing further evidence for the support of an NMDA receptor complex.

While the past history of success in enzyme isolation is often used as an example of what might be achieved by isolating receptors, receptor function appears to be closely related to the intramembrane milieu. Binding assays can be carried out using cloned material, indicating that the recognition elements are still present [31,32]. From the expression of mRNA for a given receptor, large quantities of material can be obtained, allowing the primary structure of isolated receptors to be determined and, using matrix analysis, functionality can be provisionally ascribed to residues thought to be adjacent to one another in the native molecule. For instance, in the calcium channel blocker receptor isolated from rabbit skeletal muscle, glutamate residues at positions 87 and 90 in repeat I and aspartate residues at positions 465, 836 and 1151 in repeats II, III and IV have been implicated in high-affinity calcium binding [30]. Similarly, in the chimeric adrenoceptor [32], a dominant role for the transmembrane segment 7 (Fig. 6.2) in determining the specific binding of $\alpha 2$-specific agonists has been noted. Using site-directed mutagenesis, it will be possible to directly test this hypothesis for each new receptor sequenced. This has been done for the nicotinic ACh receptor [98]. Ideally, the use of such techniques will allow more information to be derived for building necessary databases to transform molecular modeling from theory to practice. Similarly, raising polyclonal or mono-clonal antibodies to either the isolated receptor or its ligand will provide another tool to examine the physiological role of various neuroeffector agents [99]. In addition, where receptor subtypes are thought to exist, their anatomical locale can be studied by hybridization analysis as well as autoradiographic techniques.

6.3.10   Practical aspects of ligand-based screening

From the drug discovery viewpoint, the technique of radioligand binding has become an immensely powerful tool to evaluate the affinity of an NCE with a labeled receptor. In addition to often being used as the primary step on a project flow chart, the need for small quantities of material, rapid throughput and overall efficiency of the process has led many drug companies to supplement their lead finding medicinal chemistry programs with so-called 'targeted screening' operations where many thousands of NCEs or natural product compound sources are run through an assay to identify novel structures. The 'hit rate' for such operations varies between 0.01 and 1%. Many companies run batches of ligand binding assays in parallel to increase their chances of finding new compounds as well as to control for false positives. Any compound active in 3 or 4 screens may be considered to be non-specific in its actions.

The logistics of running targeted screening operations often trivialize the actual experimental process. Sample preparation and data analysis and storage are formi-dable challenges that are often overlooked in the enthusiasm to screen a company's sample bank.

Sample preparation involves the accessing, weighing and solubilization of NCEs. Inherent in this process, from a screening viewpoint, is the need to make certain empirical assumptions. These include 'weighing' samples on the basis of an assumed molecular weight of 300 or by the use of a standard 'spatula scoop' that approximates the amount of compound to give a 1 mM solution when diluted to 10 ml. Solubilization often involves the use of solvents such as DMSO or ethanol which are added via dilution stations such as the Tecan, any insoluble compounds being designated as inactive. In the early days of radioligand binding it often took 3–4 h to get a compound in solution, which is not a feasible approach when thousands of compounds are undergoing evaluation. Increasingly, assay tube preparation including the addition of tissue and radioligand is being done via dilution stations.

The use of multiport filtration assemblies such as the Brandel Cell Harvester represent major milestones in being able to handle more samples. There is, however, a need to increase throughput, and many companies are moving to a microfilter plate format and filtration units such as the TomTec to improve efficiency. The attendant reduction in assay volumes is also cost-efficient in terms of tissue and ligand usage.

Automation is being increasingly incorporated into screening laboratories via the use of dedicated robots or the use of the more versatile Zymark and Mitsubishi robots. While the market for fully automated systems is small, many pharmaceutical companies are investigating the potential resource efficiency of such approaches.

Counting of radioactivity is currently a labor-intensive (and boring) aspect of the screening operation. Automated capping and filling machines are available while recent developments such as the 'Betaplate' liquid scintillation counter from LKB offer a means to handle filter mats as single units while reducing the use of scintillation cocktail by 98%, a not inconsiderable feat given the cost of radioactive waste disposal.

When large numbers of samples (5000–20 000 per year) are being screened, there is a need to track their progress. This is usually initiated in a centralized compound facility where the compounds are achieved and weighed. Scheduling of compounds can be done using a laboratory information management system (LIMS) and tracked via computer. This ensures that all data requested is generated and matched to the compounds chosen for screening. As a final step, the analyzed data can be automatically downloaded in batch mode to a centralized database for subsequent reference use.

6.4   ENZYMES

Enzymes are amenable to study in much the same way as receptors, using a labeled substrate as a radioligand. The various neutral peptidases including enkephalinase and other members of the 24.11 class have been studied using labeled GEMSA as a ligand [100] while protein kinase C activity can be measured using [^{3}H]phorbol ester [101]. The ability of enzymes to produce substrate that can be measured spectrophotometrically or by ELISA makes screening of compounds as enzyme ligands easier from a practical standpoint. Using an automated dilution station/microtiter plate reader such as the Beckman Biomek, samples can be assayed for activity with minimal handling and waste.

Ligands are normally evaluated as enzyme inhibitors [102] and are treated for screening purposes in much the same way as receptors. Once an active compound has been identified, however, it can be studied using classical enzymological techniques to determine the mechanism of action [103].

6.5 COMPOUND SOURCES

As binding assays, receptor or enzyme, are embraced as a potential source of new structural leads, the number of NCEs available for screening is becoming finite.

Logistically, many compounds in drug company compound banks have decomposed or evaporated such that estimates related to the number of compounds screened are wildly in error. In addition, since many companies use proprietary (and usually proven) heterocycles as the starting point for their medicinal efforts, the number of dissimilar structural classes may reduce the variety of compounds from six- to four-digit numbers. This situation can further be compounded by exhaustion of available supplies and the current trend to synthesize milligram quantities of NCEs, the latter the 'Catch-22' of binding technology, that results from the need for less compound to evaluate potential activity. Thus these irreplaceable and priceless resources are rarely replenished. This is of especial concern as new molecular targets are identified at which previously screened compounds could be re-evaluated. While no hard numbers are available, a conservative estimate would be that 60% of all documented NCEs have not undergone evaluation in the molecular assays developed since 1974.

Drug companies are increasingly seeking alternative compound sources. In some instances, chemical companies are allowing drug companies to screen their compound banks (or doing it themselves). Other companies are also exchanging compounds so that NCEs can be screened more broadly or turning to academic sources for compounds. In addition, enterprises such as Nova and Panlabs offer 'fee for service' receptor-based screens for organizations that do not have the resources to do their own.

After many years of disfavor, natural products are again seen as viable sources of new drugs. This change in philosophy has occurred for several reasons: Merck's experience with asperlicin, the avermectins and the HMGCoA reductase inhibitor, mevinolin; the discovery of the immunosuppressants cyclosporine and FK 506 and the protein kinase C inhibitor, staurosporine, from natural sources; the identification of the peptidic antibiotics, the magainins from frog skin [104]; increased competition from Japanese pharmaceutical companies skilled in fermentation techniques; and from an increased interest in holistic 'Kampoh' medicines derived from plant sources that has occurred since China entered the global economy.

Plants, microbes and marine flora and fauna are all considered viable sources of NCEs. However, the approach to screening is markedly different from that which occurred even 10 years ago. Today the crude extract is screened before any attempt is made to isolate the active ingredient(s). This is more resource efficient than isolating an interesting NCE at enormous expense to find it is devoid of biological activity in those screeens in which it is evaluated.

The availability of these sources is, however, finite, and considerable care must be exercised such that the ecosystems are able to regenerate themselves. The removal of hundreds of kilograms of marine life from the oceans to obtain milligrams of NCEs cannot be tolerated if this approach is to be supported and novel drugs to be discovered. An official from the World Wild Life Fund has noted that less than 1% of the plants from the Amazon Basin have been evaluated for biological activity and the remainder probably never will be in light of the decimation of the rain forests [105].

6.6 FUTURE ISSUES

Compound sources for drug screening are probably secure for the next decade, their number being 'increased' as new assays are introduced to rescreen compounds. However, it appears likely that nature will remain the predominant source of new ligands for the future.

In addition to ventures to exploit the seabed such as Ocean Genetics, Harbor Branch Oceanographic Institute and the MITI-sponsored Japanese pharmaceutical industry consortium, which should, based on successes to date, find many new entities that may function as clinically efficacious immunomodulators and anti-cancer agents, newer approaches such as the U.S. Department of Energy's 'Savannah River Project' which exploits the use of bacterial colonies obtained by drilling into the earth's core as well as the complementary but more opportunistic uses of oil company drilling 'plugs' may lead to the discovery of other unique NCEs.

In the next decade, several major developments will impact the drug discoverer using ligand-based binding techniques. As the technique of molecular modeling becomes a more practical 'real time' tool, more companies will follow the lead of Parke-Davis/Warner-Lambert who have entered into a collaborative venture with Chiron and Protos to study receptor function from the 'receptor-side' rather than exclusively focussing on modified ligands to understand the R–L interaction. Such advances will facilitate the study of intracellular events related to the R–L complex at the nucleic acid level.

Finally, from a logistical viewpoint, it is probable that by the early 1990s, receptors will be as readily available as enzymes are today, and these will be characterized by selective non-radioactive ligand probes.

REFERENCES

[1] Spilker, B. (1989). *Multinational Drug Companies. Issues in Drug Discovery and Development*. Raven, New York.

[2] Deniker, P. (1983). Discovery of the clinical use of neuroleptics. In: M. J. Parnham & J. Bruinvels (eds) *Discoveries in Pharmacology. Vol. 1. Psycho- and Neuro-pharmacology*. Elsevier, Amsterdam, p. 163.

[3] Haefley, W. (1983). Alleviation of anxiety — the benzodiazepine saga. In: M. J. Parnham & J. Bruinvels (eds) *Discoveries in Pharmacology. Vol. 1. Psycho- and Neuro-pharmacology*. Elsevier, Amsterdam, p. 269.

[4] Squires, R. F. & Braestrup, C. (1977). Benzodiazepine receptors in rat brain. *Nature* **266**, 732.

[5] Mohler, H. & Okada, T. (1977). Benzodiazepine receptor: demonstration in the central nervous system. *Science* **198**, 849.

[6a] Nimer, S. D., Champlin, R. E., & Golde, D. W. (1988). Serum cholesterol-lowering activity of granulocyte–macrophage colony-stimulating factor. *J. Amer. Med. Assoc.* **260**, 3297.

[6b] Black, J. W. (1989) Drugs from emasculated hormones: the principle of synoptic antagonism. *Science* **245**, 486.

[7] Kenakin, T. P. (1988). *Pharmacologic Analysis of Drug–Receptor Interaction*. Raven, New York.

[8] Williams, M. & Neil, G. L. (1988). Organizing for drug discovery. *Proc. Drug Res.* **32**, 329.

[9] Haefley, W., Kyburz, E., Gerecke, M., & Mohler, H. (1985). Recent advances in molecular pharmacology of benzodiazepine receptors and in structure–activity relationships of their agonists and antagonists. *Adv. Drug Res.* **14**, 166.

[10] Williams, M. & Olsen, R. A. (1988). Benzodiazepine receptors and tissue function. In: M. Williams, R. A. Glennon, & P. B. M. W. M. W. Timmermans (eds) *Receptor Pharmacology and Function*. Marcel Dekker, New York, p. 385.

[11] Meiners, B. & Salama, A. I. (1982). Enhancement of benzodiazepine and GABA binding by the novel anxiolytic, tracazolate. *Eur. J. Pharmacol.* **78**, 315.

[12] Bennett, D. A. & Petrack, B. A. (1984). CGS 9896: a non benzodiazepine, non sedating potential anxiolytic. *Drug Dev. Res.* **4**, 75.

[13] Petersen, E., N., Jensen, L. F., Honore, T., Braestrup, C., Kehr, J. W., Stephens, D. W., Wachtel, H., Seidelman, D., & Schmiechen, R. (1984). ZK 91296, a partial agonist at benzodiazepine receptors. *Psychopharmacology* **83**, 240.

[14] Koenig, R. & Ansberry, C. (1988). Kodak seeks new drug from its shelves, hires 2 firms to test its huge inventory. *Wall St. J.*, 23 May 1988.

[15] Wong, E. H. K., Kemp, J. A., Priestly, T., Knight, A. R., Woodruff, G. N., & Iversen, L. L. (1986). The anticonvulsant MK 801 is a potent N-methyl-D-aspartate antagonist. *Proc. Natl. Acad. Sci. USA* **83**, 7104.

[16] Ariens, E. J. (1954). Affinity and intrinsic activity in the theory of competitive inhibition. *Arch. Int. Pharmacodyn.* **99**, 32.

[17] Limbird, L. (1986). *Cell Surface Receptors: a Short Course in Theory and Methods*. Martinus Nihoff, Boston.

[18] Dean, P. M. (1987). *Molecular Foundations of Drug–Receptor Interaction*. Cambridge, New York.

[19] Williams, N. & Sills, M. A. (1989). Quantitative analysis of ligand receptor interactions. In: J. C. Emmett (ed.) *Comprehensive Medicinal Chemistry, 3*, Pergamon Press, Oxford, in press.

[20] Colquhoun, D. (1985). Imprecision in presentation of binding studies. *Trends Pharmacol. Sci.* **6**, 197.

[21] Hollenberg, M. D. (1985). Receptor models and the action of neurotransmitters and hormones: some new perspectives. In: H. I. Yamamura, S. J. Enna, & M. J. Kuhar (eds) *Neurotransmitter Receptor Binding*, 2nd edn. Raven, New York, p. 1.

[22] Leysen, J. E., Gommeren, W., De Chaffoy De Courcelles, D., Stoof, J. C., & Janssen, P. A. J. (1988). Biochemical profile of risperidone, a new antipsychotic. *J. Pharmacol. Exp. Ther.* **247**, 661.

[23] Giguere, V., Ong, E. S., Segui, P., & Evans, R. M. (1987). Identification of a receptor for the morphogen retinoic acid. *Nature* **330**, 624.

[24] Noda, M., Shimizu, S., Tanabe, T., Takai, T., Kayano, T., Ikeda, T., Takahashui, H., Inayama, H., Kanaoka, T., Minamino, N., Kangawa, K., Matsuo, H., Raftery, M., Hirose, T., Inayama, S., Hayashida, H., Miyata, T.,

& Numa, S. (1984). Primary structure of *Electrophorus electricus* sodium channel deduced from cDNA sequence. *Nature* **312**, 121.

[25] Kobilka, B. F., Matsui, H., Kobilka, T. S., Tang-Feng, T. L., Francke, U., Caron, M. G., Lefkowitz, R. J., & Regan, J. W. (1987). Cloning, sequencing and expression of the gene coding for the human platelet α_2-adrenergic receptor. *Science* **238**, 650.

[26] Dixon, R. A. F., Kobilka, B. K., Strader, D. J., Benovic, J. L., Dohlman, H. G., Frielle, T., Bolanowski, M. A., Bennett, C. D., Rands, E., Diehl, R. E., Mumford, R. A., Slater, E. E., Sigal, I. S., Caron, M. G., Lefkowitz, R. L., & Srrader, C. D. (1986). Cloning of the gene and cDNA for mammalian β-adrenergic receptor and homology with rhodopsin. *Nature* **321**, 75.

[27] Grenningloh, G., Rienitz, A., Schmitt, B., Methfessel, C., Zensen, M., Beyreuther, K., Gundelfinger, E. D., & Betz, H. (1987). The strychnine-binding subunit of the glycine receptor shows homology with nicotinic acetyl-choline receptors. *Nature* **328**, 215.

[28] Schofield, P. R., Darlinson, M. G., Fujita, N., Burt, D. R., Stephenson, F. A., Rodriguez, H., Rhee, L. M., Ramamchandran, J., Reale, V., Glencorse, T. A., Seeburg, P. H., & Barnard, E. A. (1987). Sequence and functional expression of the $GABA_A$ receptor shows a ligand gated receptor super-family. *Nature* **328**, 221.

[29] Ullrich, A., Bell, J. R., Chen, E. Y., Werrara, R., Petruzzelli, L. M., Dull, T. J., Gray, A., Coussens, L., Liao, Y-C., Tsubokawa, M., Mason, A., Seeberg, P. W., Grunfeld, G., Rosen, P. M., & Ramachandran, J. (1985). Human insulin receptor and its relationship to tyrosine kinase family of oncogenes. *Nature* **313**, 756.

[30] Tanabe, T., Takeshima, H., Mikami, A., Flockerzi, V., Takahashi, H., Kanagaw, K., Kojima, H., Matsuo, T., Hirose, T., & Numa, S. (1987). Primary structure of the receptor for calcium channel blockers from skeletal muscle. *Nature* **328**, 313.

[31] Bunzow, J. R., Van Tol, H. H. M., Grandy, D. K., Albert, P., Salon, J., Christie, M., Machida, C. A., Neve, K. A., & Civelli, O. (1988). Cloning and expression of a rat D_2 dopamine receptor cDNA. *Nature* **336**, 783.

[32] Koblika, B. K., Kobilka, T. S., Daniel, H., Regan, J. W., Caron, M. G., & Lefkowitz, R. J. (1988). Chimeric α_2, β_2-adrenergic receptors: delineation of domains involved in effector coupling and ligand binding specificity. *Science* **240**, 1310, 198.

[33] Dixon, R. A. F., Strader, C. D., & Sigal, I. S. (1988). Structure and function of G-protein coupled proteins. *Annu. Rep. Med. Chem.* **23**, 221.

[34] Evans, R. M. (1988). The steroid and thyroid hormone receptor superfamily. *Science* **240**, 889.

[35] Dixon, M. & Webb, E. C. (1979). *Enzymes*. Academic Press, New York, pp. 197, 334.

[36] Hollenberg, M. D. (1988) Receptors: their reactions and interactions. In: M. Williams, R. A. Glennon, & P. B. M. W. M. Timmermans (eds) *Receptor Pharmacology and Function*. Marcel Dekker, New York, p. 1.

[37] Loo, P., Braunwalder, A., Lehmann, J., & Williams, M. (1986). Radioligand binding to central phencyclidine recognition sites is dependent on excitatory

amino acid receptor agonists. *Eur. J. Pharmacol.* **123**, 467.

[38] Arnholt, R. R. H., Pedersen, P. L., De Sousa, E. B., & Snyder, S. H. (1986). The peripheral-type benzodiazepine receptor: localization to the mitochondrial outer membrane. *J. Biol. Chem.* **261**, 576.

[39] Daval, J-L., Post, R. M., & Marangos, P. J. (1989). Pyruvate dehydrogenase interactions with peripheral-type benzodiazepine receptors. *J. Neurochem.* **52**, 110.

[40] Verma, A., Nye, J. S., & Snyder, S. H. (1987). Porphyrins are endogenous ligands for the mitochondrial (peripheral-type) benzodiazepine receptor. *Proc. Natl. Acad. Sci. USA* **64**, 2256.

[41] Peroutka, S., J. (1988). 5-Hydroxytryptamine receptor subtypes: molecular, biochemical and physiological characterization. *Trends Neurosci.* **11**, 496.

[42] Kenakin, T. P. (1989). Challenges for receptor theory as a tool for drug and drug receptor classification. *Trends Pharmacol. Sci.* **10**, 18.

[43] Hammer, R. C., Berrie, C. P., Birdsall, N. J. M., Burgen, A. S. V., & Hulme, E. C. (1980). Pirenzepine distinguishes between different subclasses of muscarinic receptors. *Nature* **283**, 90.

[44] Bonner, T. I., Buckley, N. J., Young, A. C., & Brann, M. R. (1987). Identification of a family of muscarinic acetylcholine receptor genes. *Science* **237**, 527.

[45] Black, J. W. (1987). Should we be concerned about the state of hormone receptor classification? In: J. W. Black, D. H. Jenkinson, & V. P. Gerskowitch (eds) *Perspectives in Receptor Classification*. Liss, New York, p. 11.

[46] Simon, E. J. & Hiller, J. M. (1978). The opiate receptors. *Annu. Rev. Pharmacol.* **18**, 371.

[47] Clineschmidt, B. V., Williams, M., Witaslawski, J. J., Bunting, P. R., Risley, E. A., & Totaro, J. A. (1982). Restoration of shock suppressed behavior by treatment with (+)-5-methyl-10,11-dihydro-5H-dibenzo[a,b]-cyclohepten-5,10-amine (MK 801), a substance with potent anticonvulsant, central sympathomimetic and apparent anxiolytic properties. *Drug Dev. Res.* **2**, 147.

[48] Clark, A. J. (1933). *The Mode of Action of Drugs on Cells.* Edward Arnold, London.

[49] Tallarida, R. J., Raffa, R. B., & McGonigle, P. (1988). *Principles in General Pharmacology.* Springer-Verlag, New York.

[50] Stephenson, R. P. (1956). A modification of receptor theory. *Br. J. Pharmacol.* **11**, 379.

[51] Van Rossum, J. M. & Ariens, E. J. (1962). Receptor-reserve and threshold phenomena. II. Theories on drug action and a quantitative approach to spare receptors and threshold values. *Arch. Int. Pharmacodyn.* **136**, 385.

[52] Nickerson, M. (1956). Receptor occupancy and tissue response. *Nature* **178**, 697.

[53] Furchgott, R. F. (1964). Receptor mechanisms. *Annu. Rev. Pharmacol.* **4**, 21.

[54] Cuatrecasas, P. (1974). Membrane receptors. *Annu. Rev. Biochem.*, **43**, 169.

[55] Goldstein, A., Aronow, L., & Kalman, S. M. (1974). *Principles of Drug Action: the Basis of Pharmacology,* 2nd edn. Wiley, New York, p. 82.

[56] Paton, W. D. M. (1961). A theory of drug action based on the rate of drug–receptor combination. *Proc. Roy. Soc. Ser. B.* **154**, 21.

[57] Kenakin, T. P. (1987). Agonists, partial agonists, antagonists, inverse agonists and agonists/antagonists? *Trends Pharmacol. Sci.* **8**, 423.

[58] Gosselin, R. E. (1977). Drug–receptor inactivation: a new kinetic model. In: J. M. van Rossum (ed.) *Kinetics of Drug Action.* Springer-Verlag, New York, p. 323.

[59] Monod, J., Wyman, J., & Changeux, J-P. (1965). On the nature of allosteric transitions. A plausible model. *J. Mol. Biol.* **12**, 88.

[60] Koshland, D. E., Nemethyl, G., & Filmer, D. (1966). Comparison of experimental binding data and theoretical models in proteins containing subunits. *Biochemistry* **5**, 365.

[61] Lindstrom, J. (1985). Techniques for studying the biochemistry and cell biology of receptors. In: H. I. Yamamura, S. J. Enna, & M. J. Kuhar (eds) *Neurotransmitter Receptor Binding,* 2nd edn. Raven, New York, p. 123.

[62] Filer, C., Hurt, S., & Wan, Y-P. (1988). Radioligands: synthesis and handling. In: M. Williams, R. A. Glennon, & P. B. M. W. M. Timmermans (eds). *Receptor Pharmacology and Function.* Marcel Dekker, New York, p. 105.

[63] El-Fakahany, E. E. (1988). Intact cells: a model for studying receptor binding and function. In: M. Williams, R. A. Glennon, & P. B. M. W. M. Timmermans (eds) *Receptor Pharmacology and Function.* Marcel Dekker, New York, p. 695.

[64] Bennett, Jr., J. P. & Yamamura, H. I. (1985). Neurotransmitter, hormone, or drug receptor binding methods. In: H. I. Yamamura, S. J. Enna, & M. J. Kuhar (eds) *Neurotransmitter Receptor Binding,* 2nd edn. Raven, New York, p. 61.

[65] Foster, A. C. & Fagg, G. E. (1984). Acidic amino acid binding sites in mammalian neuronal membranes: their characteristics and relationship to synaptic receptors. *Brain Res. Rev.* **7**, 103.

[66] Murphy, D. E., Schneider, J., Boehm, C., Lehmann, J., & Williams, M. (1987). Binding of [^{3}H]CPP (3-(2-carboxypiperazin-4-yl)propyl-1-phosphonic acid) to rat brain membranes: a selective, high affinity ligand for N-methyl-D-aspartate (NMDA) receptors. *J. Pharmacol. Exp. Ther.* **240**, 778.

[67] Murphy, D. E., Hutchison, A. J., Hurt, S. D., Williams, M., & Sills, M. A. (1988). Characterization of the binding of [^{3}H]CGS 19755 a novel N-methyl-D-aspartate antagonist with nanomolar affinity in rat brain. *Br. J. Pharmacol.* **95**, 932.

[68] Bruns, R. F., Lawson-Wendling, K., & Pugsley, T. A. (1983). A rapid filtration assay for soluble receptors using polyethylenimine-treated filters. *Anal. Biochem.* **132**, 74.

[69] Middlemiss, D. N. & Fozard, J. (1983). 8-Hydroxy-2-(di-n-propylamino)-tetralin discriminates between subtypes of the 5HT$_1$ recognition site. *Eur. J. Pharmacol.* **90**, 151.

[70] Norman, A. B., Battaglia, G., Morrow, A. L., & Creese, I. (1985). [^{3}H]WB 4101 labels S1 serotonin receptors in rat cerebral cortex. *Eur. J. Pharmacol.* **106**, 461.

[71] Quirion, R. & Gaudreau, P. (1985). Strategies in neuropeptide receptor binding research. *Neurosci. Biobehav. Rev.* **9**, 413.

[72a] Chang, R. S. L., Lotti, V. J., Monaghan, R. L., Birnbaum, J., Stapley, E.

O., Goetz, M. A., Albers-Schonberg, G., Patchett, A. A., Liesch, T. M., Hensens, O. D., & Springer, J. P. (1985). A potent non-peptide cholecysto-kinin antagonist selective for peripheral tissues isolated from *Aspergillus alliaceus. Science,* **230**, 177.

[72b] Chang, R. S. L. & Lotti, V. J. (1986). Biochemical and pharmacological characteristics of an extremely potent and selective nonpeptide cholecystoki-nin antagonist. *Proc. Natl. Acad. Sci. USA* **83**, 4923.

[73] Bruns, R. F., Lu, G. H., & Pugsley, T. A. (1986). Characterization of the A2 adenosine receptor labeled by [^{3}H]NECA in rat striatal membranes. *Mol Pharmacol.* **29**, 331.

[74] Jarvis, M. F., Schulz, R., Hutchison, A. J., Do, U. H., Sills, M. A. & Williams, M. (1989). [^{3}H]CGS 21680, a selective A$_2$ adenosine receptor agonist ligand directly labels A$_2$-reception in rat brain. *J. Pharmacol. Exp. Ther.* **252**, in press.

[75] Cuatrecasas, P. & Hollenberg, M. (1976). Membrane receptor and hormone action. *Adv. Prot. Chem.,* **30**, 251.

[76] Pliska, V. (1983). Displacement reactions employing heterologous tracer ligands in peptide receptor studies. A review. *J. Receptor Res.* **3**, 227.

[77] Williams, M., Wennogle, L. P., & Jeng, A. Y. (1990). Peptide ligands: receptor interactions, second messenger systems and proteolytic metabolism. In: P. I. Nadler (ed.) *Peptides and Proteins as Drugs.* Marcel Dekker, New York, in press.

[78] Williams, M. & Enna, S. J. (1986). The receptor: from concept to function. *Annu. Rep. Med. Chem.* **26**, 619.

[79] Ferkany, J. W., Valentine, H. L., Stone, G. A., & Williams, M. (1986). Adenosine A1 receptors in mammalian brain: species differences in their interactions with agonists and antagonists. *Drug Dev. Res.* **9**, 85.

[80] Stone, G. A., Jarvis, M. F., Sills, M. A., Weeks, B., Snowhill, E. W., & Williams, M. (1988). Species differences in high-affinity adenosine A$_2$ binding sites in striatal membranes from mammalian brain. *Drug Dev. Res.* **15**, 31.

[81] Minghetti, P. P. & Norman, A. W. (1988). 1,25(OH)$_2$-Vitamin D$_3$ receptors: gene regulation and genetic circuitry. *FASEB J.* **2**, 3043.

[82] Huber, B. E. (1989). Therapeutic opportunities involving cellular oncogenes: novel approaches fostered by biotechnology. *FASEB J.* **3**, 5.

[83] Sudol, M. (1989). Expression of proto-oncogenes in neural tissues. *Brain Res. Rev.,* in press.

[84] Hurley, L. H. & Boyd, F. L. (1988). DNA as a target for drug action. *Trends Pharmacol. Sci.* **9**, 402.

[85] Kroczek, R. A., Black, C. D., Barbet, J., & Shevach, E. (1987). Mechanism of action of cyclosporin A *in vivo*: 1. Cyclosporin A fails to inhibit T lymphocyte activation in response to alloantigens. *J. Immunol.* **139**, 3597.

[86] Miller, P. S. & Ts'O, P. O. P. (1988). Oligonucleotide inhibitors of gene expression in living cells: new opportunities in drug design. *Annu. Rep. Med. Chem.* **23**, 295.

[87] Kuhar, M. J., De Souza, E. B., & Unnerstall, J. M. (1986). Neurotransmitter receptor mapping by autoradiography and other methods. *Annu. Rev. Neur-osci.* **9**, 27.

[88] Jarvis, M. F. (1988). Autoradiographic localization and characterization of brain adenosine receptor subtypes. In: F. Leslie & A. C. Altar (eds) *Receptor Localization: Ligand Autoradiography*, Liss, New York, p. 95.

[89] De Lean, A., Stadel, J. M., & Lefkowitz, R. J. (1980). A ternary complex model explains the agonist-specific binding properties of the adenylate cyclase-coupled beta-adrenergic receptor. *J. Biol. Chem.* **255**, 7108.

[90] Hunston, D. L. (1975). Two techniques for evaluating small molecules–macromolecule binding in complex systems. *Anal. Biochem.* **63**, 99.

[91] Cornish-Bowden, A. & Koshland, D. E. (1975). Diagnostic uses of the Hill (logit and Nernst) plots. *J. Mol. Biol.* **95**, 201.

[92] Cheng, Y-C. & Prusoff, W. H. (1972). Relationship between the inhibition constant (K_i) and the concentration of the inhibitor which causes 50 per cent inhibition (IC_{50}) of an enzymic reaction. *Biochem. Pharmacol.* **22**, 3099.

[93] Feldman, H. (1972). Mathematical theory of complex ligand-binding at equilibrium: some methods of parameter fitting. *Anal. Biochem.* **48**, 317.

[94] Mahan, L. C., McKernan, R. M., & Insel, P. A. (1987). Metabolism of alpha- and beta-adrenergic receptors *in vitro* and *in vivo*. *Annu. Rev. Pharmacol. Toxicol.* **27**, 215.

[95] Greengard, P. (1986). Protein phosphorylation and neuronal function. *Fidia Research Foundation Neurosciences Award Lectures*. Livian Press, Padova, p. 52.

[96] Creese, I. & Sibley, D. R. (1981). Receptor adaptation to centrally acting drugs. *Annu. Rev. Pharmacol. Toxicol.* **21**, 357.

[97] Kleckner, N. W. & Dingeldine, R. (1988). Requirement for glycine in activation of NMDA receptor expressed in *Xenopus oocytes*. *Science,* **241**, 835.

[98] Mishina, M., Tobimatsu, T., Imoto, K., Tanaka, K., Fujita, Y., Fukada, K., Kuraski, M., Takahashi, H., Morimoto, T., Inauama, S., Takahashi, T., Kino, M., & Numa, S. (1985). Location of functional regions of acetylcholine receptor α-subunit by site directed mutagenesis. *Nature* **313**, 364.

[99] Swenberg, M-L., Buck, S. H., & Lovenberg, W. (1987). Development of an anti-idiotypic antibody that blocks substance P primary antibodies and substance P membrane binding. *Brain Res.* **417**, 131.

[100] Strittmatter, M., Lynch, D. R., & Snyder, S., H. (1984). [^{3}H]Guanidinoethyl-mercaptosuccinic acid binding to tissue homogenates. Selective labeling of enkephalin convertase. *J. Biol. Chem.* **259**, 11812.

[101] Leach, K. L., James, M. L., & Blumberg, P. M. (1983). Characterization of a specific phorbol ester binding site in mouse brain cytosol. *Proc. Natl. Acad. Sci. USA* **80**, 4208.

[102] Fuller, R. W. & Steranka, L. R. (1987). Drug discovery at the enzyme level. In: M. Williams & J. B. Malick (eds) *Drug Discovery and Development*. Humana, Clifton, New Jersey, p. 177.

[103] Kraut, J. (1988). How do enzymes work? *Science* **242**, 533.

[104] Zasloff, M. (1987). Magainins, a class of antimicrobial peptides from Xenopus skin: isolation characterization of two active forms, and partial cDNA sequence of a precursor. *Proc. Natl. Acad. Sci. USA* **84**, 5449.

[105] Plotkin, M. (1988). World Wildlife Fund, McNeil–Lehrer News Report, WNET Channel 13, Public Television, New York, 24 November 1988.

[106] Hirsch, J. D., Beyer, C. F., Malkowitz, L., Beer, B., & Blume, A. J. (1989). Mitochondrial benzodiazepine receptors mediate inhibition of mitochondrial respiratory control. *Mol. Pharmacol.* **34**, 157.

[107] Behling, R. W., Yamane, T., Navon, G., & Jelinski, L. W. (1988). Conformation of acetylcholine bound to the nicotinic acetylcholine receptor. *Proc. Natl. Acad. Sci. USA* **85**, 6721.

7

Ion channels

David J. Triggle
School of Pharmacy, State University of New York, Buffalo, New York, USA

7.1 INTRODUCTION

The cell is an excitable system and is sensitive to a variety of informational inputs — both physical and chemical — and including light, heat and chemical changes. These informational inputs are coupled to cellular responses through a variety of transducing mechanisms that include enzyme activation, substrate internalization and ion channel opening and closing. Ion channels are components of both intracellular and extracellular membranes and serve, with variable selectivity, to permeate ions, notably the physiologic cations and anions Na^+, K^+, Ca^{2+} and Mg^{2+} and the anion Cl^-, in response to cell stimuli.

An asymmetric distribution of ions is maintained across the cell membrane with Na^+ and Ca^{2+} being maintained at low intracellular levels and K^+ at a high intracellular level relative to the extracellular environment. This asymmetric distribution is maintained because of the selective permeability of membranes to ions and because of the existence of selective ion transporters (pumps) that serve to maintain ionic gradients in the face of leakage and to restore them post-stimulus. These pumps include Na^+, K^+-ATPase, Na^+:Ca^{2+} transporters and Ca^{2+}-ATPases. The asymmetric distribution of ions serves two principal purposes: it contributes to the generation and maintenance of a potential gradient and the subsequent generation of ionic current, and it permits the ions themselves to act as cellular messengers. The ionic currents may be the end response, as in the electric organ of the electric eel, they may serve to generate or modulate other electrical or chemical responses as with action potential propagation, or they may serve, as in the case of the calcium ion, an additional role as an intracellular messenger species. Ion channels represent necessary and likely early events in cellular evolution. The lipid bilayer represents a major energetic barrier to ion transport and the uncontrolled transmembrane movement of ions has lethal impact on the cell. Ion channels must, therefore, be regulated species. It is the regulation process that provides the key to the understanding of physiologic and pharmacologic control of ion channels. A comprehensive discussion of ion channels, their properties and their function is provided by Hille [1].

The asymmetric distribution of ions across the cell membrane indicates that each ion has a corresponding potential, the equilibrium potential, at which concentration and electrical gradients balance (Fig. 7.1). When two or more ion channels are

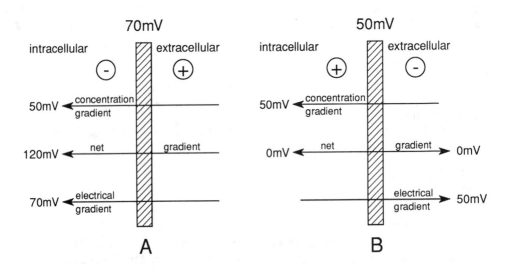

Fig. 7.1 — The concentration and potential gradients for Na^+ distribution. At a resting membrane potential of -70 mV, Na^+ ions are subject to two inward driving forces (A). When the cell is depolarized to $+50$ mV, the inwardly directed concentration gradient is balanced by the outwardly directed potential gradient (B). At this potential, the equilibrium potential, there is no net movement of Na^+ ions.

opened simultaneously or when an ion channel is not perfectly selective for a single ionic species, the measured equilibrium potential will reflect the net contribution of the several events. If the regulation of only single categories of ion channels is considered, then the opening of Na^+ and Ca^{2+} channels is of excitatory character, driving the cell to depolarized states, while opening of K^+ or Cl^- channels will be inhibitory, serving to maintain membrane potential or to hyperpolarize the cell. Conversely, the closing of a Cl^- or K^+ channel may be regarded as a disinhibitory signal, leading to cell excitation. The control of these ion channels should not be viewed in isolation, but rather should be seen as linked events. Thus, an increase in intracellular Ca^{2+} concentration can activate Ca^{2+}-dependent K^+ channels, hyperpolarize the cell, close Ca^{2+} channels and stabilize the cell. Accordingly, Ca^{2+} channel antagonists and K^+ channel activators exert similar effects on cell excitability leading to potentially similar roles in the control of smooth muscle excitability (section 7.6). Similarly, K^+ channel antagonism can lead to cell excitation and the opening of voltage-dependent Ca^{2+} channels: this process underlies the actions of the hypoglycemic sulfonylureas (section 7.6).

7.2   APPROACHES TO THE STUDY OF ION CHANNELS

Ion channels may be studied at a variety of levels from the measurement of
membrane potential changes in a cell or organ to the study of single ion channels
either in membrane patches or reconstituted into artificial membranes. Ion channels
may be studied both in bulk and at the single-channel level. Increasingly, the use of
single-channel recording techniques has permitted molecular insights into the nature
of the molecular permeation properties of ion channels [1–3]. The ability to isolate
channel components in purified form and to resolve their several components makes
possible the study of channel function in reconstituted systems that permit an
environment different from that of the native cell [3]. There are increasingly
important contributions from molecular biology with the elucidation of channel
amino acid sequences, the 'designer synthesis' of new channel sequences and the
generation of models of channel structure and function [4].

   The principle of the voltage clamp, originally described for giant axons, has been
of particular virtue in defining the magnitudes and time courses of ionic currents that
underlie electrical changes. The principle is depicted in Fig. 7.2 whereby the step and

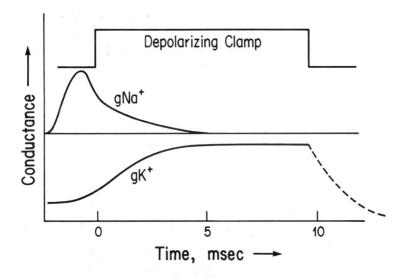

Fig. 7.2 — Schematic representation of Na^+ and K^+ conductance changes in axon. A step
depolarization (as shown) evokes a rapid and transient Na^+ conductance followed by a slower
and sustained K^+ conductance. Modified from Hodgkin, A. L. & Huxley, A. F. (1952). *J.
Physiol. (Lond.)* **117**, 500.

maintenance for defined times of a specified membrane potential permits the analysis
of the separate Na^+ and K^+ currents that underlie the action potential. Subsequent
developments have permitted the application of this principle to membrane and cell
patches in a variety of configurations to permit the detection and recording of single-
channel events.

7.3   GENERAL PROPERTIES OF ION CHANNELS

Ion channels represent one of several pathways through which ions cross cellular membranes. Ion channels are similar to carriers such as valinomycin and vectorial enzymes such as Na^+, K^+-ATPase in one important respect — ionic discrimination. Ion channels discriminate ions both on the basis of their cation/anion characteristics and, within ion series, on the basis of their size and hydration characteristics. However, ion channels may be distinguished from other ion-using species by their high conductance and high ion transport rates. Thus, channels permeate ions at rates, $> 10^7$ ions/s, that approach diffusion-controlled limits. Enzymes and carriers operate at orders of magnitude less efficiency. Consistent with this high effectiveness of operation, ion channels may exist at low densities relative to many other membrane proteins. Thus, the transfer of monovalent cations of 10–12 mol/cm^2, corresponding to 6000 ions per square micrometer, will charge the membrane by 100 mV. This amount of ion traffic can be carried by a single channel carrying 1 pA of current in 1 ms [1].

This discussion indicates that ion channels must have certain minimal organizational features that are independent of the specific channel class. These features include a pore through which the ions can permeate, a 'selectivity filter', which confers upon the channel its ionic selectivity and 'gates' which open and close to permit ion permeation. Additionally, channels possess sensors that permit them to respond to cell signals of chemical or physical nature, including neurotransmitters, hormones, odorants, light, pressure and membrane potential (Fig. 7.3). The gates

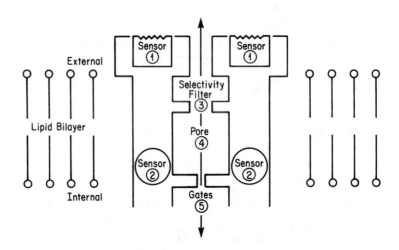

Fig. 7.3 — Schematic representation of ion channel depicting the essential components including both chemical sensors (1) and voltage sensors (2).

and sensors may be linked, directly or indirectly, through guanine nucleotide coupling proteins or biochemical intermediates including cyclic nucleotides and phospholipid metabolites.

The relative selectivity of ion channels for ions depends upon a number of factors including charge (nature and magnitude), size of the hydrated and unhydrated ions, hydration energy and affinities for binding sites that are components of the channel. In Eisenman's treatment of ion selectivity, only certain permeability sequences are predicted according to relative energies of ion binding and dehydration [5]. Ion channels possess varying degrees of ionic discrimination. Thus, the Na^+ and K^+ channels involved in the action potential generation depicted in Fig. 7.2 have absolute mutual discrimination ratios of approximately 12:1 and the voltage-dependent Ca^{2+} channel has a $Ca^{2+}:Na^+$ permeability ratio of approximately 1000:1. In contrast, the nicotinic acetylcholine receptor channel is quite promiscuous, showing little discrimination between inorganic or organic cations. In principle, ion channels may exhibit ionic selectivity through two fundamentally different mechanisms. Ions may be differentiated by charge or size: they may be of the wrong charge type, they may be of the wrong size or the dehydration energy may be excessive to permit passage of the dehydrated ion. Alternatively, ionic selectivity may arise from interactions at specific binding sites. The latter mechanism is increasingly favored. For the voltage-dependent Ca^{2+} channel, several lines of evidence, including current saturation and ion competition, have led to a model of the channel as a single-file pore with two divalent cation binding sites. Double occupancy of the binding sites and mutual cation–cation repulsion are associated with high Ca^{2+} flux rates [6].

7.4 CLASSIFICATION OF ION CHANNELS

In principle, a variety of schemes may be advanced to provide a classification of ion channels. The problem is very similar to that of the classification of pharmacologic receptors for neurotransmitters and polypeptide hormones. Channels may be classified very simply according to the nature of the ion or ions to which they are dominantly permeant — Na^+, K^+, Cl^-, etc. Although descriptive, this classification is becoming less useful since it is quite clear that multiple classes of channels exist for single ions. Classification may depend upon electrophysiologic features including conductance and other kinetic properties including rates of activation and inactivation. These can be highly discriminating properties. Fig. 7.2 shows that the Na^+ and K^+ channels of axons differ markedly in their rates of activation and even more in their inactivation rates, the Na^+ channel inactivating very rapidly even in the presence of a maintained depolarizing clamp.

Classification may also be achieved according to the stimuli to which the channels are sensitive. A division of particular importance is that between potential-dependent and receptor-operated channels. The former class is principally sensitive to changes in membrane potential over defined ranges, whereas the latter are principally sensitive to changes in chemical potential through drug–receptor interactions. The division is not, however, absolute and voltage-dependent channels are frequently modulated by endogenous chemical signals. Voltage-dependent channels may be viewed as having specific components — voltage sensors — responsive to changes in membrane potential (section 7.7). However, this sensitivity to membrane potential may be modulated through drug–receptor interactions. The cardiac Ca^{2+} channel is activated by a depolarizing stimulus; however, the opening probability is increased by phosphorylation through the beta-adrenoceptor adenylate cyclase complex. Activation of beta-adrenoceptors by isoproterenol and other beta-receptor stimulants or the intracellular administration of c-AMP or the catalytic subunit of protein kinase A serve to activate the cardiac Ca^{2+} channel [7]. Thus, the total current is given by

$$I = N_f P_o i$$

where N_f is the number of functional channels, P_o is the opening probability and i is the unitary current. The number of functional channels is given by

$$N_f = N_t P_f$$

where N_t is the total number of channels and P_f is the probability that the channel is available.

Receptor-operated channels may be considered according to several models where the chemical sensor is an intrinsic or remote component of the system (Fig. 7.4). There are important mechanistic and conceptual differences between the

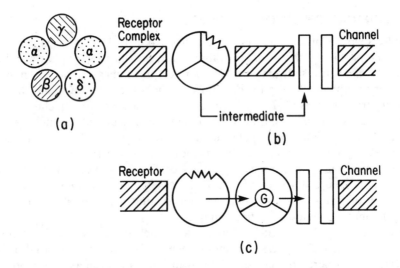

Fig. 7.4 — Possible organizational models or receptor-operated ion channels. (a) The subunits comprise both the channel and the receptor; (b) the channel and receptor are linked through one or more intermediates; (c) the channel and receptor are linked through a guanine nucleotide binding protein.

several models depicted. In Fig. 7.4(a), which depicts the nicotinic acetylcholine receptor, the five subunits comprise both the channels and the receptor. In the other models, the channel and receptors are linked through second-messenger species that may be delivered through the cytosol or membrane. Such second messengers will be derived from biochemical events initiated by drug–receptor interactions and may include c-AMP, inositol phosphates, arachidonic acid metabolites and 1,2-diacylglycerols. Some illustrative differences between channels with intrinsic and remote sensors are listed in Table 7.1.

Table 7.1 — Differentiation between channel types

	Intrinsic sensor	Remote sensor
Speed of response	Very rapid	Slower
Second messengers	No effect	Have effect
Response in patch	Maintained	May be lost
Response reconstituted	Maintained	Lost

Finally, channels may be classified according to drugs with which they may interact [8]. A fundamental distinction is thereby provided between the Na$^+$ and K$^+$ currents making up the action potential of Fig. 7.2 by the discriminative actions of tetrodotoxin and tetraethylammonium (Fig. 7.5). Tetrodotoxin and tetraethylam-

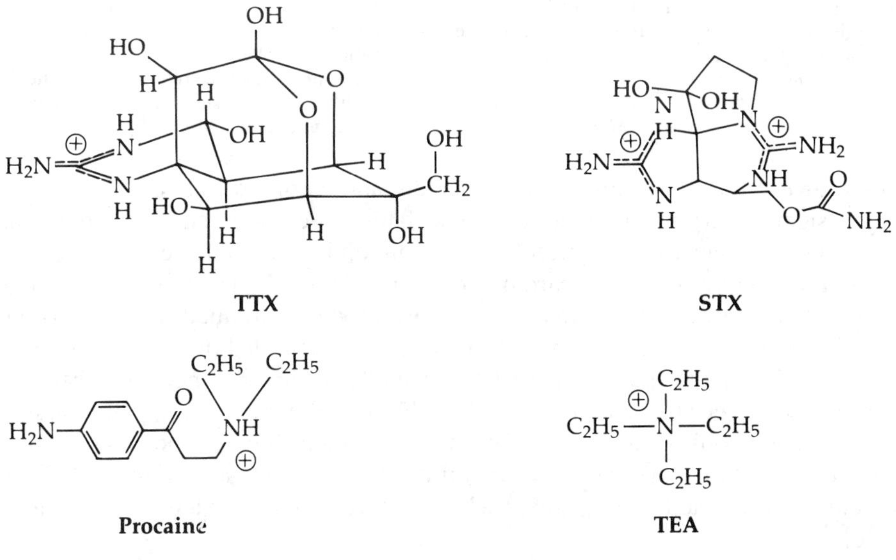

Fig. 7.5 — The structural formulae of drugs active at Na$^+$ channels including tetrodotoxin (TTX), saxitoxin (STX), procaine and at K$^+$ channels including tetraethylammonium (TEA).

monium have specific affinities for the Na^+ and K^+ channels respectively, and they serve to eliminate the corresponding component of the current from the action potential (Fig. 7.6). Toxins of both plant and animal origin have been of particular

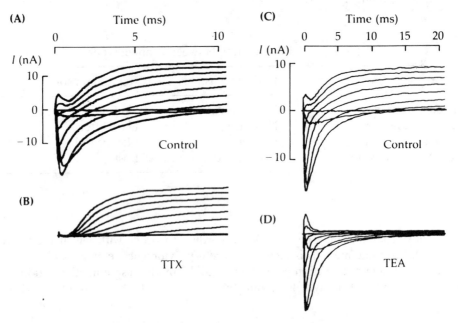

Fig. 7.6 — The specific block of Na^+ and K^+ channels by tetrodotoxin (TTX) and tetra-ethylammonium (TEA) respectively in a node of Ranvier under voltage clamp conditions. The preparation is held at a hyperpolarized membrane potential and is then depolarized to various potentials from $-60\,mV$ to $+60\,mV$ in $15\,mV$ steps either in the absence (control) or in the presence of drug. Reproduced with permission from Hille, B., (1984), *Ionic Channels in Excitable Membranes*, Sinauer Associates, Sunderland, MA.

importance to the classification of ion channels, and synthetic drugs continue to be of major significance as therapeutic agents. Thus, the Ca^{2+} channel antagonists including the clinically available verapamil, nifedipine and diltiazem (Fig. 7.7) are major therapeutic agents in cardiovascular medicine. Drug classification of ion channel type is becoming increasingly important with continued discovery of new channel types with the same primary ion sensitivity, but with different electrophysio-logic and pharmacologic characteristics. Examples of ion channel classification by pharmacologic sensitivity are provided in Table 7.2. However, a complete classifica-tion is provided only from combined electrophysiologic, permeation and pharmaco-logic considerations together with structural data. This is illustrated in Table 7.3 for the currently defined three primary classes of voltage-dependent Ca^{2+} channels [9,10].

7.5   ION CHANNELS AS PHARMACOLOGIC RECEPTORS

Ion channels may be regarded as pharmacologic receptors: they possess, or are linked to, drug binding sites. Drugs acting at these sites may have activator or

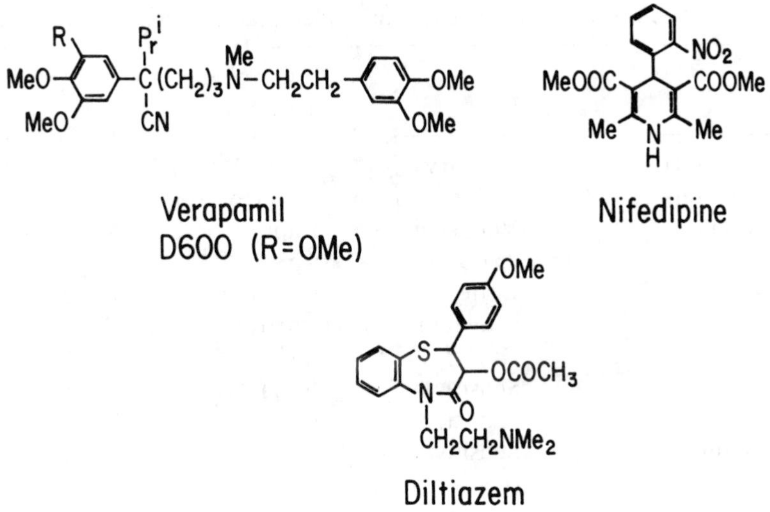

Fig. 7.7 — Structural formulae of drugs active at the L class of voltage-dependent Ca^{2+} channel.

Table 7.2 — Pharmacologic classification of ion channels

Channel type	Pharmacologic agent
Na^+	Tetrodotoxin; saxitoxin and other toxins (Table 7.4); local anesthetics
Ca^{2+}	Phenylalkylamines (verapamil); benzothiazepines (diltiazem); 1,4-dihydropyridines (nifedipine); ω-conotoxin, divalent cations (Table 7.3)
K^+	Quaternary ammonium ions; aminopyridines, quinine, toxins (apamin, dendrotoxin, charybdotoxin); sulfonylureas (Table 7.9)

antagonist properties and these sites are characterized by the existence of specific structure–activity relationships. Ion channels may possess a number of specific and discrete binding sites that are linked both one to the other and to the permeation and gating machinery of the ion channel by a set of, frequently complex, allosteric relationships. These relationships are particularly well illustrated for the voltage-dependent Na^+ channel where five or more discrete binding sites exist for toxins and synthetic agents at which channel function is regulated [11,12]. The several categories of agent include tetrodotoxin and saxitoxin (site 1), the lipid soluble toxins,

Table 7.3 — Properties of plasmalemmal Ca^{2+} channels

	Channel class		
	L	T	N
Activation range, mV	$-10\,mV$	$-70\,mV$	$-30\,mV$
Inactivation range, mV	-60 to $-10\,mV$	-100 to $-60\,mV$	-120 to $-30\,mV$
Inactivation rate	Very slow	Rapid	Moderate
Conductance	25 pS	8 pS	13 pS
Kinetics	Little activation	Brief burst, inactivation	Long burst
Permeation	$Ba^{2+} > Ca^{2+}$	$Ba^{2+} = Ca^{2+}$	$Ba^{2+} > Ca^{2+}$
Cd^{++} sensitivity	Sensitive	Insensitive	Sensitive
1,4-DHP sensitivity	Sensitive	Insensitive	Sensitive
ω-Conotoxin sensitivity	Sensitive? (neurons) Insensitive (muscle)	Insensitive	Sensitive

Data computed from a variety of sources and are not intended to suggest that these properties are singularly characteristic of each channel class.

batrachotoxin, veratridine and grayanotoxins (site 2), the alpha-scorpion toxins and sea anemone toxin (site 3), the beta-scorpion toxins (site 4) and the brevetoxins (site 5). These structurally diverse agents (Fig. 7.8) serve to antagonize or to activate channels either by blocking conductance or by promoting activation/inhibiting inactivation (Table 7.4). The brevetoxins are unique polyether products of the dinoflagellate *Ptychodiscus brevis* whose toxicity underlies the red tides of the Gulf of Mexico [13]. The relative effectiveness of these agents can be used to characterize subtypes of channels [14]. The pharmacologic subdivision of voltage-dependent Na^+ channels is paralleled by molecular biologic studies that indicate the existence of at least three mRNAs in rat brain coding for Na^+ channels [15].

The existence of both activator and antagonist agents active at ion channels raises the question of the existence of endogenous regulators, molecules that would serve as physiologic controllers of the appropriate channel and that are mimicked in function by synthetic agents or by naturally occurring toxins. No unambiguous example of an endogenous ligand active at any channel class has thus far been provided and it is likely that the search will be long and may prove to be negative. However, there has been an intensive search for agents active at the Ca^{2+} channel, reflecting the therapeutic importance of this channel, and putative endogenous species have been indicated [16].

It is anticipated that ion channels, viewed as pharmacologic receptors, should share other properties of these receptors including up- and down-regulation by both homologous and heterologous influences and the alteration of channel number and function associated with disease states and pathologic conditions. Thus, by analogy to other well described receptor systems, chronic channel stimulation and blockade may be associated with down- and up-regulation processes respectively [17]. Since

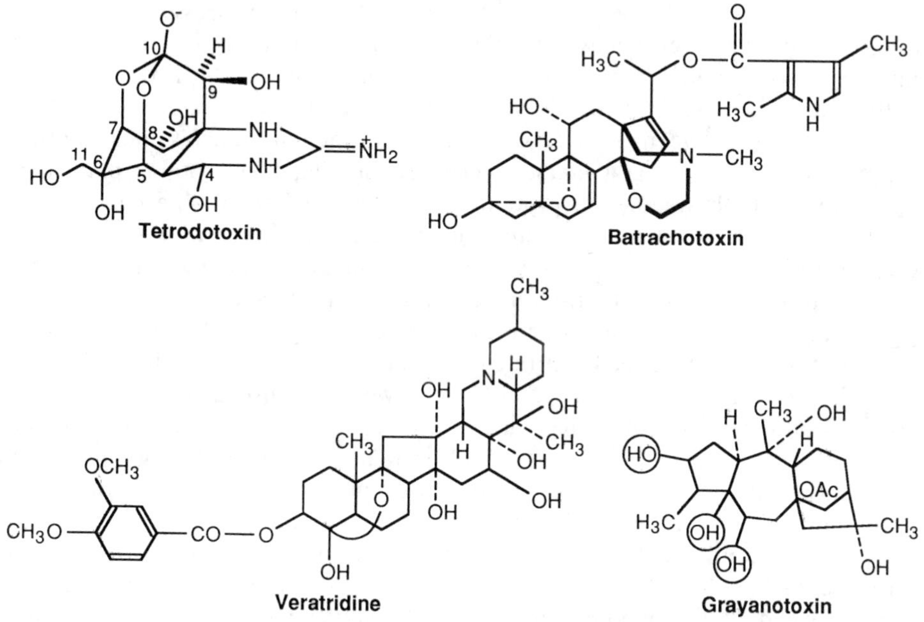

Fig. 7.8 — Structural formulae of drugs active at Na$^+$ channels.

Table 7.4 — Sodium channel toxin binding sites

Site number	Toxins	Pharmacologic effect
I	Tetrodotoxin saxitoxin	Block Na$^+$ permeation
II	Veratridine Batrachotoxin	Prolonged activation
III	Alpha-Scorpion toxins (North Africa) Sea-anemone toxins	Inhibit inactivation
IV	Beta-Scorpion toxins (American)	Shift activation
V	Brevetoxins	Prolonged activation, firing

ion channels are membrane proteins it is expected that the processes of regulation, long-term and short-term, may parallel those seen for other membrane proteins and involve internalization, uncoupling, and phosphorylation events. The regulation of voltage-dependent Ca^{2+} channels is reviewed in section 7.6.

The analogy between pharmacologic receptors and ion channels finds additional support in the roles that guanine nucleotide binding (G) proteins play in the regulation of both systems. G proteins are a family of dissociable heterotrimers composed of alpha-, beta- and gamma-subunits that couple receptor activation and effector response. The alpha-subunit is the GTP ligating component that serves to link receptor and effector [36]. G proteins link receptors and ion channels and, in principle, may do so through biochemical intermediates (c-nuc, IP_3, arachidonic acid metabolites, etc.) or directly through association with the ion channel protein [37,38]. Examples of the first category are well established and include beta-adrenoceptor activation of cardiac Ca^{2+} channels. However, evidence is accumulating that voltage-dependent ion channels can be regulated through G protein interactions that do not involve intermediary events: however, the possibility of an undetermined membrane coupling process remains. Atrial K^+ channels in isolated inside-out membrane patches are activated by a pertussis-toxin-sensitive protein of the G_i class and Ca^{2+} channels are subject to a variety of G protein mediated excitatory and inhibitory processes. G_s may serve to activate cardiac Ca^{2+} channels by a c-AMP independent process and pertussis-toxin-sensitive G_i and G_o proteins may mediate Ca^{2+} channel stimulation in endocrine cells and hormonal inhibition of Ca^{2+} channels in neuronal and endocrine cells. The G protein-channel association represents a new biological interface that may present new opportunities for ion channel modulation.

Drug interactions with ion channels present, however, a number of subtleties and complexities that are not generally shared by other receptors. In particular, the state of an ion channel — resting, open or inactivated — may determine the affinity and/or access of drug to binding sites (Fig. 7.9). Such state-dependent interactions can be demonstrated in a number of ways. Blockade of K^+ channels by intracellularly applied quaternary ammonium ions depends upon channel opening, and blockade can be reversed by inward K^+ current, consistent with blockade of the ion channel by internal occupancy with the quaternary ammonium ion and its expulsion by the inflowing K^+ ions ([1,39]; Fig. 7.10). The interaction of some agents with ion channels may show frequency-dependence whereby the apparent activity increases with increasing frequency of depolarizing stimulus. According to the modulated receptor hypothesis, such agents may bind preferentially to a channel state favored by depolarization and which is accessed by hydrophilic species through an open state of the channel made more available by the elevated frequency of stimulation [40–42]. Such frequency-dependence is exhibited by a number of local anesthetics and underlies their usefulness in some disrhythmic situations since they have a selective action in those situations where an abnormally rapid Na^+ channel activation is occurring. Other agents may exhibit selectivity for channels in states favored by prolonged depolarization. Thus, nifedipine and other 1,4-dihydropyridine Ca^{2+} channel antagonists active at the L class of voltage-dependent Ca^{2+} channels have significantly enhanced affinity for channel states favored by depolarization ([43,44]; reviewed in [45] and [46]). This preferential affinity for the inactivated state (Fig. 7.9)

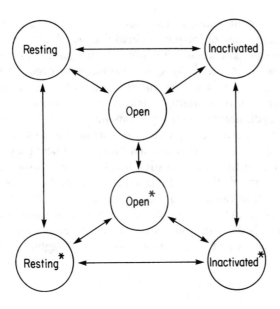

Fig. 7.9 — Schematic representation of ion channel cycling through resting, open and inactivated states. The * represents a state stabilized by drug interaction.

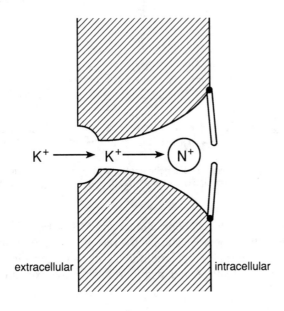

Fig. 7.10— Representation of 'trapping' of intracellularly applied quaternary ammonium ion in the K^+ channel and its displacement by an inwardly directed K^+ current. See text for further details.

is a likely significant contributor to the observed tissue selectivity of these agents since the persistent depolarization present in tonically active vascular smooth muscle will favor action in this tissue relative to other nonstimulated or paced preparations.

Such state-dependent interactions are also likely to occur at ligand-gated ion channels. Excitatory amino acids, primarily L-glutamate and L-aspartate, are the dominant excitatory neurotransmitters in the central nervous system. At least three (and possibly more) different receptor types are involved in the transmission process — the kainate, quisqualate and N-methyl-D-aspartate (NMDA) receptors [47]. The last-mentioned receptors are of particular interest since they exhibit voltage-dependent activation attributed to resting block by Mg^{2+} which is relieved by an appropriate depolarizing stimulus [48]. When activated, the NMDA receptor–channel complex is permeable to Na^+, K^+ and Ca^{2+} ions. It is the permeability to Ca^{2+} that likely underlies the excitotoxic effects of receptor activation in the central nervous system. The NMDA receptor possesses a number of binding sites including a glycine site, occupancy of which potentiates NMDA antagonism (Fig. 7.11). Non-

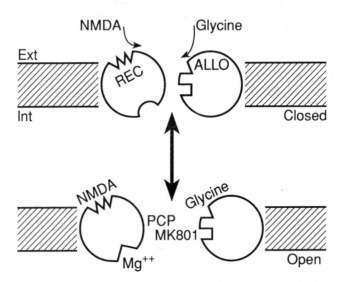

Fig. 7.11 — The NMDA receptor–channel complex depicting the allosteric glycine site, the open state binding of phencyclidine (PCP) and MK 801 and the voltage-dependent interaction of Mg^{2+}.

competitive antagonists such as phencyclidine and MK 801 exhibit use-dependence and bind preferentially to the open state of the receptor–channel complex. Such use-dependence is likely to underlie the potential use of such agents in the prevention or reduction of neuronal damage and death following hypoxia and other noxious stimulants.

7.6 SPECIFIC CHANNEL CLASSES

Although drugs active at Na^+ channels have long been of considerable pharmacologic interest, and some, notably the local anesthetics, of therapeutic interest as antiarrhythmic agents, interest in drug action at ion channels has increased considerably with the advent of the Ca^{2+} channel antagonists, major cardiovascular agents effective at one class of voltage-dependent Ca^{2+} channel. Considerable attention is, however, now being directed at other channel classes, particularly the K^+ channel, where new drug classes are becoming available.

The Ca^{2+} channel antagonists are a heterogeneous group of agents including verapamil, nifedipine and diltiazem (Fig. 7.7) that find major use in the control of angina, hypertension and other peripheral cardiovascular disorders and some cardiac arrhythmias (Table 7.5). Additional uses, both peripheral and central, are

Table 7.5 — Therapeutic uses of Ca^{2+} channel antagonists

Use	Antagonist		
	Verapamil (I)†	Nifedipine (II)	Diltiazem (III)
Angina			
exertional	+ + + ‡	+ + +	+ + +
Prinzmetal's	+ + +	+ + +	+ + +
variant	+ + +	+ +	+ + +
Paroxysmal			
supraventricular			
tachyarrhythmias	+ + +	−	+
Atrial			
fibrillation and			
flutter	+ +	−	+
Hypertension	+ +	+ + +	+
Hypertrophic			
cardiomyopathy	+	−	−
Raynaud's			
phenomenon	+ +	+ +	+ +
Cardioplegia	+	+	+
Cerebral			
vasospasm	−	+	−
(post hemorrhage)			

† Classes I, II and III as defined by the World Health Organization.
‡ Number of plus signs indicates extent of use: + + + , being very common; − , not used.

likely [45]. These agents interact with one subclass of voltage-dependent Ca^{2+} channel (Table 7.3) at sites on a major protein of the oligomeric assembly, the alpha 1 subunit. These sites of interaction are likely to be closely associated with the functional machinery of the channel and are linked allosterically both one to the other and to the channel (Fig. 7.12). Additional discrete binding sites have been indicated for other structural classes ([49]; Fig. 7.13) including the diphenylbutylpi-

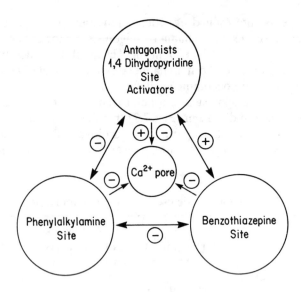

Fig. 7.12 — The arrangement of drug binding sites at the L class of voltage-dependent Ca^{2+} channels. The + and − symbols depict the direction of the allosteric linkages.

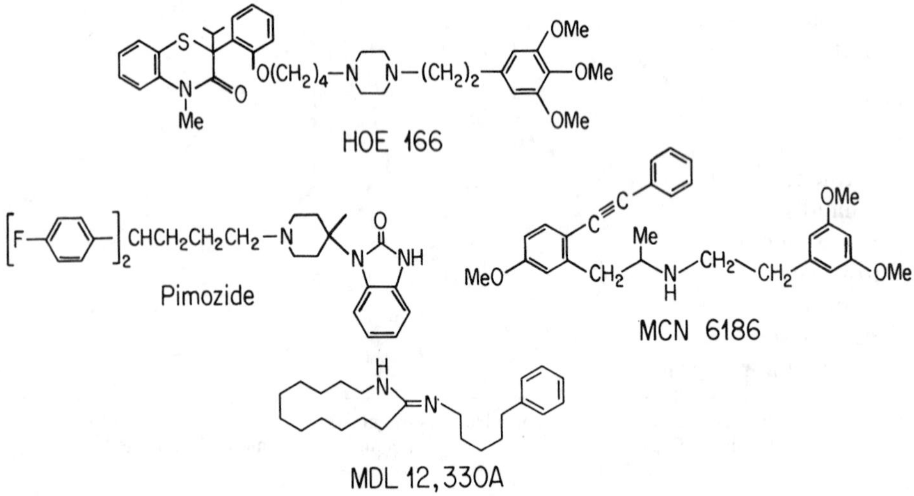

HOE 166

Pimozide

MCN 6186

MDL 12,330A

Fig. 7.13 — Structural formulae of new Ca^{2+} channel ligands.

peridines [50; pimozide, fluspiriline], the benzolactams [51; HOE 166], the indoli-
zines [52; SR 33557] and the lactamides [53; MDL 12,330]:

Consistent with a view of the Ca^{2+} channel as a pharmacologic receptor, each of
the binding sites for ligands is described in terms of structure–activity relationships
[45,46]. These have been most comprehensively defined for the 1,4-dihydropyridines
whose structure embraces both potent antagonist and activator molecules (Fig.
7.14). The binding site exerts a remarkable stereochemical discrimination whereby

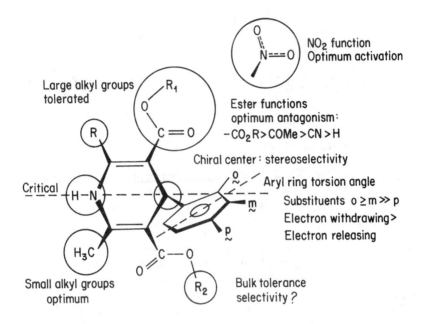

Fig. 7.14 — The general structural requirements for activity in the 1,4-dihydropyridines.

one enantiomer may function as an antagonist and the other as an activator (Fig.
7.15). The general structural requirements for activator and antagonist activities in
the 1,4-dihydropyridines are outlined in Fig. 7.14; several efforts have attempted to
define quantitatively the relationships between structure and pharmacologic activity.
Thus, in a series of analogs of nifedipine carrying different phenyl ring substituents,
activity has been described by [54]

$$\log 1/IC_{50} = 0.62\pi + 1.96\sigma\,m - 0.44\,\text{Lmeta} - 3.26\,\text{B1para} - 1.51\,\text{Lmeta}' + 14.23$$

$$n = 46, \quad r = 0.90, \quad s = 0.67, \quad F = 33.93$$

where $\sigma\,m$ is the electronic parameter, π a hydrophobicity parmeter and L and B1
Verloop steric parameters. The stereochemical requirements for activity have been

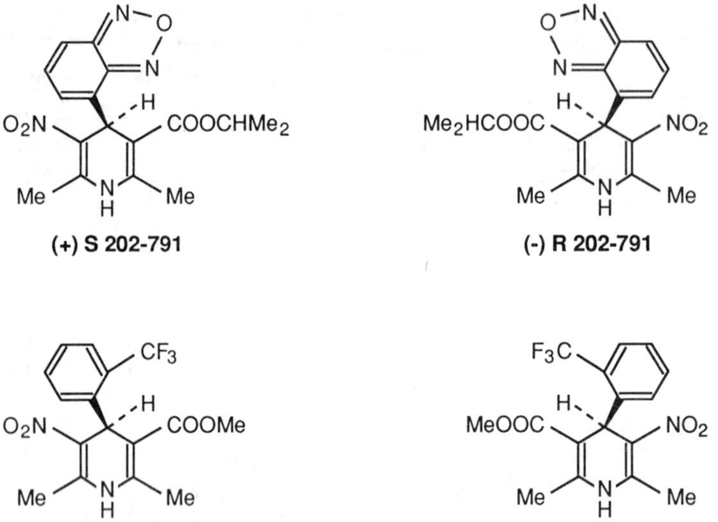

Fig. 7.15 — Structural formulae of enantiomeric 1,4-dihydropyridine activator–antagonist pairs.

examined through solid-state structures, solution conformations and the synthesis of rigid analogs (reviewed in [45,46]). There is general agreement that the steric requirements for activity include a flattened-boat conformation for the 1,4-dihydro-pyridine ring, a pseudoaxial aryl ring oriented orthogonally to the 1,4-dihydropyri-dine ring with the aryl substituents oriented away from the 1,4-dihydropyridine ring. The planarity of the 1,4-dihydropyridine ring correlates directly with the activity of these agents and with the forward orientation of the aryl ring. The latter observation is consistent with a binding model in which the aryl ring is inserted into a nonpolar cleft with stabilizing H-bonding interactions being made with the keto-oxygen atoms of the ester groups and with the NH group of the 1,4-dihydropyridine ring [55]. However, those structural features that discriminate activator and antagonist properties have yet to be determined unambiguously, although clearly the stereo-chemistry of the C-3 and C-5 ester and nitro groups is of considerable importance (Fig. 7.15).

The ability to use a variety of radioligands to quantitate the L type of Ca^{2+} channel has been of critical significance to both the elucidation of structure–activity relationships and the establishment of mechanisms of action (reviewed in [45,46]). The early established correlations between pharmacologic and radioligand binding affinities showed, consistent with both pharmacologic and therapeutic observations, that the 1,4-dihydropyridines exhibit potent smooth muscle relaxant effects in excellent accord with their radioligand binding activities, and that these correlations were weaker or absent in cardiac and neuronal preparations. These widely divergent pharmacologic activities are, however, associated with similar or identical binding affinities apparently independent of the tissue. It is likely that this selectivity of action has a significant origin in the voltage-dependent binding behavior of the 1,4-dihydropyridine antagonists: affinity increases with decreasing membrane potential consistent with a preferential interaction with the inactivated state of the channel [43–46]. In contrast, verapamil and diltiazem exhibit frequency-dependence of action whereby their affinity increases with increasing frequency of stimulation [42]. This process underlies their antiarrhythmic actions and differentiates these agents from the 1,4-dihydropyridines although all of the agents interact with the same protein of the L channel. These differential interactions may well represent different modes of access by hydrophilic and hydrophobic ligands to the inactivated state of the channel.

There are important implications to this concept of state-dependent interactions for the effective interpretation of structure–activity data. The selective interaction of drugs with the resting, open or inactivated states of the channel may demonstrate the operation of qualitatively and quantitatively different structure–activity relationships according to channel state. Thus the 1,4-dihydropyridine antagonists exhibit strong voltage-dependent interactions whereas the activators are only weakly voltage-dependent ([46,56]; Fig. 7.16, Table 7.6): this differential dependence

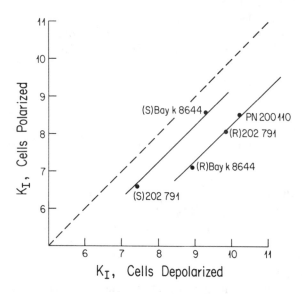

Fig. 7.16 — Correlation between binding affinities for a series of 1,4-dihydropyridines in polarized and depolarized neonatal rat ventricular myocytes. Data from [56].

presumably reflects the relative discrimination by antagonists and activator ligands for the several channel states.

Ca^{2+} channels show further analogy to pharmacologic receptors since they are regulated under both homologous and heterologous conditions ([17]; Table 7.7).

Table 7.6 — Voltage-dependent interactions of 1,4-dihydropyridines in cardiac cells [56]

	K_D $\times 10^{-9}$ M	B_{max} fmol/mg	K_D $\times 10^{-9}$ M	B_{max} fmol/mg
	Polarized		Depolarized	
[^{3}H]PN 200 110	3.57	50.1	0.06	47.2
[^{3}H]Bay K 8644	5.15	63.1	5.56	62.3

Thus, they exhibit both up- and down-regulation in response to chronic activation and drug exposure to hormone levels and to pathologic influences including alcohol, ischemia and lead. Ca^{2+} channel changes are associated with a number of discrete pathologic states including an elevation in human hypertrophic obstructive cardio-myopathy and an absence of 1,4-dihydropyridine binding sites and functional channels in embryonic muscular dysgenesis. It is highly probable that other defects associated with Ca^{2+} channel numbers and functions will also be recognized to be components of specific disease states.

Although the role of K^+ channels as a major determinant of membrane potential and cellular excitability is well established, they have not until recently been seen as major targets for therapeutic drug action. In part this has been due to the lack of specific high-affinity ligands, a situation in marked contrast to that for Na^+ and Ca^{2+} channels [57,58]. However, the availability of toxins, including apamin, dendrotox-ins and charybdotoxin, has greatly facilitated the pharmacologic and electrophysio-logic analyses of K^+ channels [59]. Consequently, some existing drugs have been characterized as K^+ channel ligands and a more rational development of new agents is likely. A complete classification of K^+ channels is not available and it is apparent from structural studies (section 7.7) that a large number of subtypes exist. A provisional classification of major classes of K^+ channels is presented in Table 7.8. According to their electrophysiologic characteristics and cellular distribution, these K^+ channels play a number of important roles in controlling cell excitability. Thus the delayed rectifier channel underlies repolarization and is an important determi-nant of action potential duration. Ca^{2+}-activated K^+ channels, which are of several different types, are involved in the regulation of Ca^{2+} entry, contribute to after-hyperpolarizations and are likely to underlie oscillatory firing patterns. There are a large number of neurotransmitter and second-messenger-gated K^+ channels. Thus the 'M' channel is turned off by acetylcholine action at muscarinic receptors and so contributes to the excitation mediated through these receptors. ATP-dependent channels are regulated by the intracellular concentrations of ATP and other adenine nucleotides which serve as channel blockers [60]. Metabolism of the major insulin secretagogues, glucose and amino acids, elevates cellular ATP levels to control K^+ channel activity. When ATP levels rise, the cell is depolarized to permit excitation, Ca^{2+} entry and insulin release, and when ATP levels fall, the cell is hyperpolarized and Ca^{2+} entry is prevented or reduced (Fig. 7.17).

Table 7.7 — Regulation of Ca^{2+} channels [17]

Treatment/condition	Species	Radioligand/tissue	Effects K_d	B_{max}	Other	Ref.
A. Homologous regulation:						
Chronic drug action:						
Oral nitrendipine, verapamil, diltiazem (28 day)	Mouse	Nitrendipine Brain	nc	↓ 40% (not diltiazem)	$^{45}Ca^{2+}$ uptake decreased	[18]
IV nifedipine (20 day)	Rat	Nitrendipine				
		Heart	nc	↓ 49%	↓ 62% β-rec	[19]
		Brain	nc	↓ 23%	↓ 65% β-rec	
Nifedipine	PC12	PN 200 110	nc	↑ 29% nifedipine		[20]
S Bay K 8644	PC12			↓ 24% Bay K 8644		
Chronic activation:						
K^+ depolarization (4 day)	PC12	Nitrendipine		↓ 50%	↓ Ca^{2+} influx	[21]
K^+ depolarization (4 day)	Chick retina	PN 200 110		↓ 40%	↓ Ca^{2+} influx	[17]
B. Heterologous regulation:						
Isoproterenol (10 day)	Rat	Nitrendipine/heart	nc	nc		[19]
Atropine (23 day)	Rat	Nimodipine/brain	nc	nc		
DFP (14 day)	Rat	Nimodipine/brain	nc	nc		
Phenylephrine (6 day)	Rat	Nitrendipine/heart	nc	↓ 32%	↓ 39% α-rec	[22]
Morphine	Mouse	Nitrendipine/brain	nc	↑ 60%		[23]
C. Other chronic regulation:						
Ethanol	Rat	Nimodipine/brain	nc	↑ 50%		
Lead	Rat	Nitrendipine/brain	nc	↑ 48%		[25]
NaCl (21 day)	Rat					
	(SHR/SP)	Nitrendipine/heart	nc	↑ 65%	↑ bp	[26]
D. Hormone regulation:						
Insulin (21 day)	Human	PN 200 110/muscle	nc	↑ 250%		[27]
Thyroid:	Rat	Nitrendipine/heart				
hyperthyroid (5 day)			nc	↓ 42%	↑ 36% β-rec	[28]
hypothyroid (PYU)			nc	↑ 26%	↓ 23% β-rec	
Estrogen (4 day)	Rat	Nitrendipine/uterus	nc	↑ 96%	↑ 45 Ca^{2+}	[29]
E. Disease states:						
Experimental:						
Hypertension	Rat, SHR	Nitrendipine/heart (24 week)	↑ 55%	↑ 43%		[30]
Hypertension	Rat, SHR (4–15 weeks)	Nitrendipine/brain	nc	↑ 21–40% (striatum, thalamus, hippocampus)		[31]
Ischemia 60 min hypoxia	Rat	Nitrendipine/heart	nc	↓ 14%		[32]
Ischemia bilateral ligation	Gerbil	Nitrendipine/brain (frontal cortex)	↓ 48%	↓ 26%		[33]
Muscular dysgenesis	Mouse	Nitrendipine/ skeletal muscle	absent			[34]
Clinical:						
Cardiomyopathy	Human	PN 200 110	nc	↑ 25%	nc β-rec nc Na^+ chan	[35]

nc = no change. rec = receptor. chan = channel. SHR = spontaneously hypertensive rat.

Table 7.8 — Provisional classification of K^+ channels [1,57–61]

Channel type	Characteristics	Pharmacology	Function
I. Voltage-dependent:			
Delayed rectifier (outward)	Rapidly activated by depolarization: slowly inactivating	Blocked by TEA, Cs^+, Ba^{2+}, quinine tetracaine, amino pyridines (weak)	Repolarization and action potential duration
Transient outward	Fast, transient activated by depolarization from a hyperpolarizing step	Aminopyridines (potent): TEA (weak)	Regulation of firing rate
II. Ca^{2+}-activated:			
regulation of Ca^{2+}	Several different conductances. Main types small and large	Blocked by apamin (small): TEA and charybdotoxin (large)	Entry: after hyperpolarization: regulation of firing rate
III. Receptor-regulated:			
M current	Activated by AcCh above $-60\,mV$	TEA (weak)	Facilitate APs: initiate EPSPs
ATP regulated	ATP reduces channel opening	Tolbutamide and sulfonylureas: diazoxide (activates)	Control membrane potential: insulin release

Two recent developments in K^+ channel ligands have been of particular interest. The hypoglycemic sulfonylureas, including tolbutamide, glibenclamide and glipizide, are antagonists of the ATP-dependent K^+ channel [60,61]. An excellent correlation exists between the binding affinities of these agents and their potencies as insulin secretagogues indicating that the sulfonylurea receptor is a component of or is associated with ATP-dependent K^+ channels [62]. Although the physiologic role of this class of K^+ channel is best understood for pancreatic beta-cells, the channels are widely distributed in other tissues including neurons and cardiac cells: additional roles for these channels are thus likely although speculative at the present time. Such roles may include shortening of the action potential duration during anoxia when ATP levels fall with associated preservation of ATP levels and the lowering of skeletal muscle excitability during extreme fatigue. Additionally, the K^+ release will serve to vasodilate, thus potentially coupling blood flow and energy demands. However, the K^+ loss from cardiac cells through these channels may underlie the occurrence of ventricular fibrillation subsequent to myocardial infarction.

The discovery of channel activators represents a second major advance in K^+ channel ligands. A group of agents, including the benzopyran BRL 34915 (cromokalim), the cyanoguanidine pinacidil and the nicotinamide derivative nicorandil (Fig. 7.18), all possess smooth muscle relaxant activity, increase K^+ or Rb^+ efflux and hyperpolarize smooth muscle membranes [57,63,64]. Additionally, nicorandil has vasodilating activity associated with the organic nitrates and functioning through guanylate cyclase activation. Other members of this class of agent may include the vasodilators diazoxide and minoxidil (as the sulfate). Minoxidil, pinacidil and diazoxide all possess the side-effect of hypertrichosis (excess hair growth), but the relationship of this effect to K^+ channel opening activity remains to be established. The type of K^+ channel(s) activated by these agents remains to be defined: it is

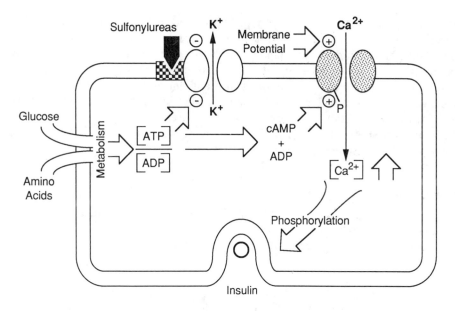

Fig. 7.17 — The role of Ca^{2+} channels and ATP-dependent K^+ channels in the control of insulin release from pancreatic beta cells. Depicted are K^+ channels with receptor sites for ATP (intracellular) and the sulfonylureas (extracellular) and voltage-dependent Ca^{2+} channels. Modulation of the K^+ channels by the ATP/ADP ratio and by the sulfonylureas alters the membrane potential and controls the activity of the Ca^{2+} channels. Reproduced with permission from Boyd [61].

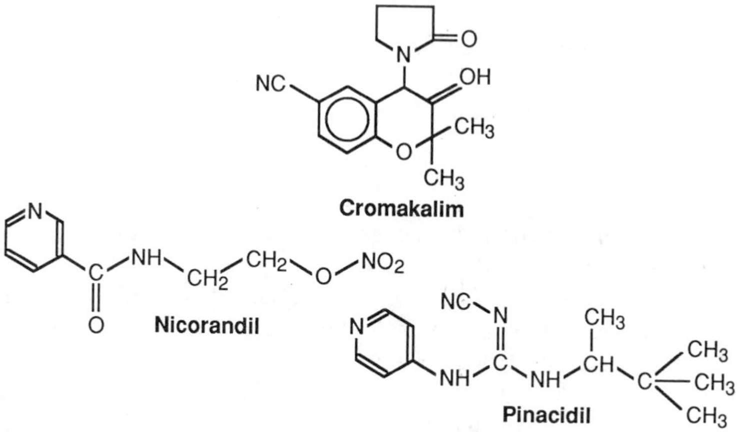

Cromakalim

Nicorandil

Pinacidil

Fig. 7.18 — Chemical formulae of K^+ channel activators.

possible that more than one channel type is involved or that these agents activate different classes of K^+ channel. A limited amount of evidence suggests the involvement of an ATP-dependent K^+ channel [65,66]. The actual and potential therapeutic applications of these agents are of substantial interest. Nicorandil and pinacidil are available in Japan and Denmark as anti-anginal and antihypertensive drugs respectively, and cromokalim is under active investigation as an antihypertensive agent. However, additional areas of application are clearly attractive, including asthma and other hyperreactivity disorders of nonvascular smooth muscle and peripheral vascular ischemic diseases.

7.7 ION CHANNEL STRUCTURES AND FUNCTION

The application of molecular biological approaches has permitted the elucidation of the sequences of protein components of a number of ion channel species, both ligand-and voltage-gated (Table 7.9), and the generation of structural and functional

Table 7.9 — Structures and sequences of voltage-gated and ligand-gated ion channels

Channel type	Reference
Voltage-gated:	
Sodium	[15,67,68]
Calcium	[69,70]
Potassium	[71,72]
Ligand-gated:	
Acetylcholine (nicotinic)	[73,74]
γ-Aminobutyric acid	[75,76]
Glycine	[77,78]

maps to describe their functions in the generation and regulation of membrane excitability (reviewed in [76,78–81]).

Considerable homology exists between the sequences and proposed transmembrane arrangements of the voltage-dependent Na^+, Ca^{2+} and K^+ channels [81,82]. This homology is consistent with evolution from a common ancestral ion channel protein and indicative of potential cross-interaction between drug categories putatively selective for specific channel types [46]. Each of the channel types consists of a major peptide that appears to contain or express the dominant channel activity. However, each of these channel types also possesses unique characteristics.

Na^+ channels consist of alpha (260 kDa), beta 1 (36–38 kDa) and beta 2 (33 kDa) subunits, differentially expressed according to species and tissue type. It is likely that the alpha subunit is sufficient to express channel activity and that it is associated in tissue-dependent fashion with the beta subunits which are likely to contribute to the structural integrity of the channel complex. Eel electroplax Na⁺ channels have alpha subunits, skeletal muscle channels have alpha and beta 1 subunits and brain Na⁺ channels have alpha, beta 1 and beta 2 subunits. The beta 2 subunit is attached to the alpha subunit via a disulfide bridge (Fig. 7.19). Sodium

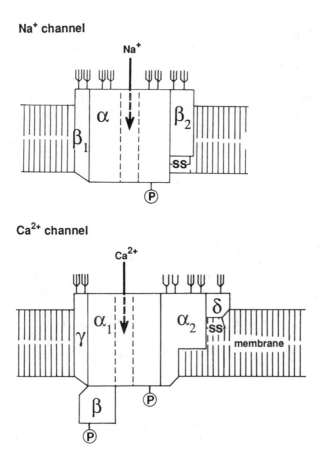

Fig. 7.19 — Proposed subunit organizations of the Na⁺ and Ca²⁺ channels. Reproduced with permission from Catterall [81]; copyright 1988 by the AAAS.

channels exhibit distinctive toxin pharmacology [14], and several distinct alpha subunits exist that are highly homologous one to the other; rat brain has three mRNAs defining channel subtypes I, II and III that are some 200 residues longer (2008 to 2012 residues) than the alpha protein from electroplax with the insert being between the first two homologous domains [14,15,83].

The L-type of voltage-dependent Ca²⁺ channel also possesses a number of subunits (Table 7.10; reviewed in [81,84]). The alpha 1 subunit from skeletal muscle

Table 7.10 — Characteristics of subunits of voltage-dependent Ca^{2+} channels/sensors of skeletal muscle†

Property	Subunit number				
	Alpha 1	Alpha 2	Beta	Gamma	Delta
Size kDa:	175	170	50	33	24–32
(approximate)		$(140 + 30)$			
1,4-DHP binding site	Yes	No	No	No	
Aryalkylamine binding site	Yes	No			
Glycosylation	Light?	Heavy	No	Yes	
Disulfide linked	No	Yes	No	No	Yes
Phosphorylation	Yes	No?	Yes	No	No
Transmembrane	Yes	No?	No	No?	No?
Effect of antibodies on subunits	Inh.	—	Act.	Inh.	—

†The corresponding subunits from other tissues may not be identical. The alpha 1 subunit from cardiac muscle has a higher MW, 195 kDa, and is immunologically different.

(2005 residues) shows considerable homology to rat brain Na^+ channel type II with 29% sequence identity and 55% similarity based on conservative substitution. The alpha 2 protein has also been sequenced (1106 residues) and is unique in being dominantly hydrophilic and heavily glycosylated [85]. The proposed structural assembly of the Ca^{2+} channel subunits is shown in Fig. 7.19. Analogously to the Na^+ channel, the alpha 1 subunit of the Ca^{2+} channel is considered from expression experiments to be sufficient for the generation of channel activity. It is likely that a number of different Ca^{2+} channel classes exist and that these contain different alpha 1 subunits.

In contrast to the voltage-dependent Na^+ and Ca^{2+} channels, the K^+ channel structures thus far available consist of only a single peptide. Additionally, the single peptides are of small size, approximately 70 kDa, with some 500–700 residues, about one quarter the size of the major proteins of the Na^+ and Ca^{2+} channels. Our knowledge of the structures of K^+ channels derives heavily from work on Drosophila where X-linked Shaker mutations linked to behavioral variations have been associated with the A type of K^+ channel [71,72,80–82]. Subsequent work has shown a remarkable diversity of K^+ channel types, quite consistent with earlier electrophysiologic evidence, derived from both an extended gene family and alternate splicing processes.

Despite the differences in channel ionic selectivity, in pharmacologic sensitivity and in size the substantial sequence homologies between the Na^+, Ca^{2+} and K^+ channels suggest common organizational and functional determinants. A very similar membrane topology is indicated in Fig. 7.20 which depicts the Na^+ and Ca^{2+} channels as composed of four homologous domains and the K^+ channel as having one domain. Each domain is depicted as composed of six transmembrane helices (some suggested arrangements indicate seven or eight transmembrane helices), S1 through S6. Major differences between the Na^+ and Ca^{2+} channels are depicted as

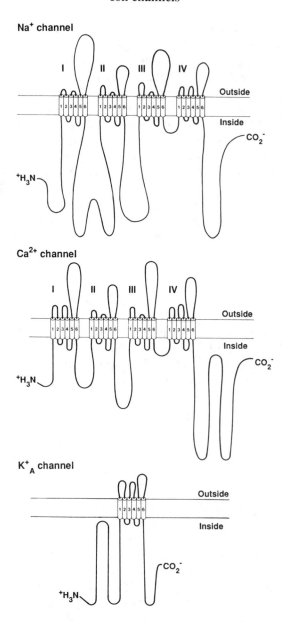

Fig. 7.20 — Proposed transmembrane organization of the principal subunits of the Na^+, Ca^{2+} and A-current K^+ channels. The models are from rat brain Na^+, skeletal muscle Ca^{2+} and *Drosophila* K^+ channels. Reproduced with permission from Catterall [81]; copyright 1988 by the AAAS.

the shortened cytoplasmic loop in the Ca^{2+} channel between domains I and II and the extended carboxy terminal cytoplasmic loop in this protein. The K^+ channel may be viewed as a monomeric species whereas the Na^+ and Ca^{2+} channels are tetrameric structures. If functional K^+ channels are formed by the oligomerization of subunits, then through the existence of a gene family, of multiple splicing and of both homo- and hetero-association of subunits, the number of different types of K^+ channel can be exceedingly large and the properties correspondingly diverse.

Functional correlates are now being associated with the structural features of the voltage-dependent channels. The drug binding sites for both Na^+ and Ca^{2+} channels are associated with the homologous alpha and alpha 1 subunits respectively. A common component of all three channel types is represented by the highly conserved S4 region which consists of repeated motifs of a positively charged amino acid (usually arginine) followed by two hydrophobic residues. It is suggested that this may represent the voltage sensor region and that its 'helical sliding' under conditions of changing membrane potential is responsible for the observed transfer of gating charges underlying the voltage-dependent channel activation processes. Drug binding sites are now being localized to discrete protein regions. The binding site for alpha-scorpion toxins (binding site 3, Table 7.4) is associated with domain I of the Na^+ channel between residues 335 and 378 in the extracellular loop between transmembrane helices S5 and S6 [86]. Additionally, antibodies directed against the highly conserved intracellular segment linking domains III and IV slow inactivation, and antibodies directed against the S4 segment of domain I accelerate inactivation and shift voltage dependence to more positive membrane potentials [87,88]. General confirmation of these conclusions derives from *in vitro* mutagenesis [89]. Neutralization or inversion of the charges of the S4 region of the first domain reduces the potential dependence of activation. Expression of only the first three homologous domains produces a nonfunctional channel, but coexpression of this sequence with repeat 4 produces a channel that does not inactivate.

Ligand-gated ion channels (Table 7.9) also show substantial homology and are likely to belong to another superfamily of ion channels including the nicotinic acetylcholine, the $GABA_A$ and the glycine receptors. The nicotinic acetylcholine receptor is made up of a number of subunits, four distinct types in muscle but only two in brain, that are very similar one to the other and all have a very similar pattern of alternating hydrophilic and hydrophobic stretches. Four domains of some 20 hydrophobic amino acids are believed to constitute the membrane spanning regions of each subunit. The alpha subunits of the nicotinic acetylcholine receptor (the acetylcholine binding subunit), the alpha and beta subunits of the $GABA_A$ receptor and a subunit of the glycine receptor all show significant homology, 37 to 59% [76]. All of these subunits have the same pattern of four transmembrane domains, which is illustrated in Fig. 7.21 for the alpha, beta subunit pair of the $GABA_A$ receptor. These homologies are likely to underlie observations that although these receptor–channel systems recognize different physiological transmitters, they do show some crossover specificity among drugs [90]. Although expression of the alpha- and beta-subunits of the $GABA_A$ receptor generates much of the functionality of the system, the benzodiazepine binding site is associated with a third subunit which has some 40% homology to the other subunits, particularly in the four transmembrane domains [91].

Although the voltage-gated and the ligand-gated channels described here belong to two different channel families, it is of interest to note how both are composed of

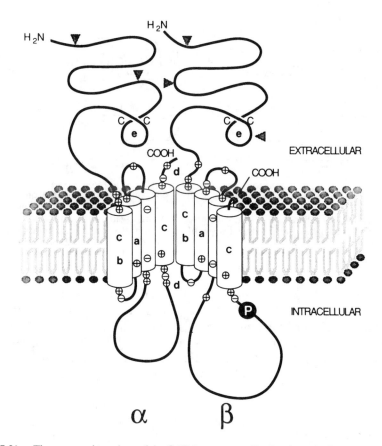

Fig. 7.21 — The proposed topology of the GABA$_A$ receptor. Depicted are the four transmembrane helices of each of the alpha- and beta-subunits. Potential glycosylation sites are indicated by triangles, a phosphorylation site (beta-subunit) by P, features common to the glycine structure by letters a through e and charged residues within or close to the transmembrane helices by + and − sign. Reproduced from Schofield *et al.* [75]; *Nature*, **328**. 221. Copyright © 1987 Macmillan Magazines Ltd.

homologous domains or homologous subunits (Fig. 7.22). This may well indicate that these two channel types evolved from a common ancestral transport protein.

7.8   SUMMARY

The past several years have seen major advances in our understanding of ion channel structure and function. An important role has been played by drugs active at Ca^{2+} channels, for these agents have fueled the simultaneous therapeutic and basic development of a major new therapeutic category of agents. Simultaneous developments in electrophysiologic and molecular biologic techniques have permitted the analysis of channel function at the molecular level and have enabled a significantly

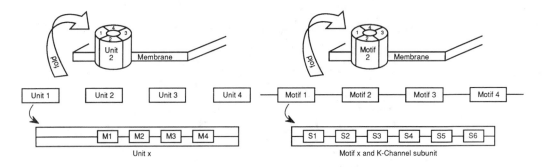

Fig. 7.22 — Comparison of organizational features of ligand- and voltage-gated ion channels. (a) Ligand-gated channels are composed of two or more distinct subunits and each unit has four hydrophobic transmembrane helices (M1–M4). (b) Voltage-gated channels (Na$^+$ and Ca^{2+}) are composed of four similar domains (motifs 1–4) each of which have 6 transmembrane helices. K$^+$ channels have a single motif with the same structure, Reproduced from Stevens [79]; *Nature*, **328**, 198. Copyright © 1987 Macmillan Magazines Ltd.

more sophisticated analysis of drug–channel interactions to be obtained. Ion channels, like pharmacologic receptors, appear to be members of superfamilies, and the time is appropriate for evolutionary speculations on the developmental pathways of ion channels. The future appears to be exceedingly bright for new drug development directed at ion channels. New classes and subclasses of channels are being uncovered and the concepts of state-dependent interactions lend new subtlety to the potential modes of drug interactions.

Natural toxins have played a major role in our generating the current knowledge of ion channel structure and function. Although recent therapeutic developments, particularly for the Ca^{2+} channel, have focussed principally on synthetic ligands, it is likely that there is still a considerable future for the role of toxins in the discovery of new channel classes. Toxins from the *Conus* genus of molluscs have proved to be of value in defining Na$^+$ and particularly Ca^{2+} channels [92,93]. The ω-conotoxins GVIA (ωCgTX) and MVIIA (ωCmTX; Fig. 7.23) define neuronal Ca^{2+} channels involved in neurotransmitter release. There are no synthetic ligands that are both potent and specific for N channels. The ω-toxin sensitive channels are of the N category, but the toxins may also block neuronal, but not muscle L-type channels. It is possible that at least two classes of N channels exist that may be distinguished by ωCgTX and ωCmTX, and in mammalian species it has been suggested that the release of inhibitory transmitters may be more sensitive to these toxins [93].

Spider venoms are now proving to be valuable sources of toxins active at a variety of channel types [94]. From the funnel-web spider *Agelenopsis aperta* come acyl-polyamine toxins (alpha-agatoxins) that block the post synaptic glutamate receptor–channel complex and a group of μ-agatoxin peptides (36–38 residues) that cause repetitive firing at presynaptic terminals [95]. The alpha-agatoxins appear to be very similar to toxins isolated from the North American spider *Argiope lobata* ([94]; Fig. 7.23). The funnel-web spider also yields ω-Aga-I, a polypeptide of approximate mass 7.5 kDa, a presynaptic calcium channel antagonist which appears to block neuronal Ca^{2+} channels in both vertebrates and invertebrates [96].

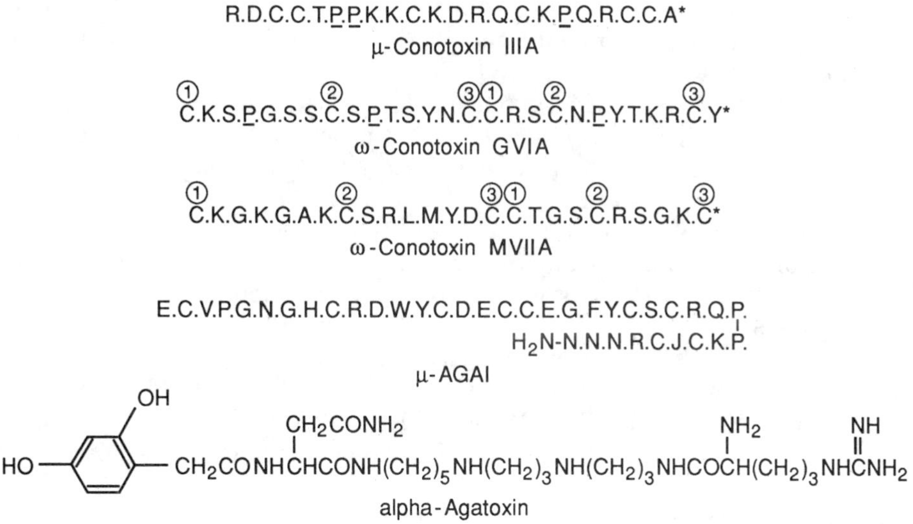

R.D.C.C.T.P̱.P̱.K.K.C.K.D.R.Q.C.K.P̱.Q.R.C.C.A*
μ-Conotoxin IIIA

①   ②   ③①   ②   ③
C.K.S.P̱.G.S.S.C.S.P̱.T.S.Y.N.C.C.R.S.C.N.P̱.Y.T.K.R.C.Y*
ω-Conotoxin GVIA

①   ②   ③①   ②   ③
C.K.G.K.G.A.K.C.S.R.L.M.Y.D.C.C.T.G.S.C.R.S.G.K.C*
ω-Conotoxin MVIIA

E.C.V.P.G.N.G.H.C.R.D.W.Y.C.D.E.C.C.E.G.F.Y.C.S.C.R.Q.P̱.
H₂N-N.N.N.R.C.J.C.K.P̱.

μ-AGAI

alpha-Agatoxin

Fig. 7.23 — Mollusc and scorpion toxins active at Na⁺ and Ca²⁺ channels. μ-Conotoxin IIIa is active at Na⁺ channels, the ω-conotoxins at Ca²⁺ channels, the μ-AGA I toxin at Na⁺ channels and the alpha-agatoxin at Ca²⁺ channels. The conotoxins are derived from *Conus* molluscs and the agatoxins from spider venom (see text for further details). The single letter amino acid code is used where P- is hydroxyproline and * is an amidated carboxy terminal. The circled numbers in the conotoxins represent the disulfide bridges.

It is likely that new clues derived from the continued study of these and related toxins will prove to be helpful in defining not only new classes of ion channels but also of new chemical entities that will have significant therapeutic application.

REFERENCES

[1] Hille, B. (1984). *Ionic Channel of Excitable Membranes*. Sinauer Associates, Sunderland, MA.

[2] Sakman, B. & Neher, E. (eds.) (1983). *Single Channel Recording*. Plenum Press, New York.

[3] Miller, C. (ed.) (1986). *Ion Channel Reconstitution*. Plenum Press, New York.

[4] Agnew, W. S., Claudio, T., & Sigworth, F. (eds) (1988). *Molecular Biology of Ion Channels. Vol. 33. Current Topics in Membranes and Transport*. Academic Press, San Diego, CA.

[5] Eisenman, G. & Dani, J. A. (1987). An introduction to molecular architecture and permeability of ion channels. *Annu. Rev. Biophys. Biophys. Chem.* **16**, 205.

[6] Tsien, R. W., Hess, P., McCleskey, E. W., & Rosenberg, R. L. (1987). Calcium channels: mechanisms of selectivity, permeation and block. *Annu. Rev. Biophys. Biophys. Chem.* **16**, 265.

[7] Kameyama, M., Hescheler, J., Hofmann, F., & Trautwein, W. (1986). Modulation of Ca current during the phosphorylation cycle in the guinea pig heart. *Pflug. Arch.* **407**, 123.

[8] Triggle, D. J. (1990). Drugs acting on ion channels and membranes. Chapter 14. In: C. Hansch, J. C. Emmett, P. D. Kennewell, C. A. Ramsden, P. G. Sammes, & J. B. Taylor (eds) *Comprehensive Medicinal Chemistry*. Pergamon Press, Oxford, England.

[9] McCleskey, E. W., Fox, A. P., Feldman, D., & Tsien, R. W. (1986). Different types of calcium channel. *J. Exp. Biol.* **124**, 177.

[10] Bean, B. P. (1989). Classes of calcium channels in vertebrate cells. *Annu. Rev. Physiol.* **51**, 367.

[11] Catterall, W. (1980). Neurotoxins that act on voltage-sensitive sodium channels in excitable membranes. *Annu. Rev. Pharmacol. Toxicol.* **20**, 15.

[12] Strichartz, G., Rando, T., & Wang, G. K. (1987). An integrated view of the molecular toxicology of sodium channel gating in excitable cells. *Annu. Rev. Neurosci.* **10**, 237.

[13] Baden, D. G. (1989). Brevetoxins: unique polyether dinoflagellate toxins. *FASEB J.* **3**, 1807.

[14] Trimmer, J. S. & Agnew, W. S. (1989). Molecular diversity of voltage-sensitive Na^+ channels. *Annu. Rev. Physiol.* **51**, 401.

[15] Noda, M., Ikeda, T. Kayano, T., Suzuki, H., Takeshima, H., Kurasaki, M., Takahashi, H., & Numa, S. (1986). Existence of distinct sodium channel messenger RNAs in rat brain. *Nature* **320**, 188.

[16] Triggle, D. J. (1988). Endogenous ligands for the calcium channel: myths and realities. In: M. Morad, W. Nayler, S. Kazda, & M. Schramm (eds). *Calcium Channel: Structure, Function and Implications*. Springer-Verlag, Berlin, p. 549.

[17] Ferrante, J. & Triggle, D. J. (1989). Drug- and disease-induced regulation of voltage-dependent calcium channels. Submitted to *Pharmacol. Rev.*

[18] Panza, G., Grebb, J. A., Sanna, E., Wright, A. G., & Hanbauer, I. (1985). Evidence for down-regulation of [³H]nitrendipine recognition sites in mouse brain after long term treatment with nifedipine or verapamil. *Neuropharmacology* **24**, 1113.

[19] Genego, P., Skattebol, A., Moran, J. F., Gallant, S., Hawthorn, M., & Triggle, D. J. (1988). Regulation by chronic administration of neuronal and cardiac calcium channel, beta-adrenoceptor and muscarinic receptor levels. *Biochem. Pharmacol.* **37**, 627.

[20] Skattebol, A., Brown, A. M., & Triggle, D. J. (1989). Homologous regulation of voltage-dependent calcium channels by 1,4-dihydropyridines. *Biochem. Biophys. Res. Comm.* **160**, 929.

[21] DeLorme, E. M., Rabe, C. S., & McGee, R. (1988). Regulation of the number of functional voltage-dependent Ca^{2+} channels on PC12 cells by chronic changes in membrane potential. *J. Pharmacol. Exp. Ther.* **244**, 838.

[22] Gengo, P., Bowling, N., Wyss, V. L., & Hayes, J. S. (1988). Effects of prolonged phenylephrine infusion on cardiac adrenoceptors and calcium channels. *J. Pharmacol. Exp. Ther.* **244**, 100.

[23] Ramkumar, V. & El-Fakahany, E. E. (1984). Increase in [³H]nitrendipine

binding sites in the brain in morphine-tolerant mice. *Eur. J. Pharmacol.* **102**, 371.

[24] Dolin, S., Little, H., Hudspith, M., Pagonis, C., & Littleton, J. (1987). Increased dihydropyridine-sensitive calcium channels in rat brain may underlie ethanol physical dependence. *Neuropharmacology* **26**, 275.

[25] Rius, R. A., Lucchi, L., Govoni, S., & Trabucchi, M. (1984). *In vivo* chronic lead exposure alters [³H]nitrendipine binding in rat striatum. *Brain Res.* **322**, 180.

[26] Garthoff, B. & Bellemann, P. (1987). Effects of salt loading and nitrendipine on dihydropyridine receptors in hypertensive rats. *J. Cardio. Pharmacol.* **10**(Suppl. 10), 171.

[27] Desnuelle, C., Askanas, V., & Engel, W. K. (1986). Insulin increases voltage-dependent Ca^{2+} channels in membrane of aneurally cultured human muscle. *Neurology* **36** (Suppl. 1), 171.

[28] Hawthorn, M., Gengo, P., Wei, X-Y., Rutledge, A., Moran, J. F., Gallant, S., & Triggle, D. J. (1988). Effect of thyroid status on beta-adrenoceptors and calcium channels in rat cardiac and vascular tissue. *Naunyn-Schmied. Arch. Pharmacol.* **337**, 539.

[29] Batra, S. (1987). Increase by estrogen of calcium entry and calcium channel density in uterine smooth muscle. *Brit. J. Pharmacol.* **92**, 389.

[30] Chatelain, P., Demol, D., & Roba, J. (1984). Comparison of [³H]nitrendipine binding to heart membranes of normotensive and spontaneously hypertensive rats. *J. Cardio. Pharmacol.* **6**, 220.

[31] Ishii, K., Kano, T., Ando, J., & Yoshida, H. (1986). Binding of [³H]nitrendipine to cardiac and brain membranes from normotensive and spontaneously hypertensive rats. *Eur. J. Pharmacol.* **123**, 271.

[32] Nayler, W. G., Dillon, J. S., Elz, J. S., & McKelvie, M. (1985). An effect of ischemia on myocardial dihydropyridine binding sites. *Eur. J. Pharmacol.* **115**, 81.

[33] Kenny, B. A., Kilpatrick, A. T., & Spedding, M. (1986). Changes in [³H]nitrendipine binding in gerbil cortex following ischemia. *Brit. J. Pharmacol.* **89**, 858P.

[34] Pincon-Raymond, M., Rieger, F., Fosset, M., & Lazdunski, M. (1985). Abnormal transverse tubule system and abnormal amount of receptors for Ca^{2+} channel inhibitors of the dihydropyridine family in skeletal muscle from mice with embryonic muscular dysgenesis. *Dev. Biol.* **112**, 458.

[35] Wagner, J. A., Sax, F. L., Weisman, H. F., Porterfield, J., McIntosh, C., Weisfeldt, M. L., Snyder, S. H., & Epstein, S. E. (1989). Calcium antagonist receptors in the atrial tissue of patients with hypertrophic cardiomyopathy. *New Engl. J. Med.* **320**, 755.

[36] Weiss, E. R., Kelleher, D. J., Woon, C. W., Soparkar, S., Osawa, S., Heasley, L. E., & Johnson, G. L. (1988). Receptor activation of G proteins. *FASEB J.* **2**, 2841.

[37] Rosenthal, W., Hescheler, J., Trautwein, W., & Schultz, W. (1988). Control of voltage-dependent Ca^{2+} channels by G protein-coupled receptors. *FASEB J.* **2**, 2784.

[38] Brown, A. M. & Birnbaumer, L. (1988). Direct G protein gating of ion channels. *Am. J. Physiol.* **254**, H401.

[39] Armstrong, C. M. (1971). Interaction of tetraethylammonium ion derivatives with the potassium channels of giant axons. *J. Gen. Physiol.* **58**, 418.

[40] Hille, B. (1977). Local anesthetics: hydrophilic and hydrophobic pathways for the drug–receptor reaction. *J. Gen. Physiol.* **69**, 497.

[41] Hondegehm, L. M. & Katzung, B. G. (1977). Time- and voltage-dependent interactions of antiarrhythmic drugs with cardiac Na$^+$ channels. *Biochim. Biophys. Acta* **472**, 373.

[42] Hondeghem, L. M. & Katzung, B. G. (1984). Antiarrhythmic agents: the modulated receptor mechanism of action of sodium and calcium channel blocking drugs. *Annu. Rev. Pharmacol. Toxicol.* **24**, 387.

[43] Sanguinetti, M. C. & Kass, R. S. (1984). Voltage-dependent block of calcium channel current in the calf cardiac Purkinje fiber by dihydropyridine calcium channel antagonists. *Circ. Res.* **55**, 336.

[44] Bean, B. P. (1984). Nitrendipine block of cardiac calcium channels: high affinity binding to the inactivated state. *Proc. Natl. Acad. Sci. USA*, **81**, 6388.

[45] Janis, R. A., Silver, P., & Triggle, D. J. (1987). Drug action and cellular calcium regulation. *Adv. Drug Res.* **16**, 309.

[46] Triggle, D. J., Langs, D. A., & Janis, R. A. (1989). Ca^{2+} channel ligands: structure–function relationships of the 1,4-dihydropyridines. *Med. Res. Rev.* **9**, 123.

[47] Stone, T. W. & Burton, N. R. (1988). NMDA receptors and ligands in the vertebrate CNS. *Prog. Neurobiol.* **30**, 333.

[48] Cotman, C. W. & Iversen, L. L. (1987). Excitatory amino acids in the brain — focus on NMDA receptors. *Trends Neurosci.* **10**, 263.

[49] Rampe, D. & Triggle, D. J. (1990). New ligands for calcium channels. *Trends Pharmacol. Sci.*, in press.

[50] Galizzi, J.-P., Fosset, M., Romey, G., Laduron, P., & Lazdunski, M. (1986). Neuroleptics of the diphenylbutylpiperidine series as potent calcium channel inhibitors. *Proc. Natl. Acad. Sci. USA* **83**, 7513.

[51] Striessnig, J., Meusburger, E., Grabner, M., Knaus, H.-G., Glossmann, H., Kaiser, J., Scholkens, B., Becker, R., Linz, W., & Henning, R. (1988). Evidence for a distinct Ca^{2+} antagonist receptor for the novel benzothiazinone compound HOE 166. *Naunyn-Schmied. Arch. Pharmacol.* **337**, 331.

[52] Nokin, P., Clinet, M., Polster, P., Beaufort, P., Meysmans, L., Gougat, J., & Chatelain, P. (1989). SR 33557, a novel calcium-antagonist: interaction with [^{3}H]nitrendipine and [^{3}H]-(−)desmethoxyverapamil binding sites in cerebral membranes. *Naunyn-Schmied. Arch. Pharmacol.* **339**, 31.

[53] Rampe, D., Triggle, D. J., & Brown, A. M. (1987). Electrophysiologic and biochemical studies on the putative Ca^{2+} channel blocker MDL 12,330A in an endocrine cell. *J. Pharmacol. Exp. Ther.* **243**, 402.

[54] Coburn, R. A., Wierzba, M., Suto, M. J., Solo, A. J., Triggle, A. M., & Triggle, D. J. (1988). 1,4-Dihydropyridine antagonist activities at the calcium channel: a quantitative structure–activity relationship approach. *J. Med. Chem.* **31**, 2103.

[55] Langs, D. A., Strong, P. D., & Triggle, D. J. (1989). Receptor model for the molecular basis of tissue selectivity of 1,4-dihydropyridine calcium channel drugs. Submitted for publication.

[56] Wei, X.-Y., Rutledge, A., & Triggle, D. J. (1989). Voltage-dependent binding of 1,4-dihydropyridine Ca^{2+} channel antagonists and activators in cultured neonatal rat ventricular myocytes. *Mol. Pharmacol.* **35**, 541.

[57] Cook, N. S. (1988). The pharmacology of potassium channels and their therapeutic potential. *Trends Pharmacol. Sci.* **9**, 21.

[58] Rudy, B. (1988). Diversity and ubiquity of K^+ channels. *Neuroscience* **25**, 729.

[59] Moczydlowski, E., Lucchesi, K., & Ravindran, A. (1988). An emerging pharmacology of peptide toxins targeted against potassium channels. *J. Membrane Biol.* **105**, 95.

[60] Ashcroft, F. M. (1988). Adenosine-5′-triphosphate-sensitive potassium channels. *Annu. Rev. Neurosci.* **11**, 97.

[61] Boyd, A. E. (1988). Sulfonylurea receptors, ion channels and fruit flies. *Diabetes* **37**, 847.

[62] Schmid-Antomarchi, H., De Weille, J., Fosset, M., & Lazdunski, M. (1987). The receptor for antidiabetic sulfonylureas controls the activity of the ATP-modulated K^+ channel in insulin-secreting cells. *J. Biol. Chem.* **262**, 15840.

[63] Ashwood, V. A., Buckingham, R. E., Cassidy, F., Evans, J. M., Faruk, E. A., Hamilton, T. C., Nash, D. J., Stemp, G., & Willcocks, K. (1986). Synthesis and antihypertensive activity of 4-[cyclic amido]-2-H-1-benzopyrans. *J. Med. Chem.* **29**, 2194.

[64] Hamilton, T. C. & Weston, A. H. (1989). Cromokalim, nicorandil and pinacidil: novel drugs which open potassium channels in smooth muscle. *Gen. Pharmacol.* **20**, 1.

[65] Sanguinetti, M. C., Scott, A. L., Zingaro, G. J., & Siegl, P. K. S. (1988). BRL 34915 (cromokalim) activates ATP-dependent K^+ current in cardiac muscle. *Proc. Natl. Acad. Sci. USA.* **85**, 8360.

[66] Buckingham, R. E., Hamilton, T. C., Howlett, D. R., Mootov, S., & Wilson, C. (1989). Inhibition by gliblenclamide of the vasorelaxant action of cromokalim in the rat. *Brit. J. Pharmacol.* **97**, 57.

[67] Noda, M., Shimizu, S., Tanabe, T., Takai, T., Kayano, T., Ikeda, T., Takahashi, H., Nakayuma, H., Kanaoka, Y., Minamino, N., Kangawa, K., Matsuo, H., Raftery, M. A., Hirose, T., Inayama, S., Hayashida, H., Miyata, T., & Numa, S. (1984). Primary structure of *Electrophorus electricus* sodium channel deduced from cDNA sequence. *Nature* **312**, 121.

[68] Slakhoff, L., Butler, A., Wei, A., Scavarda, N., Giffen, K., Ifure, C., Goodman, R., & Mandel, G. (1987). Genomic organization and deduced amino acid sequences of a putative sodium channel gene in Drosophila. *Science* **237**, 744.

[69] Tanabe, T., Takeshima, H., Mikami, A., Flockerzi, V., Takahashi, H., Kangawa, K., Kojima, M., Mitusuo, H., Hirose, T., & Numa, S. (1987). Primary structure for the receptor for calcium channel blockers from skeletal muscle. *Nature* **328**, 313.

[70] Vaghy, P. L., Striessnig, J., Miwa, K., Knaus, H.-G., Itagaki, K., McKenna,

E., Glossmann, H., & Schwartz, A. (1987). Identification of a novel 1,4-dihydropyridine- and phenylalkylamine-binding polypeptide in calcium channel preparations. *J. Biol. Chem.* **262**, 14337.

[71] Tempel, B. L., Papazian, D. M., Schwartz, T. L., Jan, Y. N., & Jan, L. Y. (1987). Sequence of a probable potassium channel component encoded at Shaker locus of Drosophila. *Science* **237**, 770.

[72] Schwartz, T. L., Tempel, B. L., Papazian, D. M., Jan, Y. N., & Jan, L. Y. (1988). Multiple potassium-channel components are produced by alternative splicing at the Shaker locus in Drosophila. *Nature* **331**, 137.

[73] Kubo, T., Noda, M., Takai, T., Tanabe, T., Kayanao, T., Shimizu, S., Tanaka, K., Takahashi, H., Hirose, T., Inagama, S., Kituno, R., Miyata, T., & Numa, S. (1985). Primary structure of subunit precursor of calf muscle acetylcholine receptor deduced from DNA sequence. *Eur. J. Biochem.* **149**, 5.

[74] Popot, J.-L. & Changeux, J.-P. (1984). Nicotinic receptor of acetylcholine: structure of an oligomeric integral membrane protein. *Physiol. Rev.* **64**, 1162.

[75] Schofield, P. R., Darlison, M. G., Fujita, N., Burt, D. R., Stephenson, F. A., Rodriguez, H., Rhee, L. M., Ramachandrian, J., Reale, V., Glencorse, T. A., Seeburg, P. H., & Barnard, E. A. (1987). Sequence and functional expression of the GABA A receptor shows a ligand-gated receptor superfamily. *Nature* **328**, 221.

[76] Barnard, E. A., Darlison, M. G., & Seeburg, P. (1987). Molecular biology of the GABA A receptor: the receptor/channel superfamily. *Trends Neurosci.* **10**, 502.

[77] Grenningloh, G., Rienitz, A., Schmitt, B., Methfessel, C., Zensen, M., Beyreuther, K., Gundelfinger, E. D., & Betz, H. (1987). The strychnine-binding subunit of the glycine receptor shows homology with nicotinic acetylcholine receptors. *Nature* **328**, 215.

[78] Betz, H. & Becker, C.-M. (1988). The mammalian glycine receptor: biology and structure of a neuronal chloride channel protein. *Neurochem. Int.* **13**, 137.

[79] Stevens, C. F. (1987). Channel families in the brain. *Nature* **328**, 198.

[80] Agnew, W. S. (1988). A Rosetta stone for K^+ channels. *Nature* **331**, 114.

[81] Catterall, W. S. (1988). Structure and function of voltage-sensitive ion channels. *Science* **242**, 50.

[82] Jan, L. Y. & Jan, Y. N. (1989). Voltage-sensitive ion channels. *Cell* **56**, 13.

[83] Kayano, T., Noda, M., Flockerzi, V., Takahashi, H., & Numa, S. (1988). Primary structure of rat brain sodium channel III deduced from the cDNA sequence. *FEBS Lett.* **228**, 187.

[84] Vaghy, P. L., McKenna, E., Itagaki, K., & Schwartz, A. (1988). Resolution of the identity of the Ca^{2+} antagonist receptor in skeletal muscle. *Trends Pharmacol. Sci.* **9**, 398.

[85] Ellis, B., Williams, M. E., Ways, N. R., Brenner, R., Sharp, A. H., Leung, A. T., Campbell, K. P., McKenna, E., Koch, W.-J., Hui, A., Schwartz, A., & Harpold, M. M. (1988). Sequence and expression of mRNAs encoding the alpha 1 and alpha 2 subunits of a DHP-sensitive calcium channel. *Science* **241**, 1661.

[86] Tejedor, F. J. & Catterall, W. A. (1988). Site of covalent attachment of α-

scorpion toxin derivatives in domain I of the sodium channel α-subunit. *Proc. Natl. Acad. Sci. USA* **85**, 8742.

[87] Gordon, D., Merrick, D., Wollner, D. A., & Catterall, W. A. (1988). Biochemical properties of sodium channels in a wide range of excitable tissues studied with site-directed antibodies. *Biochemistry* **27**, 7032.

[88] Meiri, H., Spira, G., Sammal, M., Namir, M., Schwartz, A., Komoriya, A., Kosower, E. M., & Palti, Y. (1987). Mapping a region associated with Na channel inactivation using antibodies to a synthetic peptide corresponding to a part of the channel. *Proc. Natl. Acad. Sci. USA* **84**, 5058.

[89] Stuhmer, W., Conti, F., Suzuki, H., Wang, X., Noda, M., Yahagi, N., Kubo, H., & Numa, S. (1989). Structural parts involved in activation and inactivation of the sodium channel. *Nature* **339**, 597.

[90] Triggle, D. J. (1981). *Chemical Pharmacology of the Synapse*. Academic Press, London.

[91] Pritchett, D. B., Sontheimer, H., Shivers, B. D., Ymer, S., Kettenmann, H., Schofield, P. R., & Seeburg, P. H. (1989). Importance of a novel GABA A receptor subunit for benzodiazepine pharmacology. *Nature* **338**, 582.

[92] Olivera, B. M., Gray, W. R., Zeikus, R., McIntosh, J. M., Varga, J., Rivier, J., de Santos, V., & Cruz, L. J. (1985). Peptide neurotoxins from fish-hunting cone snails. *Science* **230**, 1338.

[93] Gray, W. R., Olivera, B. M., & Cruz, L. J. (1988). Peptide toxins from venomous Conus snails. *Annu. Rev. Biochem.* **57**, 665.

[94] Jackson, H. & Usherwood, P. N. R. (1988). Spider toxins as tools for dissecting elements of excitatory amino acid transmission. *Trends Neurosci.* **11**, 278.

[95] Skinner, W. S., Adams, M. E., Quistad, G. B., Kataoka, H., Cesarin, B. J., Enderline, F. E., & Schooley, D. A. (1989). Purification and characterization of two classes of neurotoxins from the funnel web spider, *Agelenopsis aperta*. *J. Biol. Chem.* **264**, 2150.

[96] Bindokas, V. P. & Adams, M. E. (1989). ω-Aga I: a presynaptic calcium channel antagonist from venom of the funnel web spider, *Agelenopsis aperta*. *J. Neurobiol.* **20**, 171.

8

Intracellular second-messenger generation: the role of inositol lipids

Stephen K. Fisher
Neuroscience Laboratory and Department of Pharmacology, University of
Michigan, Ann Arbor, Michigan, USA

8.1 INTRODUCTION

In the early 1900s, the recognition that some drugs exhibited an extraordinary degree of potency and specificity in eliciting a biological response led to the concept that 'receptor' molecules must exist for these substances on the surface of biological membranes. Subsequently, quantitative descriptions of the competitive interaction between agonists and antagonists for these specific receptors were formulated. The receptor concept has successfully stood the test of time and has led to the biochemical isolation and characterization of many of these molecules. Furthermore, in some instances, the reconstitution of their activity in synthetic membranes has been accomplished. Earlier work envisaged that the interaction of agonists with cell-surface receptors resulted in the opening of ion channels within the membrane, followed by a redistribution of ions down their electrochemical gradients. It was subsequently recognized that the binding of a neurotransmitter or hormone at the cell-surface could also lead to the alteration of enzyme activities within the cell and (usually) a rise in the concentration of an intracellular 'second-messenger' molecule which would mediate the action of the agonist (the 'first-messenger'). The best characterized of these is undoubtedly cyclic 3',5'-adenosine monophosphate (cAMP), first identified by Earl Sutherland in the 1960s. Since the intracellular concentration of many compounds may rise following cell activation, it is necessary that a number of criteria be satisfied before the assignment of second-messenger status can be made. Thus, for example, a putative second-messenger molecule should be produced rapidly and in sufficient amounts in a stimulated cell. There should also be a means of rapid inactivation of the molecule to terminate the signal. Furthermore, application of the putative second messenger (possibly as a lipophilic derivative) should be able to mimic the effect of the naturally occurring transmitter or hormone. cAMP satisfied all of these criteria, and the discovery that cellular responses could be influenced by *both* a reduction and an increase in its concentration attests further to the importance of this molecule in cell physiology. A further link in our understanding of the mode of action of cAMP on cell responses came with the discovery that certain protein kinases were specifically activated by the cyclic nucleotide. This led to the suggestion that activation of adenylate-cyclase-linked receptors initiates a cascade of events involving the production of cAMP, the activation of protein kinases, the phosphorylation of cellular proteins and ultimately the physiological response.

However, a large number, possibly a majority, of cell-surface receptors do not couple to the opening or closing of plasma membrane channels nor do they modulate the activity of adenylate cyclase. Instead, they appear to exert their effects through the increased breakdown of a quantitatively minor pool of plasma membrane lipids, the inositol phospholipids or phosphoinositides (PPIs). The ability of a number of ligands to enhance the radiolabeling and degradation of specific membrane phospholipids was first recognized over 30 years ago by L. E. and M. R. Hokin [1], but the physiological significance of these metabolic changes remained enigmatic until the early 1980s. While it has been recognized that activation of these receptors coupled to inositol phospholipid turnover also resulted in a rise in intracellular calcium [2], the causative link between these two events remained unknown. However, this 'missing link' between PPI turnover and Ca^{2+} signaling events was provided in 1983 by Berridge and colleagues who demonstrated that a water-soluble inositol phosphate (inositol 1,4,5-triphosphate) derived from the breakdown of phosphatidylinositol 4,5-bisphosphate could mobilize calcium from intracellular stores [3]. A further observation of seminal importance was the discovery by Nishizuka's group that diacylglycerol, which is formed concomitantly with inositol 1,4,5–trisphosphate, could activate a unique type of protein kinase (protein kinase C; PKC), thereby providing a link between lipid and protein phosphorylation events [4,5]. Interest in the phosphoinositide pathway and intracellular second-messenger generation has expanded rapidly in the intervening years such that it is now one of the most actively investigated areas of biomedical research. The objectives of this chapter are threefold. First, to provide an overview of our current understanding of the molecular mechanisms underlying receptor-stimulated PPI turnover and its physiological significance; second, to critically evaluate the methods currently available for measurement of PPI turnover; and third, to indicate current approaches to the pharmacological and biochemical intervention in the inositol lipid signaling pathway.

8.2 MOLECULAR MECHANISMS FOR TRANS-MEMBRANE SIGNALING IN CELLS

Receptors in biological tissues can be classified according to the specificity with which they bind agonists and antagonists, or, alternatively, on the basis of the effector mechanism to which they couple. Using the latter categorization, at least four groups of receptor can be distinguished, all of which may be present on the same cell (Fig. 8.1). The first group includes receptors whose activation leads directly to the opening or closing of plasma membrane ion channels. An example of a receptor in

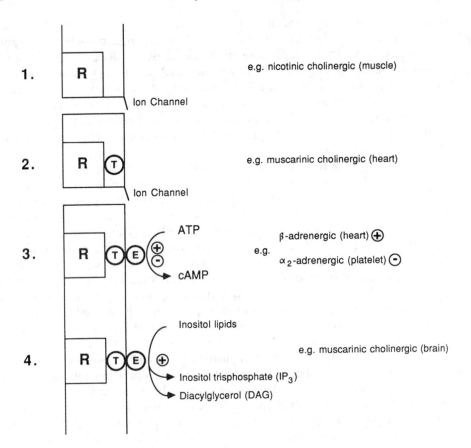

R: Receptor
T: Transducer (G-Protein)
E: Effector enzyme (adenylate cyclase or phospholipase C)

Fig. 8.1 — Four of the mechanisms used by cells for trans-membrane signaling.

this category would be the nicotinic cholinergic receptor, a trans-membrane protein that undergoes a conformational change upon the binding of acetylcholine to the two α subunits of the receptor, thereby opening a central pore and allowing the influx of Na$^+$ ions. A second, recently identified, mechanism of signal transduction also involves the opening of ion channels in the membrane, but in this instance requires the additional mediation of a transducer (guanine–nucleotide binding: G) protein. It is not yet certain whether the production of additional molecules may also be required [6 and references therein]. The mechanisms linking the third and fourth groups of receptor to cellular activation is more complex in that for each group of receptors there exist specific G-proteins and *effector* enzymes. In the case of cAMP generation, the enzyme activated or inhibited is adenylate cyclase and this is modulated through either a stimulatory or an inhibitory G protein (G_s or G_i [7]). Guanylate cyclase activity may also be regulated in some tissues (e.g. retina), but the physiological significance of changes in the concentration of intracellular cyclic guanosine monophosphate in other tissues has been debated [8]. For PPI turnover, there exists a specific phospholipase C activity which preferentially hydrolyzes one of the inositol-containing lipids, namely phosphatidylinositol 4,5-bisphosphate, through an as yet unknown G-protein (G_p). In most cell types, the number of pharmacologically distinct receptors that operate through the PPI pathway exceeds that of the adenylate-cyclase-linked receptors. This is particularly true of the central nervous system in which over 20 distinct receptors coupled to PPI turnover have been identified [9]. As discussed in the following section, receptors linked to PPI turnover are ubiquitous in distribution and subserve several diverse physiological functions.

8.2.1 Receptors linked to enhanced phosphoinositide turnover

Most eukaryotic cells appear to possess receptors that are linked to PPI turnover. In the original studies by the Hokins [1], the muscarinic cholinergic receptor was the first to be implicated in PPI turnover; but since these early studies, the list of receptors coupled to PPI turnover continues to grow and now numbers up to 40 (see [9–12] for reviews, and Table 8.1). Included in this list are cholinergic, adrenergic,

Table 8.1 — Receptor-stimulated phosphoinositide turnover

Receptor (subtype)	Tissue
Cholinergic (m_1, m_3, m_5 muscarinic)	Brain, parotid, pancreas, smooth muscles, gastric mucosa, neuroblastoma, astrocytoma
Adrenergic (α_1)	Brain, smooth muscles
Histaminergic (H_1)	Brain
Serotonergic ($5HT_2$, $5HT_{1c}$)	Blowfly salivary gland, choroid plexus, brain, platelets
Glutamate (quisqualate)	Brain
Substance P	Parotid, brain
Vasopressin (V_1)	Superior cervical ganglion, liver, brain
Neurotensin	Brain, gastric parietal cells
Angiotensin	Liver, adrenal cortex, anterior pituitary
Bombesin	3T3 fibroblasts
Cerulein	Pancreas
Bradykinin	Kidney tubules
	NG 108-15 cells
Platelet-derived growth factor	3T3 fibroblasts
f-Met–Leu–Phe	Neutrophils
	HL-60 cells
Thrombin	Platelets, fibroblasts
Platelet-activating factor	Platelets, liver
Antigen	B-lymphocytes
	T-cells
	Rat basophil leukemic cells
Concanavalin A	Thymocytes
Phytohemagglutinin	T-cell leukemia

histaminergic, serotonergic and acidic amino acid receptors, while an increasing number of neuropeptides, growth factors and other hormones are also known to exert their effects on target tissues through this pathway. Even more impressive is the list of physiological functions ultimately ascribed to activation of these receptors such as contraction, secretion, cell–cell communication in the central nervous system, immune responses, chemotaxis, and platelet aggregation. Furthermore, PPI turn over has been linked to both acute and proliferative stimuli [13]. Given the importance of Ca^{2+} in the regulation of cellular activity, and that PPI turnover is intimately linked to Ca^{2+} homeostasis, it is perhaps not surprising that this pathway appears to be of major physiological importance.

8.2.2   Inositol lipids — quantitatively minor components of biological membranes

The presence of inositol-containing phospholipids in mammalian tissues was first described by Folch in the 1940s, who isolated the lipids from extracts of ox brain [14]. Subsequently, phosphoinositides were isolated from a number of other tissues. At least three inositol-containing phospholipids can be identified, i.e. phosphatidylinositol (PI), phosphatidylinositol 4-phosphate (PIP) and phosphatidylinositol 4,5-bisphosphate (PIP_2) (Fig. 8.2). The presence of an additional phosphoinositide, namely phosphatidylinositol 3,4,5-trisphosphate, has been suggested, both in earlier and in more recent work [16,17]. However, the existence of this lipid awaits further independent confirmation. The inositol-containing lipids are trace components of membranes and rarely comprise more than 5% of the total cellular phospholipids [18]. The phosphorylated forms of PI, i.e. PIP and PIP_2, known collectively as the polyphosphoinositides, are present in even lower concentrations, especially PIP_2 which is now widely recognized to be the initial inositol lipid broken down by phospholipase C action following the ligand–receptor interaction. Both PIP and PIP_2 are localized predominantly, if not exclusively, to plasma membranes and as a consequence, tissues enriched in plasma membranes, such as brain and kidney, are also enriched in the polyphosphoinositides.

   In their plasma membrane location, the inositol lipids are thought to be present at the cytoplasmic surface with the apolar fatty acid side chains radiating into the membrane while the polar inositol head group faces towards the cytoplasm. Upon phospholipase C activation and subsequent hydrolysis of PIP_2, the apolar diacylglycerol molecule is released into the plane of the membrane while the polar inositol 1,4,5-trisphosphate ($I(1,4,5)P_3$) can freely diffuse into the cytoplasm. Cells appear to maintain the concentrations of their inositol lipids within narrow limits such that the hydrolysis of PIP_2 is followed by a rapid resynthesis of the lipid in a metabolically expensive series of reactions (see section 8.2.3). An increased concentration of inositol lipids in membranes has been linked to cell proliferation and loss of cellular regulation [19].

8.2.3   Molecular mechanism of enhanced phosphinositide turnover and its
physiological sequelae

The mechanism underlying the enhanced turnover of inositol phospholipids in tissues has been intensively investigated over the last five years, and while much progress has been made, it must be admitted that certain gaps in our knowledge still exist. While a detailed description of the individual studies pertaining to the

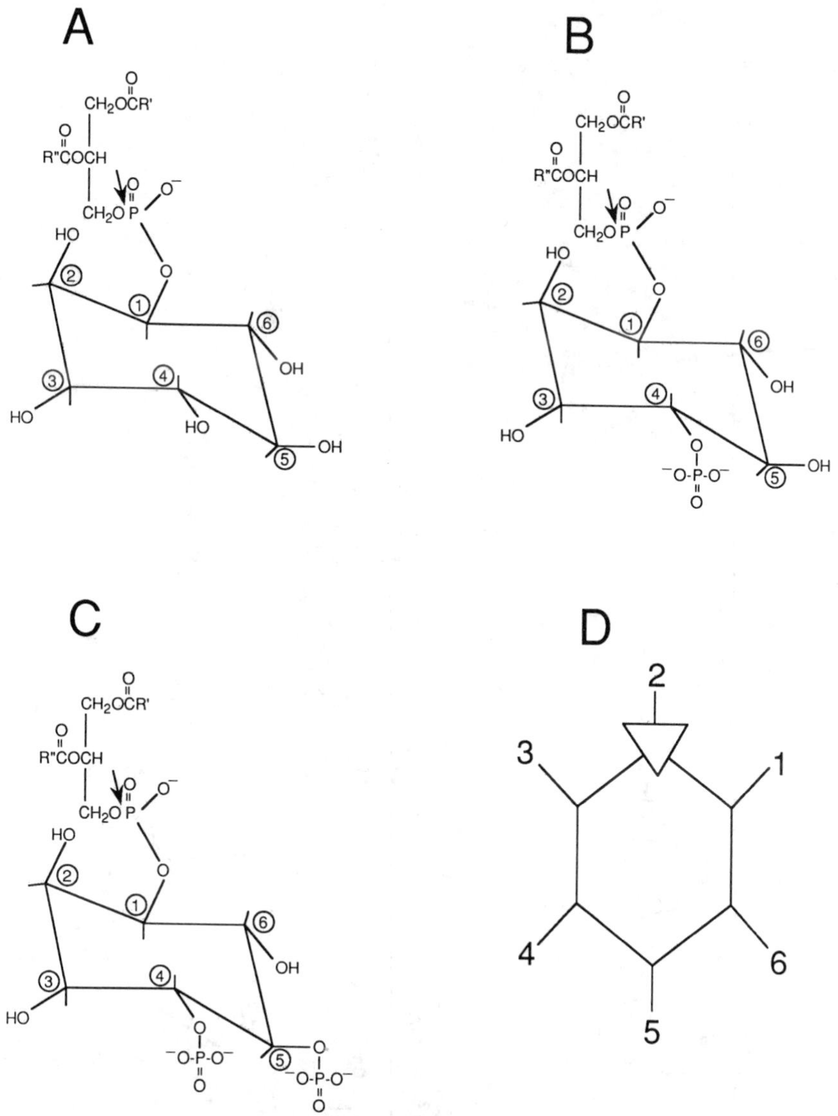

Fig. 8.2 — The inositol lipids. (a) Phosphatidylinositol (PI), (b) Phosphatidylinositol 4-phosphate, (c) Phosphatidylinositol 4,5-bisphosphate. All three inositol lipids may be cleaved by a Ca^{2+}-activated phosphodiesterase at a site designated by the arrow. R' and R" are predominantly 18:0 (stearate) and 20:4 ω 6 (arachidonate) esters, respectively. (d) A convenient representation of *myo*-inositol as recommended by Agranoff [15]. The open triangle at the d-2 position represents the axial hydroxyl projecting out of the plane of the paper towards the reader.

molecular mechanism is outside the scope of this chapter, a brief overview of the putative series of events which link agonist occupancy of the receptor to an enhanced PPI turnover is appropriate (see Fig. 8.3). Receptors coupled to an increased inositol

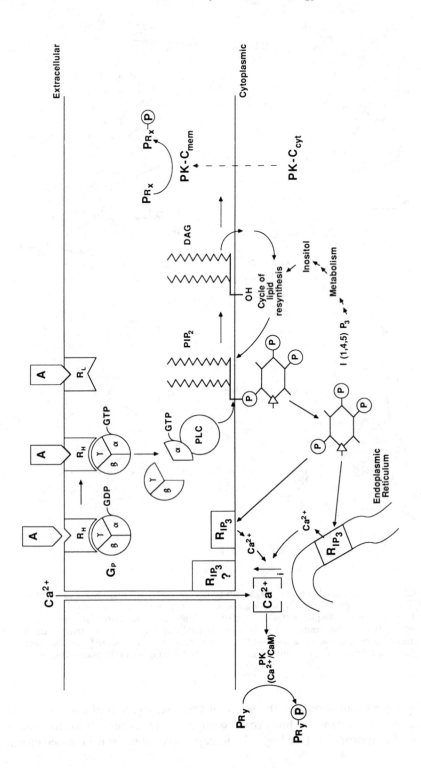

Fig. 8.3 — Putative sequence of events linking occupancy of a receptor to phosphoinositide hydrolysis, Ca²⁺ mobilization, protein kinase C activation and protein phosphorylation. See text for details.

lipid hydrolysis are believed to operate through an as yet unidentified heterotrimeric guanine nucleotide-binding protein (G_p) [20]. Following occupancy of the receptor by an agonist, a high-affinity ternary complex is formed between the receptor (R_H), the agonist (A) and G_p. Following the exchange of guanosine triphosphate (GTP) for guanosine diphosphate (GDP), G_p is presumed to dissociate into its α and $\beta\gamma$ subunits (in a manner analogous to that established for other G-proteins such as G_s or G_i [7], and in doing so the receptor's affinity for A is reduced (R_L). This mechanism is consistent with the observation made in radioligand binding studies that the addition of guanine nucleotides or their non-hydrolyzable analogs reduces the affinity with which agonists, which elicit PPI turnover, can bind to their receptors. The α subunit of G_p which possesses the GTP binding site is then thought to activate phosphoinositide specific phospholipase C (PLC), probably through a reduction of the concentration of Ca^{2+} required for its activation such that physiologically relevant concentrations of the cation ($\approx 10^{-7}M$) are sufficient [21–23]. PLC, which is localized to both the plasma membrane and the cytosol in proportions which vary according to tissue source [10], preferentially catalyzes the phosphodiesteratic hydrolysis of phosphatidylinositol 4-5-bisphosphate (PIP_2), and as a consequence, two intracellular second messengers are formed, namely $I(1,4,5)P_3$ and diacylglycerol (DAG). Both of these molecules can undergo a variety of metabolic fates. For example, $I(1,4,5)P_3$ may interact with specific receptor sites (R_{IP_3}) on either the endoplasmic reticulum or/and the plasma membrane, thereby mobilizing intracellular Ca^{2+} [24,25]. In addition, $I(1,4,5)P_3$ may cause the opening of plasma membrane Ca^+ channels, thereby further increasing (transiently) the concentration of intracellular Ca^{2+} $[Ca^{2+}]_i$ [26]. These receptor sites on the plasma membrane or endoplasmic reticulum are highly specific for the 1,4,5 isomer of IP_3, such that other positional isomers are ineffective [27]. The elevated $[Ca^{2+}]_i$ may then activate a number of protein kinases (PK), including a Ca^{2+}/calmodulin (Ca^{2+}/CaM)-dependent PK which may in turn result in the subsequent phosphorylation of cellular protein(s) — (PR_y). Rapid sequestration of released Ca^{2+} into the mitochondrial and endoplasmic reticulum fractions then occurs and reduces cytoplasmic Ca^{2+} concentrations back to resting levels. Following the interaction of $I(1,4,5)P_3$ with its receptor, $I(1,4,5)P_3$ can be metabolized via a number of different pathways, as shown in Fig. 8.4. The most rapid metabolic route of degradation is via 5′-phosphatase action which yields $I(1,4)P_2$ (structure (b)). Since this molecule is ineffective at mobilizing intracellular Ca^{2+}, this reaction can be considered to be the major 'off' signal for Ca^{2+} mobilization. A separate pathway of possible physiological significance is that of 3′-kinase which converts $I(1,4,5)P_3$ to $I(1,3,4,5)P_4$ (structure (e)). $I(1,3,4,5)P_4$ has previously been implicated in the mediation of Ca^{2+} influx into cells, although this now seems less likely [28,29]. $I(1,3,4,5)P_4$ may be dephosphorylated to $I(1,3,4)P_3$ (structure (f)) which, unlike $I(1,4,5)P_3$, cannot mobilize intracellular Ca^{2+}. As shown in Fig. 8.4, the various IP_3 and IP_2 isomers are metabolized to $I(1)P$, $I(4)P$ or $I(3)P$ and then dephosphorylated to free inositol which becomes available for the resynthesis of inositol lipid (Fig. 8.3). In the presence of mM concentrations of Li^+, inositol monophosphatase activity is completely inhibited. Li^+ may also inhibit the $I(1,4)P_2$ bisphosphatase but does not exert a significant inhibitory influence on dephosphorylation of $I(1,4,5)P_3$ [30]. Diacylglycerol may similarly undergo a number of metabolic fates. Once liberated into the

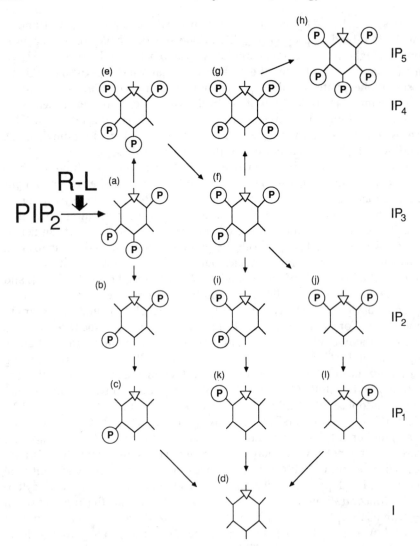

Fig. 8.4 — Metabolic interconversion of inositol phosphates. $I(1,4,5)P_3$ (structure (a)) produced by the phosphodiesteratic cleavage of PIP_2 can be either converted to $I(1,4)P_2$ (structure (b)) via a 5′-phosphatase action, or alternatively to $I(1,3,4,5)P_4$ (structure (e)) via a 3′-kinase. 5′-phosphatase action can in turn convert $I(1,3,4,5)P_4$ to the physiologically inactive isomer $I(1,3,4)P_3$, (structure (f)). $I(1,3,4,6)P_4$ (structure (g)) is synthesized by 6′-kinase action on $I(1,3,4)P_3$ and can then be further phosphorylated to $I(1,3,4,5,6)P_5$ (structure (h)). $I(1,3,4)P_3$ may also be dephosphorylated to either $I(3,4)P_2$ (structure (i)) or $I(1,3)P_2$ (structure (j)). Bisphosphatase action on structures (b), (i) and (j) yields $I(4)P$ (structure (c)), $I(3)P$ (structure (k)) and $I(1)P$ (structure (l)). Monophosphatase action on the latter inositol phosphates yields *myo*-inositol. This final step in inositol phosphate dephosphorylation is inhibited by Li^+ ions. For the sake of clarity, the cyclic derivatives of the inositol phosphate isomers are not included (for details of these, see [9]).

plane of the plasma membrane, DAG may activate PKC for which seven isoenzymes can be distinguished on the basis of the molecular and biochemical characteristics [31]. Activation of PKC involves its translocation from a cytosolic to a membrane compartment and in the presence of DAG, Ca^{2+} ions and phosphatidylserine, the membrane form of PKC (PKC_{mem}), can catalyze the phosphorylation of one or more protein substrates (PR_x) [32,33]. When in a membrane bound form, PKC is subject to proteolytic cleavage, and is split into 50 kDa and 30 kDa subunits. The 50 kDa subunit possesses protein kinase activity (PKM), but is not subject to regulation by DAG. DAG may also undergo phosphorylation to phosphatidic acid (PA), the initial step in a cycle of reactions which results in the resynthesis of PIP_2 as outlined in Fig. 8.5. The process whereby PIP_2 is resynthesized following degrada-

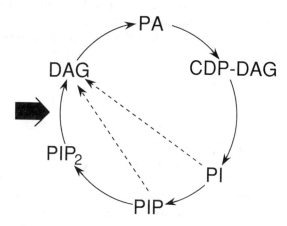

Fig. 8.5 — Cycle of inositol lipid resynthesis. Following an initial receptor-mediated breakdown of PIP_2 (as indicated by the arrow), DAG can be phosphorylated in the presence of ATP and DAG kinase to form phosphatidic acid (PA). PA may then be converted to a liponucleotide intermediate, cytidine diphosphodiacylglycerol (CDP-DAG [34]). Phosphatidyl inositol (PI) is then synthesized from CDP-DG in the presence of inositol and a transferase [35]. PIP and PIP_2 are then synthesized via sequential phosphorylations of PI and PIP, at the 4′ and 5′ positions of inositol in the presence of respective kinases and ATP. High-energy phosphate consumption occurs at the levels of DAG kinase, PI kinase, PIP kinase and at the PA:cytidyl transferase reactions. Although PIP_2 is believed to be selectively cleaved following receptor–ligand activation, direct phosphodiesteratic breakdown of either PI or/and PIP may occur during receptor activation (– – –). In the later case, only one known second messenger is formed, i.e. DAG, since IP_2 and IP_1 do not mobilize intracellular calcium.

tion is metabolically expensive in that for each mol of PIP_2 hydrolyzed by PLC, 3 mol of ATP and 1 mol of CTP are consumed [9]. While it might be anticipated that the energy demands of such a process would place serious constraints on the cell, the fact that the two limbs of this bifurcating pathway interact synergistically limits the amount of PIP_2 degradation necessary to elicit a full physiological response [36]. The PLC-mediated hydrolysis of PIP_2 is thought to be terminated by the hydrolysis of GTP bound to G_p via an intrinsic GTPase. This would allow the α and $\beta\gamma$ subunits of G_p to reassemble and the cycle may then be reinitiated. When PPI hydrolysis is measured in the presence of a non-hydrolyzable GTP analog such as guanosine-5'-0-(3-thiotrisphosphate) (GTPγS), G_p remains dissociated and PLC is continuously activated.

8.3 MEASUREMENT OF PHOSPHOINOSITIDE TURNOVER

Under ideal conditions, stimulated phosphoinositide turnover would be monitored by measurement of the chemical mass of the inositol phosphates or DAG rapidly, reliably and without the requirement for the extensive training of personnel or their exposure to harmful chemicals or radioisotopes. Unfortunately, this situation does not yet pertain to the measurement of inositol lipid turnover. However, methods are presently available which monitor one or more aspects of PPI turnover. Some of these are more applicable to the pharmaceutical industry than others, since in this setting there is often the need for methods that can handle relatively large numbers of samples efficiently. It is important to state at the outset that none of the methods described is without some drawbacks, and, further, that the methodology for DAG determination is in its infancy. In this section, various methodological approaches are critiqued and where appropriate, examples of results obtained in the author's laboratory using cultures of human neuroblastoma cells (SK-N-SH) will be presented.

8.3.1 Radiolabeling of phospholipids

This is the traditional method that was used fairly exclusively until the development within the last 4–5 years of techniques that directly monitor the release of labeled inositol phosphates. The principle underlying the method is that when tissues are incubated in a medium which supports oxidative phosphorylation (such as a Krebs–Ringer buffer) and in the presence of tracer amounts of ^{32}P-orthophosphate, the radiolabel is converted into [^{32}P]ATP and this in turn can enter the lipid resynthesis cycle depicted in Fig. 8.5 at either the diacylglycerol kinase step, or the PI- and PIP-kinase reactions. Endogenous DAG is phosphorylated in the presence of [^{32}P]ATP and DAG kinase to form [^{32}P]PA, and subsequently [^{32}P]phosphatidylinositol (PI). It should be noted that while all of the ^{32}P-label in PI resides in a phosphodiester linkage, the majority of radiolabel in PIP and PIP_2 is in the monoester phosphates. In the cycle shown in Fig. 8.5, the availability of DAG in quiescent tissues is *rate-limiting*. Thus, following the ligand-stimulated breakdown of PIP_2, more DAG is formed and this is reflected in an increased labeling of [^{32}P]PA and [^{32}P]PI. Reactions are terminated by the addition of chloroform/methanol, lipids extracted under the acidic conditions necessary for quantitative recovery, and then separated by thin-layer chromatography [37]. Following detection of radiolabeled lipids by autoradiography, an enhanced turnover of PI and PA is readily evident (see for example, Fig. 8.6, in which the addition of a cholinergic agonist — carbachol — significantly increases the ^{32}P-labeling of PA and PI). Although it might be anticipated that a loss of label from PIP_2 should also be evident, in actuality this is not usually observed since rapid resynthesis of the lipid obscures its transient breakdown. An alternative approach is first to prelabel tissue lipids to isotopic equilibrium with $^{32}P_i$ (such that the specific activity of the precursor [^{32}P]ATP approaches that of the lipid), remove excess $^{32}P_i$ by washing and then expose the

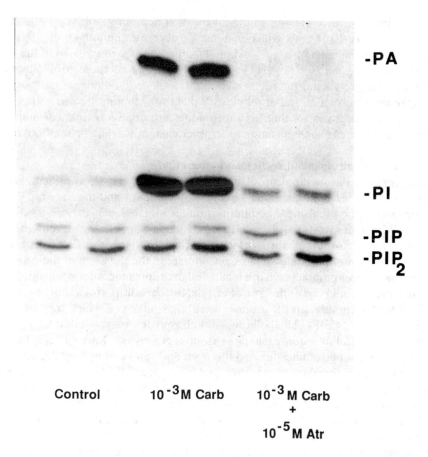

Fig. 8.6 — Thin-layer chromatographic (TLC) separation of ^{32}P-labeled phospholipids obtained from human (SK-N-SH) neuroblastoma cells. Cells were incubated for 30 min in the presence of ^{32}P$_i$, reactions terminated by the addition of chloroform/methanol, lipids extracted under acidic conditions and separated on TLC by the method of Jolles *et al.* [38] and visualized by autoradiography. The concentrations of carbachol and atropine were 1 mM and 10μ M respectively. Note that the addition of carbachol enhanced the ^{32}P-labeling of both PA and PI over control incubations. Inclusion of atropine blocked this increased labeling, indicating the involvement of a muscarinic cholinergic receptor.

prelabeled tissue to the agent of interest. Using this paradigm, a rapid breakdown of [^{32}P]PIP$_2$ following receptor activation is detected as a *loss* of label from the lipid [39]. Although changes in ^{32}P-labeling of phospholipids can be a sensitive index of receptor activation, a number of considerations are appropriate. First, from a theoretical viewpoint, PA and PI labeling monitors the secondary phase of lipid resynthesis rather than the primary breakdown event. Second, in some tissues, an increased *de novo* lipid synthesis can occur in response to a drug which might erroneously be interpreted to reflect activation of the phosphoinositide turnover pathway. For example, cationic amphiphilic drugs (e.g. propranolol, chlorproma-zine) can redirect phospholipid synthesis via an inhibition of PA phosphatase and thereby increase the labeling of PA, PI and other phospholipids [40]. A third consideration is that agents which increase or decrease the uptake of $^{32}P_i$ into the tissue will have significant effects on lipid labeling through alterations of the specific activity of the precursor $[^{32}P]ATP$ pool. While some of these problems can be avoided if the prelabeling paradigm is adopted, changes in radiolabel associated with PIP_2 are often very small and/or rapid, such that this technique becomes impractical. A further consideration is that lipid techniques are relatively time consuming and require more expertise than some of the other currently available methods.

8.3.2   Inositol phosphate detection and separation

Until recently, the metabolism of inositol phosphates has been difficult to study owing to the absence of adequate separation techniques and the very rapid rate of dephosphorylation that these compounds undergo. However, the observation that Li^+ inhibits *myo*-inositol 1-phosphatase [41] made possible the development of a specific and rapid method for assessing the ligand-induced breakdown of inositol lipids since inositol monophosphates accumulate in the presence of the cation [42]. When tissue slices or intact cells are incubated in the presence of $[^3H]$inositol and Li^+ (or alternatively allowed to first prelabel), the further addition of agonists results in a several-fold accumulation of inositol phosphates, much of which may be initially derived from $I(1,4,5)P_3$. The polar inositol phosphates are separated from the non-polar *myo*-inositol by anion-exchange chromatography on Dowex 1-formate resins. Labeled inositol phosphates bind to the resin and can be eluted by the addition of 1.0 M ammonium formate/0.1 M formic acid. The release of a total inositol phosphate fraction (i.e. a mixture of IP_4, IP_3, IP_2 and IP_1) is frequently used to provide an index of receptor-stimulated PPI turnover, and this can readily be accomplished by a batch technique separation method [42,43]. While this method of PPI turnover measurement is relatively simple, it provides little information as to the underlying biochemical events. However, a relatively large number of samples can be accommodated and the technique provides reliable data.

More information can be obtained if the inositol phosphates are fractionated by means of chromatography on Dowex-1 resin (formate form) anion-exchange columns. The water-soluble components are first applied to the column and free *myo*-inositol is eluted with 30–50 mL of water. Glycerophosphorylinositol is then eluted with 3×6 mL of 5 mM sodium tetraborate/60 mM sodium formate and IP_1, IP_2, IP_3 and IP_4 eluted sequentially with 3×6 mL volumes each of 0.1 M formic acid/0.2 M ammonium formate, 0.1 M formic acid/0.4 M ammonium formate, 0.1 M formic acid/ 0.8 M ammonium formate and 0.1 M formic acid/1.0 M ammonium formate respectively [44,45]. Using this fractionation technique, the rapid (5–10 s) appearance of labeled IP_3 and IP_2 can readily be detected following agonist addition (Fig. 8.7).

Ion-exchange HPLC can also be used to separate the individual inositol phosphates, and more importantly their positional isomers. A method that gives good separation of the various inositol phosphate isomers is that of Dean and Moyer [46] which involves use of a Partisil SAX column and a stepwise ammonium phosphate elution. Using this technique, $I(1,4,5)P_3$ and $I(1,3,4)P_3$ are readily separated as are a number of inositol bisphosphate and monophosphate isomers. While the HPLC technique offers the best resolution of the inositol phosphate mixture (and hence the most information), it is time-consuming, can handle relatively few samples (even

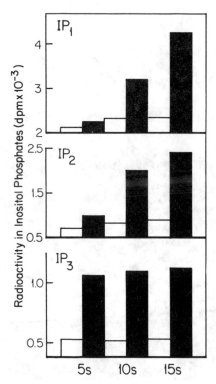

Fig. 8.7 — Rapid release of inositol phosphates from SK-N-SH cells in presence of carbachol. Cells prelabeled with [³H]inositol for 3 days were detached, washed and incubated in the presence of buffer alone (□) or 10 mM carbachol (■). Reactions were terminated by the addition of trichloroacetic acid, inositol phosphates extracted and separated by anion-exchange chromatography (from [23], *Mol. Pharmacol.* **35**, 195).

with an autosampler), and separations can be adversely affected by presence of salts and variation in column performance. Moreover, since measurement of radioactivity is required for identification of the inositol phosphate isomers, a column follower is necessary for detection if collection of individual fractions is to be avoided. However, this in itself can pose problems owing to the low sensitivity of currently available detection systems. Despite these considerations, it is likely that HPLC techniques will be increasingly important in studies of inositol lipid signaling owing to the complexity of inositol phosphate metabolism (see Fig. 8.4).

The method of high-voltage electrophoresis (HVE) has been successfully applied to the separation of inositol phosphates [47]. HVE is performed on Whatman No. 1 paper in Na⁺ oxalate buffer (pH 1.5) for 10–30 min at 4000 V. Inositol phosphates are detected either through autoradiography or by means of detection of phosphate-containing compounds by a molybdate spray [37]. For separation of the higher inositol phosphates, i.e. IP₄, inositol pentakis- and hexakisphosphates, this method offers at present the most convenient technique, even though isomer separation is not possible. An example of the results obtained with this method is shown in Fig. 8.8.

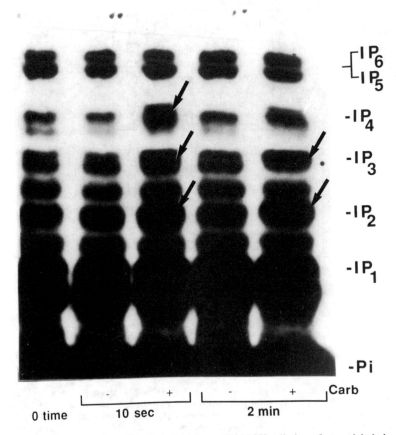

Fig. 8.8 — HVE separation of inositol phosphates. SK-N-SH cells were first prelabeled with
$^{32}P_i$ for 2 h and then exposed to carbachol for the times indicated. Reactions were terminated
and ^{32}P-labeled water-soluble compounds separated by HVE at 4000 V for 20 min. Inositol
phosphates were identified by autoradiography. Note that carbachol increases the release of
IP_4, IP_3 and IP_2 (as indicated by arrows).

8.3.3   Measurement of I(1,4,5)P₃ mass

The need for a simple, inexpensive and specific assay method for determination of
$I(1,4,5)P_3$ mass has long been recognized. The recent development of a specific
$I(1,4,5)P_3$ binding assay to determine tissue concentrations suggests that such a
technique may now be available [48]. The assay is based upon the binding of a known
amount of $[^3H]I(1,4,5)P_3$ to specific receptor sites on bovine adrenocortical membranes and competition for these sites by unlabeled $(I(1,4,5)P_3$ present in tissue
extracts. The assay is very specific for the 1,4,5 isomer of IP_3, and $I(1,3,4)P_3$,
$I(2,4,5)P_3$ and $I(1,3,4,5)P_4$ exhibit 30–50-fold lower binding. Inositol mono- and
bisphosphates exhibit an even lower affinity for the receptor. Sensitivity of the assay
is 0.2 pmol, which is adequate, since the concentration of $I(1,4,5)P_3$ is between 0.1
and 2 μM in quiescent tissues. Other normal constitutents of the assay buffer such as
ATP exhibit minimal interference. However, one drawback of this technique is that

only relatively robust changes in I(1,4,5)P$_3$ can be detected reliably. While the cost of the commercially available kit currently precludes extensive studies, preparation of adrenocortical membranes from slaughterhouse material can in part circumvent this problem. An example of the rapid increase in the intracellular concentration of I(1,4,5)P$_3$ that can be detected following receptor activation is shown in Fig. 8.9.

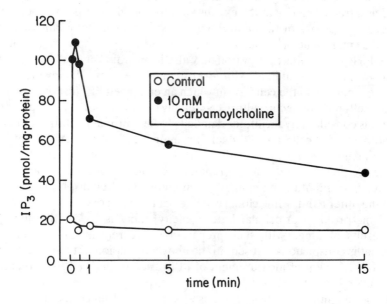

Fig. 8.9 — Time-course for the production of I(1,4,5)P$_3$ mass in SK-N-SH cells following carbachol addition. SK-N-SH cells were incubated for designated times in the absence (○) or presence (●) of carbachol. Reactions were terminated by the addition of trichloroacetic acid and water-soluble extracts assayed for I(1,4,5)P$_3$ mass. Carbachol increased I(1,4,5)P$_3$ mass by four-fold within 5 s of agonist addition.

8.3.4 Measurement of DAG mass
While measurement of the stimulated release of inositol phosphates has been extensively studied, considerably less attention has been focused on methods for determination of DAG levels. In some studies, the diacylglycerols have been labeled with [^{3}H]glycerol and their metabolism followed. Recently, an assay that allows measurement of DAG mass in crude lipid extracts of biological samples has been developed, based upon the quantitative conversion of DAG to [^{32}P]PA in the presence of bacterial DAG kinase and [^{32}P]ATP [49]. The assay is specific for *sn*-1,2-diacylglycerol and is sensitive to quantities as low as 20 pmol. While this assay technique provides the necessary quantitation of DAG mass, interfering substances derived from the tissue can sometimes pose problems. Furthermore, this method does not provide any information regarding the individual molecular species of DAG present. It is likely that other techniques for measurement of the mass and molecular species of DAG will be developed shortly to supplement the presently available assay techniques.

8.3.5 Choice of tissue preparation

Both basal and stimulated PPI turnover have been measured in a large number of mammalian tissues. However, the ease with which this turnover is determined varies considerably. For example, while blood-derived elements such as platelets and neutrophils are readily obtained, maintaining these cells for prolonged periods of time to facilitate the labeling of their lipid pools (particularly when [^{3}H]inositol is employed as a tracer) can be at the expense of physiological responsiveness. Tissue slices (e.g. from regions of the central nervous system) can be obtained relatively quickly and be maintained in a viable state for up to 3 h when appropriate conditions are selected. However, this time period may also be insufficient to allow the labeling of agonist-sensitive pools of lipid. Moreover, tissue heterogeneity may preclude any definite assessment as to the cell type in which an enhanced PPI turnover is elicited. In contrast, cells maintained in culture can readily be labeled for extended periods of time, and this considerably facilitates detailed studies. Primary cultures of neurons, glia, smooth muscle cells and adrenal chromaffin cells are examples of tissues employed in studies of receptor-mediated PPI turnover. Cultured tumor cells are even more frequently used. Both preparations can, however, be faulted since primary cultures cannot be maintained indefinitely and often display cell heterogeneity. On the other hand, while clonal cell lines can be used over a prolonged period and avoid the problem of cellular heterogeneity, there is always the question of whether results obtained with such preparations are relevant to untransformed tissues. What is conspicuously absent in the above discussion of the choice of tissue preparation is mention of measurement of PPI turnover in a *cell-free* preparation. While stimulated inositol phosphate release from prelabeled membranes has been reported, the magnitude of these responses is in general much reduced from that observed in the intact tissues [50,51]. Thus, our ability to monitor events underlying PPI turnover in a simpler membrane preparation is at present severely limited. This is in contrast to the situation that exists for the adenylate cyclase system in which agonist modulation of enzyme activity in isolated membranes can readily be detected. This one factor alone has considerably hindered progress in inositol lipid signaling studies since modulation of the intracellular components of the phosphoinositide pathway, e.g. G_p and PLC activity, is not readily accomplished. One means to partially circumvent this problem is the use of a permeabilized cell preparation [23,52–54]. Exposure of cells to low concentrations of digitonin renders the plasma membrane permeable to molecules of MW < 100 000. For example, non-hydrolyzable analogs of guanine nucleotides (which are normally membrane impermeant) can be introduced into cells and thereby directly enhance PLC activity. Similarly, other agents with the potential of interacting with G_p, PLC or other intracellular components of the pathway (e.g. IP$_3$ receptor or PKC) can be studied. In some cell types, receptor-coupling to PLC is also fully retained and the interaction between the agonist, G-protein and PLC can be directly studied (see Fig. 8.10).

8.4 PHOSPHOINOSITIDE TURNOVER AND DRUG ACTION

In the context of studies related to the identification of drugs and elucidation of their molecular mechanisms of action, measurement of PPI turnover serves two major purposes. First, by identification of the receptors that operate through this pathway,

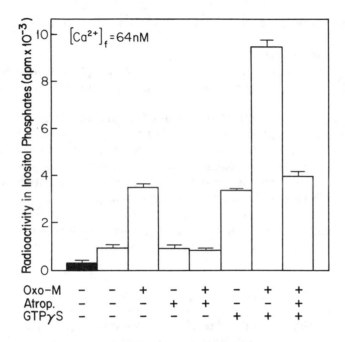

Fig. 8.10 — SK-N-SH cells were prelabeled with [^{3}H]inositol for 3 days and then permeabilized for 5 min at 37° in a medium that approximates the intracellular milieu (KGEH) and contains 20 μM digitonin. Cells were then washed free of the detergent and incubated for 15 min at 37° with KGEH in the presence of either muscarinic agonist (1 mM oxotremorine-M), antagonist (25 μM atropine) or GTPγS (50 μM). Reactions were terminated by rapid cooling to 0°, followed by centrifugation. Supernatants were collected and release of labeled inositol phosphates monitored. Note that while the addition of Oxo-M and GTPγS each elicits a release of inositol phosphates, in the combined presence of these agents, a synergistic increase in PPI hydrolysis is detected. Atropine reverses the increased release to a level similar to that seen in the presence of GTPγS alone. The solid bar indicates the release of inositol phosphates obtained at zero time (from [23], *Mol. Pharmacol.*, **35**, 195).

an insight is gained into their physiological significance and additionally, into the mechanism of action of drugs that disrupt these signaling events. Also provided is a useful delineation of individual receptor subtypes involved, e.g. of the five muscarinic receptor subtypes identified from molecular cloning studies, three (m_1, m_3/HM$_4$ and m_5) couple to PPI turnover while the remaining two (m_2 and m_4) are coupled to the inhibition of adenylate cyclase [55]. Second, PPI turnover provides a convenient biochemical measure of receptor *activity*. This is of particular importance in the central nervous system since prior to the identification of these PPI-linked receptors, only radioligand binding techniques were routinely available for their study. Furthermore, many psychotherapeutic agents, including anti-depressants and neuroleptics, are known from radioligand binding assays to interact with one or more PPI-linked receptors [56,57]. While changes in PPI turnover often parallel those of receptor number, on occasion changes in inositol lipid hydrolysis exceed those observed for receptor density [58]. Thus, PPI turnover measurement may provide clues regarding adaptive changes in chemical signaling within the CNS that are not readily apparent from radioligand binding measures alone.

8.4.1 Pharmacological and biochemical intervention in the phosphoinositide pathway

Within the series of events that link receptor occupancy to PLC activation, a number of sites exist that might be disrupted experimentally. From the standpoint of drug development, the receptor site is an obvious target, since it is extracellular and thus more accessible to drugs than intracellular sites. Furthermore, interference with subsequent steps may not retain the required degree of specificity, since this messenger system is shared by multiple receptor types, many of which may exist on the same cell. Nevertheless, as our knowledge of PPI turnover continues to increase, identification and development of agents able to block (or potentiate) one or more of these subsequent steps would not only be useful in the dissection of the regulatory aspects of this complex dual second-messenger system, but may conceivably be of potential therapeutic importance. Intervention at the level of G_p can be effected in intact cells through the addition of NaF which is presumed to dissociate the α and the $\beta\gamma$ subunits [59,60], or by the direct addition of guanine nucleotides to membranes or permeabilized cells [23,52–54]. Presently, there is no specific agent available that can interfere with this signal transduction process, perhaps reflecting the current uncertainty as to the identity of G_p. In some tissues, pertussis toxin can block stimulated PPI turnover, thereby implicating G_i, whereas in other tissues, cholera toxin is inhibitory, thereby implicating G_s [61]. However, these are the exceptions, since the two bacterial toxins are not inhibitory in most instances. One approach with the potential to probe the receptor–G_p interaction is the use of synthetic peptides corresponding to known regions of the α subunit of the G-protein. The 40 carboxyl-terminal amino acids are quite well conserved among the family of G-proteins and are presumed to be involved in receptor binding. Such synthetic peptides have been shown to compete with transducin for interaction with rhodopsin [62]. Similarly, the availability of these or similar peptides may permit studies of the receptor–G_p coupling. A similar deficit exists with regard to a selective inhibitor of the PIP_2 phosphodiesterase although U-73122 offers promise in that it readily enters intact cells, and can inhibit PIP_2 hydrolysis and physiological function in the same concentration range [63]. In some instances, aminoglycosides (e.g. neomycin) can also inhibit PIP_2 phosphodiesterase, presumably through interaction with PIP_2 substrate [64,65]. An additional complexity encountered when looking for specific inhibitors of this enzyme is that at least five separate isoenzymes of PLC have been postulated to exist and the sequence of two of these is known [66,67]. While for each of these isoenzymes, PIP_2 is the preferred substrate, differences in the guanine nucleotide regulation have been noted. Thus, the development of isoenzyme-specific inhibitors may prove feasible and certainly desirable. Limiting the availability of lipid substrates would appear to be another approach to the regulation of PPI turnover. At the level of CDP-DAG:inositol transferase (see Fig. 8.3), inositol analogs may prove to be either effective inhibitors of the enzyme [35], or, alternatively, incorporated into a species of PI which cannot readily undergo subsequent phosphorylation to PIP_2. Using this approach, Moyer *et al.* [68] have demonstrated that two analogs of inositol, 5-deoxy-*myo*-inositol and 5-deoxy-5-fluoro-*myo*-inositol, were able to permeate intact L 1210 leukemia cells and be incorporated into cellular phospholipid. However, this 'fraudulent lipid' could only be phosphorylated at the 4'-position of the inositol ring and thus PIP_2 synthesis was prevented. This type of approach may well prove fruitful in future studies, especially when trying to evaluate the relative importance of PI, PIP and PIP$_2$ breakdown to cellular physiology. Conversely, increasing the level of lipid substrates has been accomplished by transformation of cells with v-src and v-ros oncogenes [69,70]. A newly described synthetic analog of I(1,4,5)P$_3$, inositol (1,4,5)trisphosphorothioate, which is resistant to hydrolysis, offers considerable potential in the investigation of the interrelationship between the inositol phosphate, its receptor and calcium mobilization [71,72]. Inhibition of the degradation of I(1,4,5)P$_3$ in cell membranes can also be effected by inclusion of 2,3-bisphosphoglyceric acid [73]. With regard to the DAG limb of the pathway, it has long been known that synthetic analogs of DAG such as oleoyl-acetyl glycerol or phorbol esters are activators of PKC [5,32,36]. Inhibitors of DAG kinase and DAG lipase are also available although their specificity has yet to be firmly established. For example, the DAG kinase inhibitor, R 59 022, potentiates thrombin-induced increases in diacylglycerol level in platelets, and this occupies a role comparable to cAMP phosphodiesterase inhibitors in the adenylate cyclase pathway [74]. Similarly the DAG lipase inhibitor, RHC 80267, can prevent arachidonic acid release and thromboxane formation [75]. From this brief discussion, it is evident that the number of experimental tools available to probe the mechanisms of PPI hydrolysis is relatively limited. It should also be added that with the possible exceptions of diabetic neuropathy [76] or mania as discussed below, a deficit in the PPI pathway has yet to be clearly associated with a known pathological condition. This in turn may reflect the primary importance of this trans-membrane signaling mechanism to normal cell physiology.

8.4.2   Lithium, a prototypical drug affecting PPI turnover?

Although lithium salts have been effectively used in the treatment of mania for decades, the underlying mechanism of its action remains unknown. Largely as a result of studies by Sherman and colleagues, it is now established that therapeutically relevant concentrations of Li$^+$ result in the accumulation of inositol phosphates both *in vivo* and *in vitro*, the result of a selective inhibition of inositol monophosphatase [41,77,78]. The net effect is to reduce the availability of inositol which could theroetically result in the reduction of PI synthesis, especially if we consider that the blood–brain-barrier is relatively impermeable to inositol. Berridge *et al.* [42] have proposed that Li$^+$ may preferentially regulate Ca^{2+} mobilizing receptors that are hyperactive by reducing the formation of lipid-derived mediators and thereby act as a calcistat. The resultant inefficiency in neuronal communication would be particularly localized to areas of the brain that were highly active before drug treatment. Consistent with this hypothesis is the observation that chronic treatment of animals with Li$^+$ can reduce receptor-stimulated PPI turnover [79–81]. While the link between Li$^+$ and inositol lipid turnover remains an attractive hypothesis, questions still remain. For example, in the parotid gland, administration of Li$^+$ results in an accumulation of CDP-DAG (due to inositol depletion) but has no effect on receptor-mediated PIP$_2$ breakdown, a result consistent with the existence of a pool of lipid spared the effect of Li$^+$ [82]. A similar finding was obtained with GH$_3$ pituitary cells exposed to Li$^+$ [83]. Furthermore, Li$^+$ may also exert an effect at the G-protein level [84]. Despite these considerations, Li$^+$ continues to provide us with a valuable tool for the study of the intracellular regulation of the phosphoinositide pathway.

8.3 CONCLUDING REMARKS

Progress in our understanding of inositol lipid signaling continues at a daunting pace. Less than six years ago, many investigators outside this field viewed it as somewhat of an anomaly, and yet today, it is clear that there are few, if any, eukaryotic cells that do not rely on phosphoinositide-derived messages to sustain their normal physiology. What lies ahead? One area that can be expected to produce some unexpected findings is that of the metabolism of the individual inositol phosphates and their physiological functions. Presently, only two *bona fide* second messengers have been established, $I(1,4,5)P_3$ and DAG. Yet, the complexity of inositol phosphate isomer metabolism surely argues that additional PPI-derived molecules important for cell function must exist. For example, little is known of the inositol pentakis- and hexakisphosphates and yet it is possible that these molecules may serve as extracellular messengers [85]. Another candidate is $I(1,4)P_2$, which, although ineffective as a mobilizer of intracellular Ca^{2+} [27], has recently been proposed as an activator of DNA polymerase and to serve as a second messenger during the initiation of mitosis in stimulated cells [86]. While $I(1,3,4,5)P_4$ is currently out of favor as a mediator of Ca^{2+} influx across the plasma membrane, is it possible that its true function lies in the sequestration of released calcium [87]? It is also likely that the techniques of immunology and molecular biology will be increasingly used to probe the inositol lipid signaling mechanism. For example, antibodies to PIP_2 are now available, thus enabling a direct evaluation of the role of this lipid in cell differentiation [88]. Molecular cloning studies of the PLC isoenzymes have begun to yield unexpected findings relevant to the regulation of PPI turnover. For example, two regions of bovine brain PLC exhibit significant amino acid similarities to the products of various tyrosine-kinase-related oncogenes [66], while antibodies to phosphotyrosine can precipitate PLC in A-431 cells [89]. One interpretation of these results is that PLC may be a substrate for tyrosine kinase and this may have important functional consequences.

A major challenge to the pharmaceutical industry is in the application of the burgeoning body of information on the inositol lipids and their turnover to the screening and identification of compounds of potential therapeutic importance. A logical application lies in the combination of molecular biological approaches with measurement of PPI turnover to identify receptor subtype specific agents. For example, the expression of individual receptor molecules in cells following transfection of the appropriate cDNA clones and demonstration of their functional coupling to effector mechanisms allows for the identification of a 'tailored subtype specific' ligand [90]. This type of rational approach to the identification of agents targeted towards a specific receptor subtype that has previously been implicated in a clinically relevant phenomenon holds much promise for the future discovery of novel therapeutic compounds.

ACKNOWLEDGMENTS

The author wishes to thank Dr. A. Heacock for her helpful comments, Dr. B. W. Agranoff and E. B. Seguin for supplying Figs 8.6 and 8.8, and to Ms. Jo Ann Kelsch for preparation of the manuscript. This work was supported by National Institutes of Health Grant NS 23831 and National Institute of Mental Health Grant MH 42652.

REFERENCES

[1] Hokin, L. E. & Hokin, M. R. (1955). Effects of acetylcholine on the turnover of phosphoryl units in individual phospholipids of pancreas slices and brain cortex slices. *Biochim. Biophys. Acta* **18**, 102.

[2] Michell, R. H. (1975). Inositol phospholipids and cell surface receptor function. *Biochim. Biophys. Acta* **415**, 81.

[3] Streb, H., Irvine, R. F., Berridge, M. J., & Schulz, I. (1983). Release of Ca^{2+} from a nonmitochondrial intracellular store in pancreatic acinar cells by inositol-1,4,5-trisphosphate. *Nature* **305**, 67.

[4] Takai, Y., Kishimoto, A., Kikkawa, U., Mori, T., & Nishizuka, Y. (1979). Unsaturated diacylglycerol as a possible messenger for the activation of calcium-activated, phospholipid-dependent protein kinase system. *Biochem. Biophys. Res. Commun.* **91**, 1218.

[5] Nishizuka, Y. (1984). Turnover of inositol phospholipids and signal transduction. *Science* **225**, 1365.

[6] Bourne, H. R. (1989). Who carries what message? *Nature* **337**, 504.

[7] Gilman, A. G. (1987). G-proteins; transducers of receptor-generated signals. *Annu. Rev. Biochem.* **56**, 615.

[8] Waldman, S. A. & Murad, F. (1987). Cyclic GMP synthesis and function. *Pharmacol. Rev.* **39**, 163.

[9] Fisher S. K. & Agranoff, B. W. (1987). Receptor activation and inositol lipid hydrolysis in neural tisues. *J. Neurochem.* **48**, 999.

[10] Abdel-Latif, A. A. (1986). Calcium-mobilizing receptors, polyphosphoinositides, and the generation of second messengers. *Pharmacol. Rev.* **38**, 227.

[11] Berridge, M. J. (1986). Inositol phosphates as second messengers. In: J. W. Putney, Jr. (ed.) *Phosphoinositides and Receptor Mechanisms*. Alan R. Liss Press, New York, p. 25.

[12] Williamson, J. R. (1986). Role of inositol lipid breakdown in the generation of intracellular signals. *Hypertension* **8** (Suppl II), 140.

[13] Berridge, M. J. (1987). Inositol lipids and cell proliferation. *Biochim. Biophys. Acta* **907**, 33.

[14] Folch, J. (1949). Complete fractionation of brain cephalin: isolation from its phosphatidyl serine, phosphatidlyl ethanolamine and diphosphoinositide. *J. Biol. Chem.* **177**, 497.

[15] Agranoff, B. W. (1987). Receptor-mediated phosphcinositide metabolism. In: Y. H. Ehrlich, W. Berry, & R. H. Lenox (eds) *Advances in Experimental Biology and Medicine*: *Molecular Mechanisms of Neuronal Responsiveness*. Plenum Press, New York (in press).

[16] Santiago-Calvo, E., Mule, S. J., & Hokin, L. E. (1963). A new phosphoinositide containing four phosphates per inositol. *Biochim. Biophys. Acta* **70**, 91.

[17] Traynor-Kaplan, A. E., Harris, A. L., Thompson, B. L., Taylor, P., & Sklar, L. A. (1988). An inositol tetrakisphosphate-containing phospholipid in activated neutrophils. *Nature* **334**, 353.

[18] Fisher, S. K., Van Rooijen, L. A. A., & Agranoff, B. W. (1984). Renewed interest in the polyphosphoinositides. *Trends Biochem. Sci.* **9**, 53.

[19] Whitman, M., Fleischman , L., Chahwala, S. B., Cantley, L., & Rosoff, P. (1986). Phosphoinositides, mitogenesis, and oncogenesis. In: J. W. Putney, Jr. (ed.) *Phosphoinositides and Receptor Mechanisms*. Alan R. Liss Press, New York, p. 197.

[20] Fain, J. N., Wallace, M. A., & Wojcikiewicz, R. J. H. (1988). Evidence for involvement of guanine nucleotide-binding regulatory proteins in the activation of phospholipases by hormones. *FASEB J.* **2**, 2569.

[21] Smith, C. D., Cox, C. C., & Snyderman, R. (1986). Receptor-coupled activation of phosphoinositide-specific phospholipase C by an N protein. *Science* **232**, 97.

[22] Bradford, P. G. & Rubin, R. P. (1986). Guanine nucleotide regulation of phospholipase C activity in permeabilized rabbit neutrophils. *Biochem. J.* **239**, 97.

[23] Fisher, S. K., Domask, L. M., & Roland, R. M. (1989). Muscarinic receptor regulation of cytoplasmic Ca^{2+} concentrations in human SK–N–SH neuroblastoma cells: Ca^{2+} requirements for phospholipase C activation. *Mol. Pharmacol.* **35**, 195.

[24] Worley, P. F., Baraban, J. M., Supattapone, S., Wilson, V. S., & Snyder, S. H. (1987). Characterization of inositol trisphosphate receptor binding in brain. Regulation by pH and calcium. *J. Biol. Chem.* **262**, 12132.

[25] Delfert, D. M., Hill, S., Pershadsingh, H. A., Sherman, W. R., & McDonald, J. M. (1986). *myo*-Inositol 1,4,5-trisphosphate mobilizes Ca^{2+} from isolated adipocyte endoplasmic reticulum but not from plasma membranes. *Biochem. J.* **236**, 37.

[26] Guiellemette, G., Balla, T., Baukal, A. J., & Catt, K. J. (1988). Characterization of inositol 1,4,5-trisphosphate receptors and calcium mobilization in a hepatic plasma membrane fraction. *J. Biol. Chem.* **263**, 4541.

[27] Berridge, M. J. & Irvine, R. F. (1984). Inositol trisphosphate, a novel second messenger in cellular signal transduction. *Nature* **312**, 315.

[28] Irvine, R. F. & Moor, R. M. (1986). Micro-injection of inositol 1,3,4,5-tetrakisphosphate activates sea urchin eggs by a mechanism dependent on external Ca^{2+}. *Biochem. J.* **240**, 917.

[29] Snyder, P. M., Krause, K.-H., & Welsh, M. J. (1988). Inositol trisphosphate isomers, but not inositol 1,3,4,5-tetrakisphosphate, induce calcium influx in *Xenopus laevis* oocytes. *J. Biol. Chem.* **263**, 11048.

[30] Nahorski, S. R. (1988). Inositol polyphosphates and neuronal calcium homeostasis. *Trends Neurosci.* **11**, 444.

[31] Nishizuka, Y. (1988). The molecular heterogeneity of protein kinase C and its implications for cellular regulation. *Nature* **334**, 661.

[32] Nishizuka, Y. (1986). Studies and perspectives of protein kinase C. *Science* **233**, 305.

[33] Kraft, A. S. & Anderson, W. B. (1983). Phorbol esters increase the amount of Ca^{2+}, phospholipid-dependent protein ·kinase associated with the plasma membrane. *Nature* **301**, 621.

[34] Petzold, G. L. & Agranoff, B. W. (1965). Studies on the formation of CDP-diglyceride. *Fed. Proc.* **24**, 476.

[35] Benjamins, J. A. & Agranoff, B. W. (1969). Distribution and properties of CDP-diglyceride: inositol transferase from brain. *J. Neurochem.* **16**, 513.

[36] Nishizuka, Y. (1984). Turnover of inositol phospholipids and signal transduction. *Science* **225**, 1365.

[37] Hajra, A. K., Fisher, S. K., & Agranoff, B. W. (1988). Isolation, separation, and analysis of phosphoinositides from biological sources. In: A. A. Boulton, G. B. Baker, & L. A. Horrocks (eds) *Lipids and Related Compounds*. Humana Press, New Jersey, p. 211.

[38] Jolles, J., Schrama, L. H., & Gispen, W. H. (1981). Calcium-dependent turnover of brain polyphosphoinositides *in vitro* after prelabling *in vivo*. *Biochim. Biophys. Acta* **666**, 90.

[39] Weiss, S. J., McKinney, J. S., & Putney, J. W., Jr. (1982). Receptor-mediated net breakdown of phosphatidylinositol 4,5-bisphosphate in parotid acinar cells. *Biochem. J.* **206**, 555.

[40] Hauser, G. & Papu, A. (1982). Effects of propranolol and other cationic amphiphilic drugs on phospholipid metabolism. In: L. A. Horrocks, G. B. Ansell, & G. Procellati (eds) *Phospholipids in the Nervous System*, Vol. 1, Raven Press, New York, p. 283.

[41] Hallcher, L. M. & Sherman, W. R. (1980). The effects of lithium ion and other agents on the activity of *myo*-inositol-1-phosphatase from bovine brain. *J. Biol. Chem.* **255**, 10896.

[42] Berridge, M. J., Downes, C. P., & Hanley, M. R. (1982). Lithium amplified agonist-dependent phosphatidylinositol responses in brain and salivary glands. *Biochem. J.* **206**, 587.

[43] Fisher, S. K. & Bartus, R. T. (1985). Regional differences in the coupling of muscarinic receptors to inositol phospholipid hydrolysis in guinea pig brain. *J. Neurochem.* **45**, 1085.

[44] Berridge, M. J., Dawson, R. M. C., Downes, C. P., Heslop, J. P., & Irvine, R. F. (1983). Changes in the levels of inositol phosphates after agonist-dependent hydrolysis of membrane phosphoinositides. *Biochem. J.* **212**, 473.

[45] Batty, I. R., Nahorski, S. R., & Irvine, R. F. (1985). Rapid formation of inositol 1,3,4,5-tetrakisphosphate following muscarinic receptor stimulation of rat cerebral cortical slices. *Biochem. J.* **232**, 211.

[46] Dean, N. M. & Moyer, J. D. (1987). Separation of multiple isomers of inositol phosphates formed in GH_3 cells. *Biochem. J.* **242**, 361.

[47] Seiffert, U. B. & Agranoff, B. W. (1965). Isolation and separation of inositol phosphates from hydrolysate of rat tissues. *Biochim. Biophys. Acta* **98**, 574.

[48] Palmer, S., Hughes, K. T., Lee, D. Y., & Wakelam, M. J. O. (1989). Development of a novel, Ins(1,4,5)P$_3$-specific binding assay. Its use to determine the intracellular concentration in Ins(1,4,5)P$_3$ in unstimulated and vasopressin-stimulated rat hepatocytes. *Cellular Signaling* **1**, 147.

[49] Preiss, J. E., Bell, R. M., & Niedel, J. M. (1987). Diacylglycerol mass measurements in stimulated HL-60 phagocytes. *J. Immunology* **138**, 1542.

[50] Rebecchi, M. J. & Rosen, O. M. (1987). Stimulation of polyphosphoinositide

hydrolysis by thrombin in membranes from human fibroblasts. *Biochem. J.* **245**, 49.

[51] Hepler, J. R. & Harden, T. K. (1986). Guanine nucleotide-dependent pertussis-toxin-insensitive stimulation of inositol phosphate formation by carbachol in a membrane preparation from human astrocytoma cells. *Biochem. J.* **239**, 141.

[52] Eberhard, D. A. & Holz, R. W. (1987). Cholinergic stimulation of inositol phosphate formation in bovine adrenal chromaffin cells: distinct nicotinic and muscarinic mechanisms. *J. Neurochem.* **49**, 1634.

[53] Best, L. (1986). A role for calcium in the breakdown of inositol phospholipids in intact and digitonin-permeabilized pancreatic islets. *Biochem. J.* **238**, 773.

[54] Bradford, P. G. & Rubin, R. P. (1986). Guanine nucleotide regulation of phospholipase C activity in permeabilized rabbit neutrophils. *Biochem. J.* **239**, 97.

[55] Peralta, E. G., Ashkenazi, A., Winslow, J. W., Ramachandran, J., & Capon, D. J. (1988). Differential regulation of PI hydrolysis and adenylyl cyclase by muscarinic receptor subtypes. *Nature* **334**, 434.

[56] Richelson, E. & Nelson, A. (1984). Antagonism by antidepressants of neurotransmitter receptors of normal human brain *in vitro. J. Pharmacol. Exp. Ther.* **230**, 94.

[57] Richelson, E. & Nelson, A. (1984b). Antagonism by neuroleptics of neurotransmitter receptors of normal human brain *in vitro. Eur. J. Pharmacol.* **103**, 197.

[58] Kendall, D. A. & Nahorski, S. R. (1985). 5-Hydroxytryptamine-stimulated inositol phospholipid hydrolysis in rat cerebral cortex slices: pharmacological characterization and effects of antidepressants. *J. Pharmacol. Exp. Ther.* **233**, 473.

[59] Hepler, J. R., Earp, H. S., & Harden, T. K. (1988). Long-term phorbol ester treatment down-regulates protein kinase C and sensitizes the phosphoinositide signaling pathway to hormone and growth factor stimulation. *J. Biol. Chem.* **263**, 7610.

[60] Jope, R. S (1988). Modulation of phosphoinositide hydrolysis by NaF and aluminium in rat cortical slices. *J. Neurochem.* **51**, 1731.

[61] Lo, W. W. Y. & Hughes, J. (1987). Receptor-phosphoinositidase C coupling. Multiple G-proteins? *FEBS Lett.* **224**, 1.

[62] Hamm, H. E., Deretic, D., Arendt, A., Hargrave, P. A., Koenig, B., & Hofmann, K. P. (1988). Site of G protein binding to rhodopsin mapped with synthetic peptides from the α subunit. *Science* **241**, 832.

[63] Smith, R., Bleasdale, J., Bundy, G., Sam, L., & Justen, J. (1989). Effects of a phospholipase C inhibitor, U-73122, on receptor-coupled signal transduction in human neutrophils. *FASEB J.* **3**, A370.

[64] Van Rooijen, L. A. A. & Agranoff, B. W. (1986). Inhibition of polyphosphoinositide phosphodiesterase by aminoglycoside antibiotics. *Neurochem. Res.* **10**, 1019.

[65] Taylor, C. W., Blakeley, D. M., & Brown, K. D. (1988). Guanine nucleotides stimulate hydrolysis of phosphatidylinositol and polyphosphoinositides in permeabilized Swiss 3T3 cells. *FEBS Lett.* **237**, 163.

[66] Suh, P.-G., Ryu, S. H., Moon, K. H., Suh, H. W., & Rhee, S. G. (1988).

Inositol phospholipid-specific phospholipase C: complete cDNA and protein sequences and sequence homology to tryosine kinase-related oncogene products. *Proc. Natl. Acad. Sci. USA* **85**, 5419.

[67] Bennett, C. F., Balcarek, J. M., Varrichio, A., & Crooke, S. T. (1988). Molecular cloning and complete amino-acid sequence of form-I phosphoinositide-specific phospholipase C. *Nature* **334**, 268.

[68] Moyer, J. D., Reizes, O., Ahir, S., Jiang, C., Malinowski, M., & Baker, D. C. (1988). Substrate properties of analogs of *myo*-inositol. *Mol. Pharmacol.* **33**, 683.

[69] Sugimoto, Y., Whitman, M., Cantley, L. C., & Erikson, R. L. (1984). Evidence that the Rous sarcoma virus transforming gene product phosphorylates phosphatidylinositol and diacylglycerol. *Proc. Natl. Acad. Sci. USA* **81**, 2117.

[70] Macara, I. G., Marinetti, G. V., & Galduzzi, P. C. (1984). Transforming protein of avian sarcoma virus UR2 is associated with phosphatidylinositol kinase activity: possible role in tumorigenesis. *Proc. Natl. Acad. Sci. USA* **81** 2728.

[71] Willcocks, A. L., Potter, B. V. L., Cooke, A. M., & Nahorski, S. R. (1988). *Myo*-inositol(1,4,5)-triphosphorothioate binds to specific [^{3}H]inositol-(1,4,5)trisphosphate sites in rat cerebellum and is resistant to 5-phosphatase. *Eur. J. Pharmacol.* **155**, 181.

[72] Taylor, C. W., Berridge, M. J., Brown, K. D., Cooke, A. M., & Potter, B. V. L. (1988). DL-*myo*-inositol(1,4,5)trisphosphorothioate mobilized intracellular Ca^{2+} in Swiss 3T3 cells and *Xenopus* oocytes. *Biochem. Biophys. Res. Commun.* **150**, 262.

[73] Downes, C. P., Mussat, M. C., & Mitchell, R. H. (1982). The inositiol trisphosphate phosphomonoesterase of the human erythrocyte membrane. *Biochem. J.* **203**, 169.

[74] de Chaffoy de Courcelles, D., Roevens, P., & Van Belle, H. (1985). R 59 022, a diacylglycerol kinase inhibitor. Its effect on diacylglycerol and thrombin-induced C kinase activation in the intact platelet. *J. Biol. Chem.* **260**, 15762.

[75] Natarajan, R., Stern, N., & Nadler, J. (1988). Diacylglycerol provides arachidonic acid for lipoxygenase products that mediate angiotensin II-induced aldosterone synthesis. *Biochem. Biophys. Res. Commun.* **156**, 717.

[76] Greene, D. A. & Lattimer, S. A. (1985). Altered nerve *myo*-inositol metabolism in experimental diabetes and its relationship to nerve function. In: J. E. Bleasdale, J. Eichberg, & G. Hauser (eds) *Inositol and Phosphoinositides*: *Metabolism and Biological Regulation*. Humana Press, New Jersey, P. 563.

[77] Allison, J. H. & Blisner, M. E. (1976). Inhibition of the effect of lithium on brain inositol by atropine and scopolamine. *Biochem. Biophys. Res. Commun.* **68**, 1332.

[78] Allison, J. H., Blisner, M. E., Holland, W. H., Hipps, P. P., & Sherman, W. R. (1976). Increased brain *myo*-inositol 1-phosphate in lithium-treated rats. *Biochem. Biophys. Res. Commun.* **71**, 664.

[79] Casebolt, T. & Jope, R. S. (1987). Chronic lithium treatment reduces norepinephrine-stimulated inositol phospholipid hydrolysis in rat cortex. *Eur. J. Pharmacol.* **140**, 245.

[80] Kendall, D. A. & Nahorski, S. R. (1987). Acute and chronic lithium influence agonist and depolarization-stimulated inositol phospholipid hydrolysis in rat cerebral cortex. *J. Pharmacol. Exp. Ther.* **241**, 1023.

[81] Godfrey, P. P., McClue, S. J., White, A. M., Wood, A. J., & Grahame-Smith, D. G. (1989). Subacute and chronic *in vivo* lithium treatment inhibits agonist- and sodium fluoride-stimulated inositol phosphate production in rat cortex. *J. Neurochem.* **52**, 498.

[82] Downes, C. P. & Stone, M. A. (1986). Lithium-induced reduction in intracellular inositol supply in cholinergically stimulated parotid gland. *Biochem. J.* **234**, 199.

[83] Drummond, A. H. & Raeburn, C. A. (1984). The interaction of lithium with thyrotropin releasing hormone-stimulated lipid metabolism in GH_3 pituitary tumor cells. *Biochem. J.* **224**, 129.

[84] Avissar, S., Schreiber, G., Danon, A., & Belmaker, R. H. (1988). Lithium inhibits adrenergic and cholinergic increases in GTP binding in rat cortex. *Nature* **331**, 440.

[85] Vallejo, M., Jackson, T., Lightman, S., & Hanley, M. R., (1978). Occurrence and extracellular actions of inositol pentakis- and hexakisphosphate in mammalian brain. *Nature* **330**, 656.

[86] Sylvia, V., Curtin, G., Norman, J., Stec, J., & Busbee, D. (1988). Activation of a low specific activity form of DNA polymerase α by inositol-1,4-bisphosphate. *Cell* **54**, 651.

[87] Hill, T. D., Dean, N. M., & Boynton, A. L. (1988). Inositol 1,3,4,5-tetrakisphosphate induces Ca^{2+} sequestration in rat liver cells. *Science* **242**, 1176.

[88] Matuoka, K., Fukami, K., Nakanishi, O., Kawai, S., & Takenawa, T. (1988). Mitogenesis in response to PDGF and bombesin abolished by microinjection of antibody to PIP_2. *Science* **239**, 640.

[89] Wahl, M. I., Daniel, T. O., & Carpenter, G. (1988). Antiphosphotyrosine recovery of phospholipase C activity after EGF treatment of A-431 cells. *Science* **241**, 968.

[90] Lester, H. A. (1988). Heterologous expression of excitability proteins: route to more specific drugs? *Science* **241**, 1057.

9

Molecular biology of receptors and drug design

J. Craig Venter and **Claire M. Fraser***
Section of Receptor Biochemistry and Molecular Biology, Laboratory of
Molecular and Cellular Neurobiology, National Institute of Neurological
Disorders and Stroke, National Institutes of Health, Bethesda, Maryland, USA
*Section of Molecular Neurobiology, Laboratory of Physiologic and
Pharmacologic Studies, National Institute on Alcohol Abuse and Alcoholism,
Rockville, Maryland, USA

9.1 INTRODUCTION

Up until the present, the design of new drugs has relied almost completely upon
chemical modification of endogenous receptor ligands or upon serendipitous discovery of natural products with therapeutic potential. However, recent advances in the
cloning and sequence analysis of hormone and neurotransmitter receptor genes will
lead to major advances in the drug discovery process. These advances will come from
three major areas: (1) the knowledge of receptor structure (molecular modeling,
site-directed mutagenesis and X-ray crystallography); (2) more specific drug screening and *in vitro* assays using permanent cell lines expressing pure receptor populations; and (3) a thorough understanding of the mechanisms of receptor activation
and the information transfer process from the receptors to cellular activators or
effectors. This chapter will outline some of the recent advances in each of these key
areas and will explain how they will relate to the drug discovery process.

9.2 RECEPTOR GENE SUPERFAMILIES

Pharmacological and physiological classification of receptors has grouped certain
families of receptors together based on such criteria as ligand binding properties,
activation of cellular effector systems or signal transduction mechanisms. However,
recent molecular biological approaches to the study of receptor systems have

revealed that all receptors cloned and sequenced to date can be assigned to one of only a few receptor supergene families (Table 9.1).

Table 9.1 — Receptor gene superfamilies

Opsin/adrenergic/muscarinic/dopamine/serotonin/substance K

Nicotinic/GABA/glycine

Growth hormone/prolactin

Insulin/EGF

Steroid hormone

Almost a century of pharmacological and biochemical evidence suggested that adrenergic and muscarinic cholinergic receptors represented divergent proteins that interacted with distinctly different ligands and activated unique intracellular pathways. However, biochemical and immunological studies in the early 1980s led Venter *et al.* [1–3] to speculate that adrenergic and muscarinic cholinergic receptors may be closely related structurally and may represent members of a larger gene family of receptors that interact with guanine nucleotide regulatory (G) proteins. The data derived from cloning and sequence analysis of adrenergic and muscarinic cholinergic receptors have confirmed our earlier observations on the homology between receptor classes and the existence of a superfamily of receptors which includes adrenergic [4–13], muscarinic acetylcholine [14–21], serotonin [22,23], dopamine [24], angiotensin [25], substance K [26] and yeast mating factor receptors [27] as well as the visual pigments, the opsins [28–30] and bacteriorhodopsin [31]. Knowledge of the primary structure of these related proteins has also provided new information on the putative three-dimensional orientation of these receptors in the bilayer and suggested possible molecular mechanisms of signal transduction.

9.3 CLONING AND SEQUENCE ANALYSIS OF β-ADRENERGIC RECEPTOR GENES

β-adrenergic receptors are one of the best characterized receptors that mediate their effects intracellularly through the action of a stimulatory guanine nucleotide binding protein, G_s [32,33]. Agonist occupancy of the receptor initiates a series of events which ultimately lead to the activation of adenylate cyclase (Fig. 9.1). To date, the genes encoding human [7] and turkey [8] $β_1$-adrenergic receptors and human [9,10], hamster [11], rat [12] and mouse [13] $β_2$-adrenergic receptors have been cloned and sequenced.

As illustrated in Fig. 9.2, the gene for the human $β_1$-adrenergic receptor, isolated from a placental cDNA library, encodes a protein of 477 amino acid residues with a calculated molecular weight of 51 200 [7]. In contrast, the human $β_2$-adrenergic receptor gene, obtained from placental [9] and brain [10] cDNA libraries, encodes a protein of 413 amino acids with a calculated molecular weight of 46 480. These

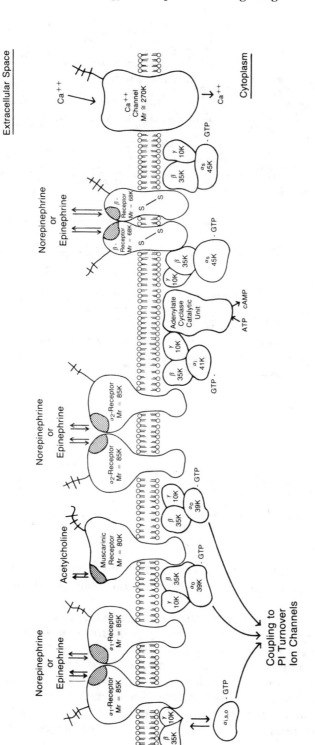

Fig. 9.1 — Schematic model of the plasma membrane depicting adrenergic and muscarinic cholinergic receptors and their respective effector systems. (See also the schematic model given in the color section.)

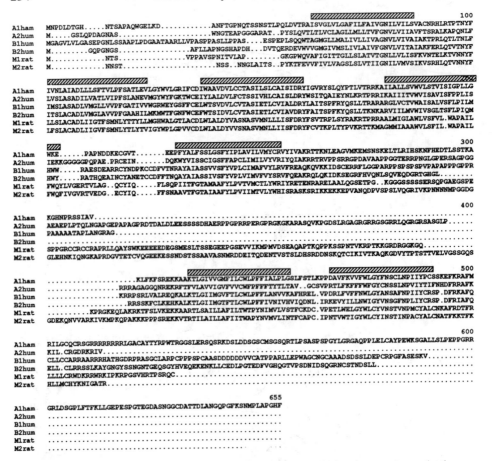

Fig. 9.2 — Comparison of the deduced amino acid sequences of the hamster α_1-adrenergic, the human α_2-adrenergic, β_1-adrenergic and β_2-adrenergic and the rat M1 and M2 muscarinic acetylcholine receptors. The sequences were aligned with gaps introduced to display maximum homology by the GAP program of the University of Wisconsin Genetics Computer Group. Putative membrane-spanning domains in each of the receptors are indicated by the hatched boxes above the sequences.

β-adrenergic receptor subtypes share 54% overall homology in protein sequence; however, there are small domains in each protein in which the homology is as high as 100%.

Analysis of the primary structure of β-adrenergic receptors reveals that both receptor subtypes possess seven stretches of hydrophobic amino acids that are of sufficient length to span the lipid bilayer ([7–13], Fig. 9.3). By analogy with bacteriorhodopsin [31,40], it has been proposed that these regions of the receptors may represent membrane-spanning domains. Thus, a model has emerged suggesting that the receptor is composed of seven transmembrane segments connected by alternating intracellular and extracellular loops ([9,10], Fig. 9.4). In the native protein, these transmembrane helices are most likely arranged in a bundle enclosing

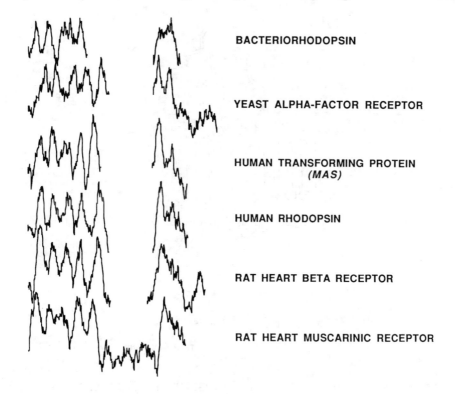

BACTERIORHODOPSIN

YEAST ALPHA-FACTOR RECEPTOR

HUMAN TRANSFORMING PROTEIN
(MAS)

HUMAN RHODOPSIN

RAT HEART BETA RECEPTOR

RAT HEART MUSCARINIC RECEPTOR

Fig. 9.3 — Hydropathy analysis of adrenergic and muscarinic cholinergic receptors and related proteins. The secondary structure of the indicated proteins was analyzed by the method of Kyte and Doolittle (1982), *J. Mol. Biol.* **157**, 105]. Peaks in the profile indicate regions containing hydrophobic amino acids. The similarity in the profiles of these proteins is striking. Each protein exhibits seven well-defined hydrophobic domains that have been postulated to represent membrane-spanning segments.

an aqueous pocket. The amino terminus of the receptors, which contains putative sites for N-linked glycosylation, is thought to be located extracellularly whereas the carboxy terminus of the protein is located intracellularly (Fig. 9.4). It is of note that the homology among all the members of this receptor gene family is highest in the putative transmembrane-spanning domains, suggesting an important role for this structure in receptor function.

9.4   CLONING AND SEQUENCE ANALYSIS OF α-ADRENERGIC RECEPTOR GENES

α-adrenergic receptors were originally subclassified into α_1- and α_2-adrenergic subtypes based on anatomical and pharmacological criteria [34,35]. α_1 and α_2-adrenergic receptors are coupled to at least two distinct second-messenger pathways through G proteins; α_1-adrenergic receptors stimulate breakdown of phosphoinositides and α_2-adrenergic receptors inhibit adenylate cyclase activity

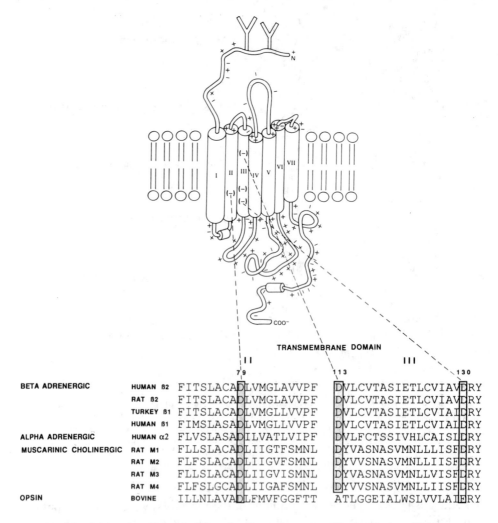

Fig. 9.4 — Schematic model of the human β₂-adrenergic receptor. The top portion of the figure illustrates a cutaway view of the human β_2-adrenergic receptor oriented in the lipid bilayer. The receptor contains seven transmembrane-spanning domains (I–VII) connected by alternating extracellular and intracellular loops. Charged residues are indicated as are regions of predicted α-helical structure (cylinders). The NH_3^+ terminus of the receptor is thought to be oriented extracellularly. This portion of the receptor contains two putative sites for N-linked glycosylation (Y). This model places the COO^- terminus of the receptor intracellularly. The bottom portion of the figure illustrates the deduced amino acid sequences of defined regions of several members of this receptor family. The conserved aspartate residues that were studied by site-directed mutagenesis are highlighted and numbered.

(Fig. 9.1). The α_1-adrenergic receptor has been implicated in a number of physiological functions including smooth muscle contraction and regulation of hepatic glycogen metabolism whereas the α_2-adrenergic receptor appears to play an important role in platelet aggregation, regulation of insulin release from the pancreas and regulation of lipid metabolism in adipose tissue.

During the past two years the genes encoding a hamster α_1-adrenergic receptor [4] and two distinct human α_2-adrenergic receptors from platelets [5] and kidney [6] have been cloned and sequenced. As illustrated in Fig. 9.2, these receptors share considerable homology among themselves and with other receptors in the gene family such as β-adrenergic and muscarinic acetylcholine receptors, possessing seven regions of hydrophobic amino acids that are presumed to represent transmembrane-spanning segments.

9.5 CLONING AND SEQUENCE ANALYSIS OF MUSCARINIC ACETYLCHOLINE RECEPTOR GENES

Muscarinic acetylcholine receptors have a distinct pharmacology and modulate a large array of effector systems including adenylate cyclase attentuation, phosphoinositide hydrolysis, Ca^{2+} channel activity and K^+ channel activity [36]. Depending on the tissue, the coupling of muscarinic receptors to these cellular effectors can produce an array of biochemical and physiological responses. One proposed explanation for this tremendous diversity has been the existence of multiple receptor subtypes; this hypothesis has been supported by extensive pharmacological data [37–39].

The notion of multiple subtypes of muscarinic receptor has been confirmed with the cloning and sequence analysis of genes encoding muscarinic receptors from pig brain [15] and heart [14] cDNA libraries, rat brain [19] and heart [12] cDNA libraries and human genomic libraries [17]. In the rat and the human, at least four muscarinic receptor subtypes have been defined pharmacologically and five distinct but highly homologous genes have been identified encoding proteins of 460 (M1, 51 368 daltons), 466 (M2, 51 543 daltons), 478 (M4, 52,695 daltons), 589 (M3, 66 133 daltons) and 531 (M5) amino acids (Fig. 9.5). All of the muscarinic receptors contain at least two potential sites for glycosylation. Differences between the calculated molecular weights of these proteins and the size of the receptors on SDS–polyacrylamide gels suggest that the receptors are glycosylated to an extent of 30–35% by weight.

As with other members of this multigene family, the primary sequence of all muscarinic receptors sequenced to date contains seven stretches of hydrophobic amino acids which presumably represent transmembrane domains in these proteins (Fig. 9.5). The most typical structure proposed for protein segments which span the cell membrane are helical; indeed, X-ray and neutron diffraction studies of bacteriorhodopsin have suggested that the transmembrane segments of bacteriorhodopsin exist as α helices roughly perpendicular to the membrane [40]. Modeling of the transmembrane segments of the rat M1 muscarinic receptor as α helices is illustrated in Fig. 9.6.

The extent of sequence homology among the five muscarinic receptors is 36% and homology increases to 52% when favored amino substitutions are considered [36]. Homology among subtypes is even higher within the transmembrane domains of these proteins which display 66% overall homology. The least conserved domain of the five muscarinic receptor subtypes is contained within the third intracellular loop of the proteins (Figs 9.5 and 9.6). It is possible that this portion of the receptors may, in part, determine the specificity of the receptors for distinct G proteins.

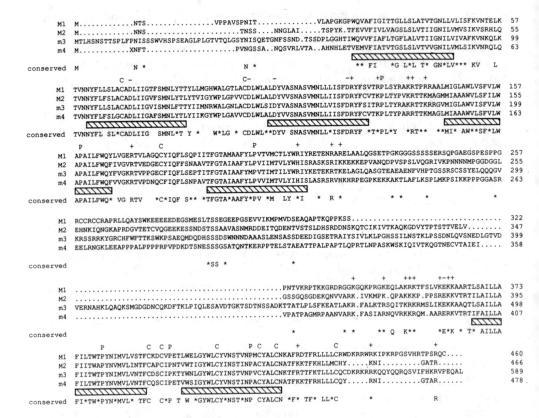

Fig. 9.5 — Comparison of the deduced amino acid sequences of the rat muscarinic cholinergic receptors. The sequences were aligned with gaps introduced to display maximum homology by the GAP program. The amino acids conserved in all four proteins are shown below the sequences, indicated by the letter for that amino acid or by an asterisk if favored substitutions are present. Charged groups, cysteines and prolines which are conserved in all four proteins are shown above the sequences. Putative membrane-spanning regions are indicated by hatched bars.

9.6 PERMANENT EXPRESSION OF RECEPTOR GENES

Characterization of the genes encoding the neurotransmitter receptors has necessitated their expression and assay in an appropriate system [41]. The development of a number of techniques for gene transfer into eukaryotic cells (transfection) provides the investigator with several options for the expression of a particular gene. In order to achieve stable expression of genes in cultured cells one requires a selection system that allows for survival of only those cells that have taken up the foreign DNA and

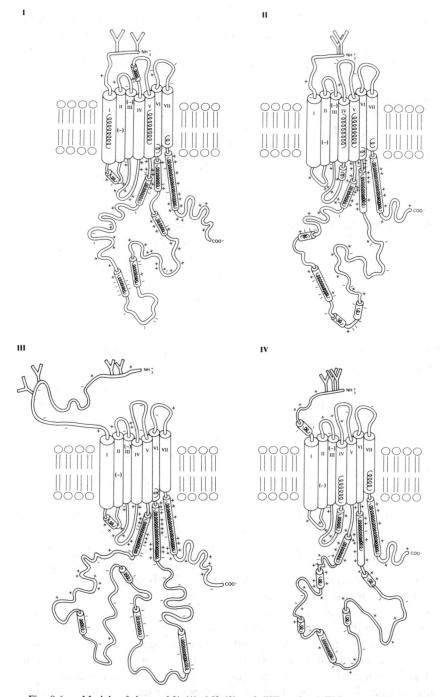

Fig. 9.6 — Models of the rat M1 (1), M2 (2), m3 (III) and m4 (IV) muscarinic receptors. Positively and negatively charged amino acid side chains are indicated. Coils represent regions calculated to be α-helical. The large intracellular loops of the receptors display the lowest structural homology.

integrated it into the cell chromatin. Surviving cells grow into discrete colonies that can be isolated, expanded and assayed for the presence of a particular gene product. When performed successfully, clonal cell lines that continuously express a gene of interest are obtained and this allows for an essentially unlimited supply of the gene products.

Establishment of a system for the continuous expression of genes in cultured mammalian cells allows for the study of the pharmacology, biochemistry and processing of a single homogeneous population of receptors in a defined membrane environment. This approach lends itself to an examination of the behavior of a particular receptor in a number of different cells types and also to a comparison of different receptor subtypes in the same cell. The expression of human receptors in cultured cells may have a marked impact on the identification and screening of new therapeutic agents as well as providing a source of receptors for structural analysis. We have extended our initial work on the expression of neurotransmitter receptors in cultured cells to produce new clonal cell lines expressing oligonucleotide-directed mutant receptors. These types of studies will allow for identification of important structural and functional domains of receptor proteins and elucidation of the mechanisms of receptor action.

9.7   EXPRESSION OF β-ADRENERGIC RECEPTOR GENES IN CULTURED CELLS

In order to identify cloned neurotransmitter receptor genes and to characterize the pharmacological and biochemical properties of these proteins, we have used plasmid expression vectors to produce stable cell lines expressing the receptors in high density (Fig. 9.7). We have used both Chinese hamster ovary (CHO) and B-82 cells for many expression studies, as these cells lack most hormone and transmitter receptors.

Addition of isoproterenol to transfected cells expressing human or rat β_2-adrenergic receptors produces a dose-dependent increase in the level of intracellular cyclic AMP, indicating that the receptor genes introduced into these cells by transfection are processed and inserted into the cell membrane and couple to endogenous G proteins to activate adenylate cyclase ([42,43], Fig. 9.8). The availability of stable cell lines expressing different densities of β_2-adrenergic receptors has provided an opportunity to examine the relationship between receptor number and receptor-mediated responsiveness in a cell where the levels of G proteins and effector units remain constant. George et al. [44] and Bouvier et al. [45] have reported that increasing densities of β-receptors in hamster fibroblasts correlated with an increased efficacy of isoproterenol in stimulating adenylate cyclase. In addition, the dose–response curves for isoproterenol stimulation of adenylate cyclase were shifted to the left as receptor density increased. This finding is consistent with an increasing population of 'spare' receptors in excess of that required for maximal stimulation of adenylate cyclase. These data have provided the first direct evidence that the maximal level of receptor-stimulated adenylate cyclase activity may, in part, be determined by receptor number.

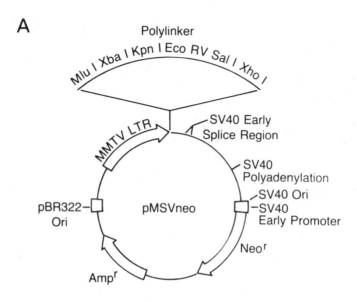

Fig. 9.7 — Schematic representation of the essential elements of a plasmid expression vector, pMSVneo. The bacterial origin of replication (pBR322 Ori) and the gene for antibiotic resistance (Amp^r) allow for replication of the plasmid in *E. coli* strains HB101 and JM109, for example. This vector contains the dominant selectable marker, Neo^r, under transcriptional control of the SV40 early promoter that enables selection of stable transformants in culture medium containing the neomycin analog, G-418. Genes for expression are inserted into one of the six unique restriction sites in the polylinker region of the vector. Genes inserted here are under the control of the MMTVLTR promoter and their expression can be induced by addition of steroids to the culture medium. This plasmid vector has been used in expression of β-adrenergic and muscarinic cholinergic receptors in B-82 and CHO cells.

9.8 EXPRESSION OF α-ADRENERGIC RECEPTOR GENES IN CULTURED CELLS

Using the plasmid expression system described above, we have obtained several lines of CHO cells permanently expressing the human α_2-adrenergic receptor normally found in platelets [46]. As illustrated in Fig. 9.9, the α_2 receptor expressed in platelets displays pharmacology characteristic of an α_{2A} receptor subtype with a high affinity for yohimbine ($K_d = 1$ nM) and a low affinity for prazosin ($K_d = 10,000$ nM) [47]. Agonists display a rank order of potency in ligand binding assays of para-aminoclonidine ⩾ UK 14304 > (−) epinephrine > (−)norepinephrine > (−) isoproterenol, consistent with the identification of this protein as an α_2 receptor (Fig. 9.9).

The role of the α_2 receptor in modulation of intracellular cAMP production was investigated in transfected CHO cells. It appears that the human α_2-adrenergic receptor in CHO cells may simultaneously couple to more than one effector including a pertussis-toxin-sensitive attenuation of adenylate cyclase and pertussis-toxin-insensitive pathway that results in potentiation of intracellular cAMP levels

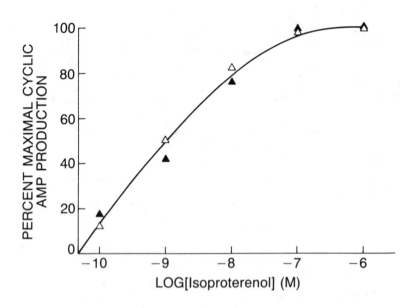

Fig. 9.8 — Iosproterenol-induced cyclic AMP production in B-82 cells transfected with rat or human β_2-adrenergic receptors. B-82 cells transfected with a rat (solid triangles) or human (open triangles) β_2-adrenergic receptor gene were incubated with the indicated concentrations of isoproterenol for 20 min at 37°C. Concentrations of intracellular cyclic AMP were determined with a radioimmunoassay for cyclic AMP. Addition of isoproterenol to control B-82 cells had no effect on levels of cyclic AMP. Maximal cyclic AMP production was defined as that produced by 10 μM forskolin.

[46]. A similar α-adrenergic receptor-mediated potentiation of cAMP production was described in rat brain by Duman *et al.* [48] in 1986; however, it was not until the gene for the α receptor was cloned and expressed in cultured cells that the dual actions of the receptor could be directly elucidated.

9.9   EXPRESSION OF MUSCARINIC ACETYLCHOLINE RECEPTOR GENES IN CULTURED CELLS

In order to attempt to correlate the molecular forms of the muscarinic receptor with the subtypes defined pharmacologically, several laboratories have begun work on the expression of these genes in cultured mammalian cells. Stable expression of the gene encoding a rat muscarinic receptor in B-82 [49] and CHO [50] cells revealed that this protein binds muscarinic antagonists with a rank order of potency of atropine > pirenzepine > AF-DX 116, consistent with that described for an M1 receptor subtype (Fig. 9.10). In murine B-82 cells [49] and CHO cells [50] expressing this muscarinic receptor, addition of carbachol produced a dose-dependent increase in the hydrolysis of phosphoinositides (PI). Pertussis·toxin attenuated carbachol-stimulated PI turnover, suggesting that the M1 muscarinic receptor is coupled to the hydrolysis of inositol lipids via a pertussis-toxin-sensitive G protein [51]. At concen-

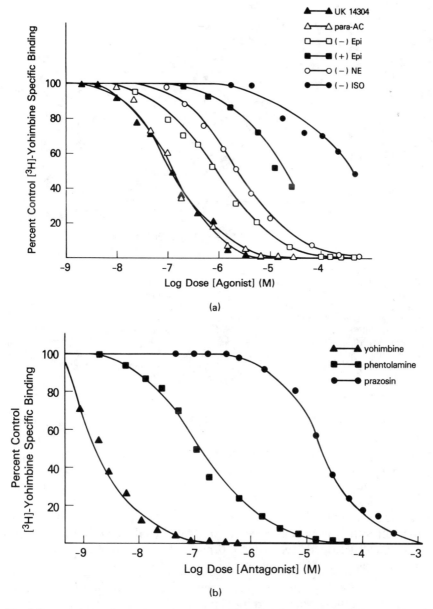

Fig. 9.9 — α-adrenergic agonist and antagonist binding to human α₂-adrenergic receptors expressed in CHO cells. Membranes from cells expressing the human α_2-adrenergic receptor were incubated with 3.5 nM [^{3}H]-yohimbine and the indicated concentrations of adrenergic agents. Samples were filtered and counted for specific yohimbine binding.

trations of carbachol up to 10 mM, no stimulatory or inhibitory effect on basal or PGE₁-stimulated cAMP formation in B-82 cells was observed [51].

In contrast to the results obtained from expression studies of the M1 muscarinic

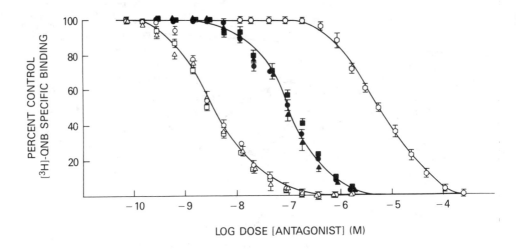

LOG DOSE [ANTAGONIST] (M)

Fig. 9.10 — Muscarinic cholinergic antagonist binding to wild-type receptors expressed in CHO cells. Membranes from CHO cells expressing wild-type M1 muscarinic receptors were incubated in 50 mM $NaPO_4$ buffer, pH 8.0 containing a K_d concentration of [³H]-QNB and the indicated concentrations of muscarinic agents for 60 min at 37°C. Samples were filtered over Whatman GF/C glass fiber filters using a Brandel M-24R cell harvester and filters were washed with 20 ml $NaPO_4$, pH 7.4. Total QNB binding in the absence of competing ligands was 15 fmol. Data are representative of two to three separate experiments performed in triplicate. Open circles, squares and triangles represent QNB binding in the presence of atropine. Solid symbols represent QNB binding in the presence of pirenzepine. Open hexagons represent QNB binding in the presence of AF-DX 116.

receptor were those of Ashkenazi *et al.* [52] on the coupling of a porcine M2 muscarinic cholinergic receptor to cellular effectors in CHO cells. The muscarinic agonist — carbachol — both inhibited adenylate cyclase and stimulated PI hydrolysis in transfected cells. The stimulation of PI hydrolysis was significantly less efficient and more dependent on high levels of receptor expression than inhibition of adenylate cyclase. Although these data suggest that one muscarinic receptor subtype may couple to multiple effector systems, the physiological relevance of M2 receptor stimulation of PI hydrolysis is questionable. Additional studies on the function of other genetically defined muscarinic receptor subtypes will aid in elucidating the nature of receptor–effector coupling.

9.10   SITE-DIRECTED MUTAGENESIS

9.10.1   Site-directed mutagenesis of β₂-adrenergic receptors

In order to examine the role of highly conserved amino acid residues in receptor function, Fraser *et al.* have used site-directed mutagenesis of neurotransmitter receptor genes to create point mutations in these proteins and have stably expressed the mutant receptors in cultured cells. There are three highly conserved aspartate residues in transmembrane segments II and III of the human β₂-adrenergic receptor [9,10]. Numerous types of evidence have suggested a role for these corresponding

amino acids in retinal binding in the opsins [53] and in proton translocation in
bacteriorhodopsin [54].

In order to examine the role of the highly conserved aspartate (Asp) residues in
transmembrane segments II and III of the human β_2-adrenergic receptor, mutants
were created in which Asp^{79} (transmembrane II) and Asp^{130} (transmembrane III)
were placed with asparagine (Asn) residues (Fig. 9.4). Both of these mutant
receptors displayed normal antagonist binding and the expected rank order of
potency for agonists. However, Asn^{79} mutant receptors exhibited significantly lower
affinity for agonists (40-fold for isoproterenol, 140-fold for epinephrine and 240-fold
for norepinephrine) than did wild-type receptors ([55], Fig. 9.11). The Hill coeffi-

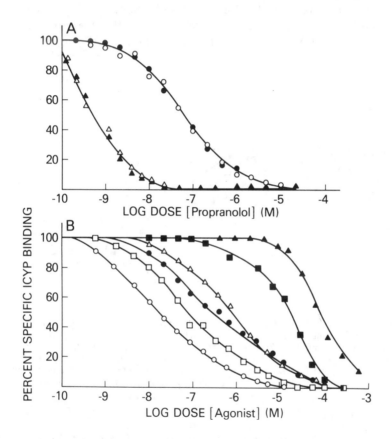

Fig. 9.11 — Agonist and antagonist binding to Asn^{79} mutant β-adrenergic receptors. Membranes prepared from cells expressing wild-type or Asn^{79} mutant β_2-adrenergic receptors were
incubated in the presence of ICYP plus the indicated concentrations of adrenergic agents. Panel
A: solid circles and triangles represent competition displacement binding with (−) propranolol
to wild-type and mutant receptors, respectively. Open circles and triangles represent competition displacement binding with (+) propanolol to wild type and mutant receptors, respectively. Panel B: Competition binding to wild-type β_2-adrenergic receptors in the presence of
(−) isoproterenol (open circles), (−) epinephrine (open squares) and (−) norepinephrine
(open triangles). Competition binding to Asn^{79} mutant receptors in the presence of (−)
isoproterenol (solid circles), (−) epinephine (solid squares) and (−) norepinephrine (solid
triangles).

cient for agonist binding was consistent with a single class of low-affinity binding sites; addition of guanine nucleotides had no effect on agonist binding affinity. Interestingly, addition of isoproterenol to cultures expressing Asn[79] mutant receptors produced a slight but significant increase in intracellular levels of cyclic AMP, indicating that this mutant receptor can effect minimal activation of adenylate cyclase [55]. The differential loss of affinity for the catecholamines supports the hypothesis advanced by Applebury and Hargrave [53] that Asp[79] may serve as a counterion for the amine substituent of the catecholamines, analogous to its role in the binding of retinal to rhodopsin.

In contrast to the findings with the Asn[79] receptors, Asn[130] mutant β receptors displayed high-affinity agonist binding (5–10-fold higher than wild-type receptor) consistent with a single class of binding sites ([56], Fig. 9.12). However, addition of saturating concentrations of isoproterenol to cell culture expressing Asn[130] receptors

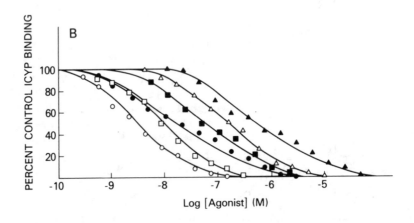

Fig. 9.12 — Agonist binding to Asn[130] mutant β-adrenergic receptors. Membranes prepared from cells expressing wild-type or Asn[130] mutant β₂-adrenergic receptors were incubated in the presence of ICYP and the indicated concentrations of adrenergic agents. Competition binding between ICYP and (−) isoproterenol (circles), (−) epinephrine (squares), and (−) norepinephrine (triangles) is shown. Binding to wild type beta receptors is indicated by the solid symbols; binding to mutant receptors is indicated by the open symbols.

had no effect on intracellular levels of cyclic AMP. It is possible that Asn[130] mutant receptors represent receptors that are irreversibly coupled to guanine nucleotide binding proteins following agonist binding or, alternatively, that Asp[130] serves as an alternative counterion for catecholamine binding to the β receptor which is differentially exposed in the unoccupied and liganded receptor [56].

Recently, Strader *et al.* [57] have described the properties of a mutant hamster β₂-adrenergic receptor in which Asp[113] in the third transmembrane domain was replaced by Asn. This mutation decreased the affinity of the receptor for antagonists by 10,000-fold. The concentration of agonists required to activate adenylate cyclase in cells expressing the Asp[113] mutant receptor was increased to the same extent.

Taken together, data obtained from the characterization of mutant human and hamster β_2-adrenergic receptors suggest a role for the conserved aspartate residues in transmembrane segments II and III in ligand binding and agonist-induced receptor activation. These data are consistent with the existence of overlapping, but not identical, binding sites for agonists and antagonists on the β-adrenergic receptor. Both Asp[79] and Asp[113] [55,57] appear to be required for the high-affinity binding of β receptor agonists. It is possible that these residues are hydrogen bonded to each other in the native receptor, providing a receptor conformation that is required for the recognition of the catecholamines. Further mutagenesis studies may help to clarify this hypothesis.

Chemical modification of the β-adrenergic receptor with disulfide bond reducing agents [58–61] has suggested that hormone binding to and activation of β-adrenergic receptors may involve disulfide bonds. These observations imply an important role for cysteinyl residues in β-receptor structure and function. Using site-directed mutagenesis, we investigated the role of five conserved cysteine residues in the human β_2-adrenergic receptor [62]. The most marked effect on receptor function was observed following substitution of two vicinal cysteine residues in the third extra-cellular loop of the receptor with serine. These mutant receptors displayed a marked loss in affinity for both agonists and antagonists (100- to 7000-fold) as compared to wild-type receptors. Consistent with the loss in mutant receptor affinity for agonists was a corresponding shift to the right in the dose–respose curve for isoproterenol-induced increases in intracellular cyclic AMP in cells expressing the mutant recep-tors. These data implicate two of the extracellular cysteine residues in the β-receptor in maintenance of a receptor conformation that allows for high affinity ligand binding or in ligand binding directly.

9.10.2 Site directed mutagenesis of M1 muscarinic cholinergic receptors
In order to investigate the role of the conserved aspartic acids in muscarinic receptor function, we made single-point mutations in the M1 muscarinic receptor gene to independently convert Asp[71] in the second transmembrane domain and Asp[105] and Asp[122] in the third transmembrane domain to asparagine (Asn) and permanently transfected CHO cells with each mutant gene ([50], Fig. 9.13).

Mutation of Asp[71] produced a mutant receptor that had normal antagonist and partial agonist binding and a 11.5-fold higher affinity for carbachol than the wide-type receptor ([50], Fig. 9.14). These data are similar to those derived from site-directed mutagenesis of Asp [79] in the β_2-adrenergic receptor [55] and suggest that different coordinates may exist for the binding of agonists in these receptor classes. Unlike the corresponding mutation in the β_2 receptor, which decreased agonist affinity, substitution of Asp[71] with Asn in the muscarinic receptor increased agonist affinity. These data support a role for the conserved Asp in agonist binding to both β-adrenergic and muscarinic receptors; however, the opposing changes in receptor affinity suggest that the nature of agonist binding to these receptors may be fundamentally different. Asn[71] mutant muscarinic receptors induced only minimal stimulation of PI hydrolysis in transfected cells (Fig. 9.15), similar to the findings with the Asn[79] mutant β receptor and agonist stimulation of adenylate cyclase [55].

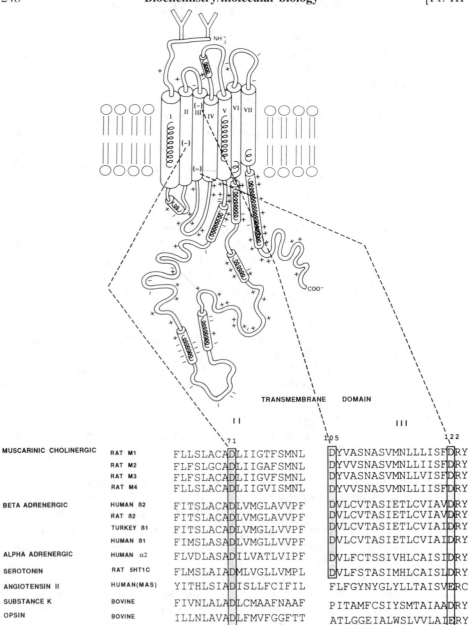

Fig. 9.13 — Schematic model of the M1 muscarinic cholinergic receptor. The top panel illustrates a cut-away view of the M1 muscarinic receptor oriented in the membrane. The receptor contains seven transmembrane-spanning domains (I–VII) connected by alternating extracellular and intracellular loops. Charged residues are indicated, as are regions of predicted α-helical structure. The NH_3^+ terminus of the receptor is thought to be oriented extracellularly. This portion of the receptor contains two putative sites for N-linked glycosylation (Y). This model places the COO^- terminus of the receptor intracellular. The bottom panel of this figure illustrates the deduced amino acid sequences of the second and third transmembrane domains of several members of this receptor family. The conserved aspartate residues that were studied by site-directed mutagenesis are highlighted and numbered.

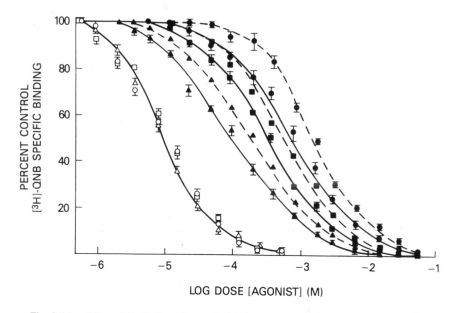

Fig. 9.14 — Muscarinic cholinergic agonist binding to wild-type and mutant M1 muscarinic receptors. Membranes from CHO cells expressing wild-type, Asn[71] or Asn[122] mutant M1 receptors were incubated with a K_d concentration of [^{3}H]-QNB and the indicated concentrations of carbachol or oxotremorine for 60 min at 37°C. Samples were filtered and counted for specific QNB binding. Open circles, squares and triangles represent QNB binding to wild-type, Asn[71] and Asn[122] mutant receptors, respectively, in the presence of oxotremorine. The corresponding solid symbols represent QNB binding to the indicated receptors in the presence of carbachol. Solid lines represent competition displacement studies performed in the absence of exogenous guanine nucleotides; dashed lines represent studies performed in the presence of 100 μM GTP.

These data suggest that the aspartic acid residue in the second transmembrane domain of all members of this gene family may play a common role in agonist activation of intracellular effectors.

Substitution of Asp[122] with Asn, in the third transmembrane domain of the muscarinic receptor, produced a mutant receptor that had normal antagonist and partial agonist affinity but a 3.2-fold higher affinity for carbachol ([50], Fig. 9.14). Both carbachol and oxotremorine were able to stimulate PI hydrolysis in cells expressing the Asn[122] receptor; however, the EC_{50} for agonist stimulation of PI turnover was shifted approximately 10-fold to the right (Fig. 9.15). The discrepancy between the increase in receptor affinity for carbachol and the decreased efficacy of full and partial agonists to elicit maximal responses suggests a change in the efficiency of receptor coupling to G proteins.

Substitution of Asp[105] with Asn produced a mutant receptor with decreased affinity for agonists and antagonists such that receptor detection with radioligand binding assays was limited [50]. These findings are similar to those from mutagenesis of the corresponding aspartic acid residue in the hamster β$_2$-adrenergic receptor [57] and implicate this amino acid directly in ligand binding or indirectly in the maintenance of a receptor conformation required for high-affinity ligand binding.

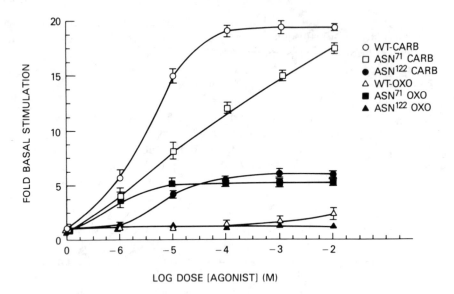

Fig. 9.15 — Measurement of phosphoinositide turnover in CHO cells transfected with wild-type and mutant M1 muscarinic receptors. CHO cells containing 200 fmol, 380 fmol, and 185 fmol/mg protein of wild-type, Asn[71] or Asn[122] mutant muscarinic receptors, respectively, were assayed for carbachol and oxotremorine-stimulated phosphoinositide turnover according to the method of Berridge [63, and references therein]. Cells were seeded on 35 mm culture dishes at a density of 2.5×105 cells/plate in Nutrient mixture F-10 (GIBCO) supplemented with 10% dialyzed fetal bovine serum. 2.5μCi [3H]-*myo*-inositol was added to each plate and cells were incubated for 16 h at 37°C. Prior to addition of agonists, culture medium containing radiolabeled *myo*-inositol was aspirated from the dishes and cells were pretreated with F-10 medium containing 10 mM LiCl for 30 min at 37°C. The indicated final concentrations of muscarinic agents were then added to the cultures and agonist-stimulated phosphoinositide accumulation was allowed to proceed for 30 min at 37°C. Incubations were stopped by the addition of 10% perchloric acid. Extracts were alkalinized and inositol phosphates were purified by chromatography on Dowex resin. Data are expressed as fold basal stimulation of PI hydrolysis. The basal level of PI accumulation in transfected cells was 6000–10 000 dpm. Data represent the mean of three experiments performed in duplicate.

9.11 CONCLUSIONS AND FUTURE DIRECTIONS

Details of receptor structure and function that were unavailable as recently as two years ago are now readily obtainable through the application of molecular biological techniques. Cloning and sequence analysis of neurotransmitter receptor genes has provided information of the primary structure of these proteins, revealing the relationship between pharmacologically diverse families of receptors. Knowledge of the primary structure of receptors has allowed for prediction of secondary structure and the construction of three-dimensional models of the proteins. These models will play an integral role in future drug development.

Permanent expression of cloned human neurotransmitter receptor genes in cultured cells lacking receptors is now providing unlimited sources of pure receptors. This recent development allows for drug screening and evaluation with single-receptor subtypes and will generate information on the subtype selectivity of pharmacological agents not possible with tissue preparations containing mixed receptor populations. Furthermore, the availability of clonal cell lines expressing human neurotransmitter receptors may reduce the need for the use of animals in initial drug screening programs. In addition, over-expression of receptors in cultured cells will provide a source of material for detailed biochemical studies and for X-ray crystallographic analysis of the three-dimensional structure of receptors.

The use of site-directed mutagenesis to elucidate the relationship between protein structure and function has provided considerable information on the role of certain conserved amino acids and has suggested possible molecular mechanisms of signal transduction across membranes. A thorough understanding of these processes may facilitate the development of new classes of therapeutic agents that interfere with or stimulate receptor activation of intracellular effectors independent of ligand binding.

At present it is clear that considerable conservation of receptor structure exists among the receptors known to interact with guanine nucleotide regulatory proteins. Limited site-directed mutagenesis studies to date have suggested that conservation of receptor structure may also reflect conservation of receptor mechanisms of activation. Consequently, advances in our understanding of the three-dimensional structure or function of any receptor in this gene superfamily may facilitate a more global appreciation of receptor transduction mechanisms and provide insight into a more rational design of diverse therapeutic agents.

REFERENCES

[1] Venter, J. C. (1983). Muscarinic cholinergic receptor. Receptor size, membrane orientation and absence of major phylogenetic structural diversity. *J. Biol. Chem.* **258**, 4842.

[2] Venter, J. C., Eddy, B., Hall, L. M., & Fraser, C. M. (1984). Monoclonal antibodies detect the conservation of muscarinic cholinergic receptor structure from *Drosophila* to human brain and detect possible structural homology with alpha$_1$-adrenergic receptors. *Proc. Natl. Acad. Sci. USA* **81**, 272.

[3] Shreeve, S. M., Fraser, C. M., & Venter, J. C. (1985). Molecular comparison of alpha$_1$ and alpha$_2$-adrenergic receptors suggests that these proteins are stucturally related isoreceptors. *Proc. Natl. Acad. Sci. USA* **82**, 4842.

[4] Cottechia, S., Schwinn, D. A., Randall, R. R., Lefkowitz, R. J., Caron, M. G., & Kobilka, B. K. (1988). Molecular cloning and expression of the cDNA for the hamster alpha$_1$-adrenergic receptor. *Proc. Natl. Acad. Sci. USA* **85**, 7159.

[5] Kobilka, B. K., Maysui, H., Kobilka, T. S., Yang-Feng, T. L., Francke, U., Caron, M. G., Lefkowitz, R. J., & Regan, J. W. (1987). Cloning, sequencing and expression of the gene coding for the human platelet alpha$_2$-adrenergic receptor. *Science* **238**, 650.

[6] Regan, J. W., Kobilka, T. S., Yang-Feng, T. L., Caron, M. G., Lefkowitz, R. J., & Kobilka, B. K. (1988). Cloning and expression of a human kidney cDNA for an alpha$_2$-adrenergic receptor subtype. *Proc. Natl. Acad. Sci. USA* **85**, 6301.

[7] Frielle, T., Collins, S., Daniel, K. W., Caron, M. G., Lefkowitz, R. J., &

Kobilka, B. K. (1987). Cloning of the cDNA for the human beta$_1$-adrenergic receptor. *Proc. Natl. Acad. Sci. USA* **84**, 7920.

[8] Yarden, Y., Rodriquez, H., Wong, S. K.-F., Brandt, D. R., May, D. C., Burnier, J., Harkins, R. N., Chen, E. Y., Ramachandran, J., Ullrich, A., & Ross, E. M. (1986). The avian beta-adrenergic receptor: primary structure and membrane topology. *Proc. Natl. Acad. Sci. USA* **83**, 6795.

[9] Kobilka, B. K., Dixon, R. A. F., Frielle, T., Dohlman, H. G., Bolanowski, M. A., Sigal, I. S., Yang-Feng, T. L., Francke, U., Caron, M. G., & Lefkowitz, R. J. (1987). cDNA for the human beta$_2$-adrenergic receptor: a protein with multiple membrane spanning domains and encoded by a gene whose chromosomal location is shared with that of the receptor for platelet derived growth factor. *Proc. Natl. Acad. Sci. USA* **84**, 46.

[10] Chung, F.-Z., Lentes, K.-U., Gocayne, J. D., FitzGerald, M. G., Robinson, D., Kerlavage, A. R., Fraser, C. M., & Venter, J. C. (1987). Cloning and sequence analysis of the human brain beta-adrenergic receptor. Evolutionary relationship to rodent and avian beta receptors and porcine muscarinic receptors. *FEBS Lett.* 211, 200.

[11] Dixon, R. A. F., Kobilka, B. K., Strader, D. J., Benovic, J. L., Dohlman, H. G., Frielle, T. Bolanowski, M. A., Bennett, C. D., Rands, E., Diehl, R. E., Mumford, R. A., Slater, E. E., Sigal, I. S., Caron, M. G., Lefkowitz, R. J., & Strader, C. D. (1986). Cloning of the gene and cDNA for mammalian beta-adrenergic receptor and homology with rhodopsin. *Nature* **321**, 75.

[12] Gocayne, J. D., Robinson, D. A., FitzGerald, M. G., Chung, F.-Z., Kerlavage, A. R., Lentes, K.-U., Lai, J., Wang, C.-D., Fraser, C. M., & Venter, J. C. (1987). Primary structure of rat cardiac beta-adrenergic and muscarinic cholinergic receptors obtained by automated DNA sequence analysis: further evidence for a multigene family. *Proc. Natl. Acad. Sci. USA* **84**, 8296.

[13] Allen, J. M., Baetge, E. E., Abrass, I. B., & Palmiter, R. D. (1988). Isoproterenol response following transfection of the mouse beta$_2$-adrenergic gene into Y1 cells. *EMBO J.* **7**, 133.

[14] Kubo, T., Maeda, A., Sugimoto, K., Akiba, I., Mikami, Takahashi, H., Haga, T., Haga, K., Ichiyama, A., Kangawa, K., Matsuo, H., Hirose, T., & Numa, S. (1986). Primary structure of porcine cardiac muscarinic acetylcholine receptor deduced from the cDNA sequence. *FEBS Lett.* **209**, 367.

[15] Kubo, T., Fukuda, K., Mikami, A., Maeda, A., Takahashi, H., Mishina, M., Haga, T., Haga, K., Ichiyama, A., Kangawa, K., Kojima, M., Matsuo, H., Hirose, T., & Numa, S. (1986). Cloning, sequencing and expression of complementary DNA encoding the muscarinic acetylcholine receptor. *Nature* **323**, 411.

[16] Allard, W. J., Sigal, I. S., & Dixon, R. A. F. (1987). Sequence of the gene encoding the human M1 muscarinic acetylcholine receptor. *Nucleic Acids Res.* **15**, 10604.

[17] Peralta, E. G., Ashkenazi, A., Winslow, J. W., Smith, D. H., Ramachandran, J., & Capon, D. J. (1987). Distinct primary structures, ligand-binding properties and tissue specific expression of four human muscarinic acetylcholine receptors. *EMBO J.* **6**, 3923.

[18] Peralta, E. G., Winslow, J. W., Peterson, G. L., Smith, D. H., Ashkenazi, A.,

Ramachandran, J., Schimerlik, M. I., & Capon, D. J. (1987). Primary structure and biochemical properties of an M2 muscarinic receptor. *Science* **236**, 600.

[19] Bonner, T. I., Buckley, N. J., Young, A. C., & Brann, M. R. (1987). Identification of a family of muscarinic acetylcholine receptor genes. *Science* **237**, 527.

[20] Bonner, T. I., Young, A. C., Brann, M. R., & Buckley, N. J. (1988). Cloning and expression of the human and rat m5 muscarinic acetylcholine receptor genes. *Neuron* **1**, 403.

[21] Liao, C.-F., Themmen, A. P. N., Joho, R., Barberis, C., Birnbaumer, M., & Birnbaumer, L. (1989). Molecular cloning and expression of a fifth muscarinic acetylcholine receptor. *J. Biol. Chem.* **264**, 7328.

[22] Julius, D., MacDermott, A. B., Axel, R., & Jessell, T. M. (1988). Molecular characterization of a functional cDNA encoding the serotonin 1c receptor. *Science* **241**, 558.

[23] Fargin, A., Raymond, J. R., Lohse, M. J., Kobilka, B. K., Caron, M. G., & Lefkowitz, R. J. (1988). The genomic clone G-21 which resembles a beta-adrenergic receptor sequence encodes the 5-HT1A receptor. *Nature* **335**, 358.

[24] Bunzow, J. R., Van Tol, H. H. M., Grandy, D. K., Albert, P., Salon, J., Christie, M., Machida, C. A., Neve, K. A., & Civelli, O. (1988). Cloning and expression of a rat D2 dopamine receptor cDNA. *Nature* **336**, 783.

[25] Jackson, T. R., Blair, L. A. C., Marshall, J. Goedert, M., & Hanley, M. R. (1988). The mas oncogene encodes an angiotensin receptor. *Nature* **335**, 437.

[26] Masu, Y., Nakaama, K., Tamaki, H., Harada, Y., Kuno, M., & Nakanishi, S. (1987). cDNA cloning of bovine substance K receptor through oocyte expression system. *Nature* **329**, 836.

[27] Marsh, L. & Herskowitz, I. (1988). STE2 protein of *Saccharomyces kluyveri* is a member of the rhodopsin/beta-adrenergic receptor family and is responsible for recognition of the peptide ligand alpha factor. *Proc. Natl. Acad. Sci USA* **85**, 3855.

[28] Nathans, J. & Hogness, D. S. (1983). Isolation, sequence analysis and intron–exon arrangement of the gene encoding bovine rhodopsin. *Cell* **34**, 807.

[29] Nathans, J. & Hogness, D. S. (1984). Isolation and nucleotide sequence of the gene encoding human rhodopsin. *Proc. Natl. Acad. Sci. USA* **81**, 4851.

[30] Zuker, C. S., Cowman, A. F., & Rubin, G. M. (1985). Isolation and structure of a rhodopsin gene from *D. melanogaster*. *Cell* **40**, 851.

[31] Martin, R. L., Wood, C., Baehr, W., & Applebury, M. L. (1986). Visual pigment homologies revealed by DNA hybridization. *Science* **232**, 1266.

[32] Stiles, G. L., Caron, M. G., & Lefkowitz, R. J. (1984). Beta-adrenergic receptors: biochemical mechanisms of physiological regulation. *Physiol. Rev.* **64**, 661.

[33] Gilman, A. G. (1987). G proteins: transducers of receptor-generated signals. *Annu. Rev. Biochem.* **56**, 615.

[34] Langer, S. Z. (1974). Presynaptic regulation of catecholamine release. *Biochem. Pharmacol.* **23**, 1793.

[35] Starke, K. (1981). Alpha-adrenoceptor subclassification. *Rev. Physiol. Biochem. Pharmacol.* **88**, 199.

[36] Kerlavage, A. R., Fraser, C. M., & Venter, J. C. (1987). Muscarinic choliner-

gic receptor structure: molecular biological support for subtypes. *Trends Pharmacol. Sci.* **8**, 426.

[37] Hammer, R., Berrie, C. P., Birdsall, N. J. M., Burgen, A. S. V., & Hulme, E. C. (1980). Pirenzepine distinguishes between different subclasses of muscarinic receptors. *Nature* **283**, 90.

[38] Birdsall, N. J. M. & Hulme, E. C. (1983). Muscarinic receptor subclasses. *Trends Pharmacol. Sci.* **4**, 454.

[39] Brown, J. H. & Brown, S. L. (1984). Agonists differentiate muscarinic receptors that inhibit cyclic AMP formation from those that stimulate phosphoinositide metabolism. *J. Biol. Chem.* **259**, 3777.

[40] Henderson, R. & Unwin, P. T. N. (1975). Three dimensional model of purple membrane obtained by electron microscopy. *Nature* **257**, 28.

[41] Fraser, C. M. (1989). Expression of receptor genes in cultured cells. In: E. Hulme (ed.) *Receptors*: *A Practical Approach*. IRL Press, Oxford, in press.

[42] Fraser, C. M., Chung, F.-Z., & Venter, J. C. (1987). Continuous high density expression of human $beta_2$-adrenergic receptors in a mouse cell line previously lacking beta-receptors. *J. Biol. Chem.* **262**, 14843.

[43] Robinson, D. A. (1988). Cloning, sequencing and expression of rat cardiac $beta_2$-adrenergic receptors. Doctoral disseration. State University of New York at Buffalo, Buffalo, New York.

[44] George, S. T., Berrios, M., Hadcock, J. R., Wang, H., & Malbon, C. C. (1988). Receptor density and cAMP accumulation: analysis in CHO cells exhibiting stable expression of a cDNA that encodes the $beta_2$-adrenergic receptor. *Biochem. Biophys. Res. Comm.* **150**, 665.

[45] Bouvier, M., Hnatowich, M., Collins, S., Kobilka, B. K., Deblasi, A., Lefkowitz, R. J., & Caron, M. G. (1988). Expression of a human cDNA encoding the $beta_2$-adrenergic receptor in Chinese hamster fibroblasts (CHW): functionality and regulation of the expressed receptors. *Mol. Pharmacol.* **33**, 133.

[46] Fraser, C. M., Arakawa, S., McCombie, W. R., & Venter, J. C. (1989). Cloning, sequence analysis and permanent expression of a human $alpha_2$-adrenergic receptor in CHO cells: evidence for independent pathways of receptor coupling to adenylate cyclase attenuation and activation. *J. Biol. Chem.* **264**, 11754.

[47] Bylund, D. B. (1985). Heterogeneity of $alpha_2$-adrenergic receptors. *Pharmacol. Biochem. Behav.* **22**, 835.

[48] Duman, R. S., Karbon, E. W., Harrington, C., & Enna, S. J. (1986). An examination of the involvement of phospholipases A2 and C in the alpha-adrenergic and gamma-aminobutyric acid receptor modulation of cyclic AMP accumulation in rat brain slices. *J. Neurochem.* **47**, 800.

[49] Lai, J., Mei, L., Roeske, W. R., Chung, F.-Z., Yamamura, H. I., & Venter, J. C. (1988). The cloned murine M1 muscarinic receptor is associated with the hydrolysis of phosphatidylinositols in transfected murine B82 cells. *Life Sci.* **42**, 2489.

[50] Fraser, C. M., Wang, C.-D., Robinson, D. A., Gocayne, J. D., & Venter, J. C. (1989). Site-directed mutagenesis of m1 muscarinic acetylcholine receptors: Conserved aspartic acids play important roles in receptor function.. *Mol. Pharmacol.* in press.

[51] Mei, L., Lai, J., Roeske, W. R., Fraser, C. M., Venter, J. C., & Yamamura, H. I. (1989). Pharmacological characterization of the M1 muscarinic receptors expressed in murine fibroblast B82 cells. *J. Pharmacol. Exp. Ther.* **248**, 661.

[52] Ashkenazi, A., Winslow, J. W., Peralta, E. G., Peterson, G. L., Schimerlik, M. I., Capon, D. J. & Ramachandran, J. (1987). An M2 muscarinic receptor subtype coupled to both adenylyl cyclase and phosphoinositide turnover. *Science* **238**, 672.

[53] Appleby, M. L. & Hargrave, P. A. (1986). Molecular biology of the visual pigments, *Vision Res.* **26**, 1881.

[54] Khorana, H. G. (1988). Bacteriorhodopsin, a membrane protein that uses light to translocate protons. *J. Biol. Chem.* **263**, 7439.

[55] Chung, F.-Z., Wang, C.-D., Potter, P. C., Venter, J. C., & Fraser, C. M. (1988). Site-directed mutagenesis and continuous expression of human beta-adrenergic receptors. Identification of a conserved aspartate residue involved in agonist binding and receptor activation. *J. Biol. Chem.* **263**, 4052.

[56] Fraser, C. M., Chung, F.-Z., Wang, C.-D., & Venter, J. C. (1988). Site-directed mutagenesis of human beta-adrenergic receptors: substitution of aspartic acid 130 by asparagine produces a receptor with high affinity agonist binding that is uncoupled from adenylate cyclase. *Proc. Natl. Acad. Sci. USA* **85**, 5478.

[57] Strader, C. D., Sigal, I. S., Candelore, M. R., Rands, E., Hill, W. S., & Dixon, R. A. F. (1988). Conserved aspartic acid residues 79 and 113 of the beta-adrenergic receptor have different roles in receptor function. *J. Biol. Chem.* **263**, 10267.

[58] Lucas, M., Hanoune, J. & Bockaert, J. (1978). Chemical modification of the β-adrenergic receptors coupled with adenylate cyclase by disulfide bridge-reducing agents. *Mol. Pharmacol.* **14**, 227.

[59] Moxham, C. P. and Malbon, C. C. (1985) Fat cell β_1-adrenergic receptor: structural evidence for existence of disulfide bridges essential for ligand binding. *Biochemistry* **24**, 6072.

[60] Pederson, S. E. and Ross, E. M. (1985). Functional activation of β-adrenergic receptors by thiols in the presence or absence of agonists. *J. Biol. Chem.* **260**, 14150.

[61] Moxham, C. P., Ross, E. M., George, S. T. & Malbon, C. C. (1988). β-Adrenergic receptors display intramolecular disulfide bridges *in situ*: analysis by immunoblotting and functional reconstitution. *Mol. Pharmacol.* **33**, 486.

[62] Fraser, C. M. (1989). Site-directed mutagenesis of β-adrenergic receptors. Identification of conserved cysteine residues that independently affect ligand binding and receptor activation. *J. Biol. Chem.* **264**, 9266.

[63] Berridge, M. J. (1986). Inositol phosphates as second messengers. In: J. W. Putney, Jr. (ed.) *Phosphoinositides and Receptor Mechanisms*. Alan R. Liss Press, New York, p. 25.

Part IV
Pharmacology

10

Animal behavioral models for drug development in psychopharmacology

Lawrence A. Dunn, Clinton D. Kilts, Charles B. Nemeroff
Division of Biological Psychiatry, Department of Psychiatry, Duke University
Medical Center, Durham, North Carolina, USA

10.1   INTRODUCTION

The use of animal behavioral models for the development and screening of new
psychoactive substances is of tremendous importance to the science of psychopharmacology as well as to the pharmaceutical industry. The use of effective, appropriate
models can identify potential products, and elucidate the mechanisms of drug action
and even the pathophysiology of disease states. A failure in the model chosen for
screening a compound could conceivably prevent the development of a clinically
efficacious compound, or result in wasted effort on studies of an ineffective
compound.

Carefully designed and characterized animal models are of particular importance
in psychiatry where the etiology and pathophysiology of the diseases treated, the
mechanisms of action of the drugs used, and even the fundamental basis of the most
salient features of normal mental function remain virtually obscure. The incomplete
understanding of human mental function, and psychiatric disease, places an added
burden on the development of useful animal models. As is often noted in the clinical
literature, the apparent power of any test of, or treatment for, a psychiatric illness is
limited by the sensitivity and specificity of the diagnostic nosology employed in its
study [1–3]. Animal models in psychopharmacology are similarly limited by a lack of
consensus on what exactly constitutes the disease(s) being modeled.

This factor is often ignored when animal models are discussed. Some have
insisted that an animal model have an etiology, and pathophysiology, which parallels
those of the disease being modeled when these features are in fact unknown [4–7].
One approach to this problem, as will be discussed later, is to model drug response
rather than disease state itself. Another is to develop both animal models and
concepts of human disease bidirectionally so that the results of each line of research
can augment rather than restrict the other [8].

Two distinct approaches to animal behavioral modeling relevant to new drug development are efforts to model the action of drugs of known clinical utility and efforts to model the disease states for which drug treatments are being developed.

10.1.1   Models of drug action

Animal models of drug action have been useful screening tools for clinically active substances for some time. The method for developing such tests can be straightforward. A known active drug is administered to a test animal which is observed for changes in behavior. Observed behavioral changes such as catalepsy, altered locomotion, altered conditioned responding, changes in social behavior, or other observable effects become the model for the activity of that drug. Such a presumed model would be tested with other available drugs with similar therapeutic effects to assess the sensitivity of the model to a class of clinically similar compounds. The model would also be tested with representative substances from other drug classes to determine whether the observed effect is specific to one therapeutic class of drugs or a general effect of a broad range of psychoactive, or even neurotoxic compounds.

Although possessing good sensitivity and specificity alone would make an animal model useful as a screening test for potential clinical agents, an ideal animal model would have other characteristics as well. Pharmacologic isomorphism is one of these [9]. An animal model exhibits pharmacologic isomorphism if the targeted behavioral change caused by the drug has a similar onset, time course, and potency to the therapeutic changes sought in clinical treatments. Antidepressants, for example, typically manifest their therapeutic effects after several days to three weeks of treatment, do not show tolerance of antidepressant activity with chronic administration, and are effective in a daily dose range of roughly 0.5 to 5.0 mg/kg [10]. A pharmacologically isomorphic model for such drugs would likewise exhibit an effect that was maximal only after chronic treatment, did not exhibit tolerance with prolonged drug administration, and occurred within a clinically relevant dose range.

Another ideal characteristic, but one that must be pursued with considerable care, is behavioral homology between the disease state and the animal model. If an animal model is predicated on a drug-induced behavioral change similar to a change sought in treating a human disease, then the model may be more effective in identifying functionally diverse compounds with unique mechanisms of action that achieve similar clinical results. In addition, good behavioral homology helps to ensure that a clinically relevant aspect of drug action is being modeled. As will be discussed, drug screening techniques based solely on clinically irrelevant side effects have unfortunately been widely used. Moreover, models demonstrating behavioral homology have value beyond drug screening. They provide tools for the study of mechanisms of drug action and have potential for helping to elucidate mechanisms of neuropsychopathology, even though they stop short of modeling psychopathology by intent.

10.1.2   Models of disease states

Animal models of psychiatric disease, though often not developed with drug testing specifically in mind, represent valuable tools for identification of novel therapeutic agents. They are useful both directly as screening tests, and indirectly insofar as a more precise understanding of psychiatric illness allows better development of effective psychopharmacologic treatment.

Animal behavioral models of psychiatric disease states involve the production of behaviors in animals which are homologous to symptoms characteristic of human disease states. Behaviors are produced in animals through the use of environmental change, infectious agents, pharmacologic treatment, neurosurgical procedures, genetic manipulations, or a combination of these. The evaluation of such models really must depend upon their type and intended application. Some models assume a specific neurochemical state as an etiology for a disease, induce that state in animals and study the resulting behaviors. Others induce behaviors in animals environmentally and assess whether a characteristic neurochemical state develops. An excellent framework for evaluating the comparative validity of such animal models is provided by Wilner [7]. The assessment of a model of a disease state for utility in drug screening and development parallels the assessment of the validity of animal models of drug action. A model should be sensitive to clinically effective agents of diverse chemical classes, and should not be similarly affected by compounds from other psychoactive classes. Pharmacologic isomorphism is also important here. The responses of the modeled behavior to drug treatment should mirror the onset, maintenance of effect with chronic treatment, and potency observed in clinical drug applications.

Behavioral homology between the laboratory model and clinical state is more closely attended to in models of disease states, as their validity and heuristic value tend to rely as much on this as in pharmacologic response parallels. Here it again seems apparent that good behavioural homology would result in a model with predictive power over a broader range of compounds with diverse mechanisms of action.

Etiologic homology is an important and difficult consideration in models of disease states. As has been mentioned, the etiologies of psychiatric diseases remain largely obscure and are very active areas of research. However, models can be designed and evaluated based on what is known or hypothesized about disease etiologies. The more accurate the assumptions about etiology are, the more effective the model will be as a screening tool for clinically active compounds and in probing mechanisms of drug action.

In this introduction, we have avoided discussing specific animal models in favor of reviewing general features of two classes of models. Members of these classes have been further adapted to solve problems specific to the diseases targeted for study. It is to models applied to three major psychiatric disorders — schizophrenia, depression, and anxiety disorders — that we now turn.

10.2   SCHIZOPHRENIA

Schizophrenia is a difficult disease to model in part because its most, salient positive symptoms — delusions, hallucinations, and thought disorder [11,12] — are difficult or impossible to model in animals. Moreover, the negative symptoms, reflected by the so-called defect state, are equally difficult to study in the laboratory. Schizophrenia does have a fairly robust etiological theory [13–15], and a number of effective drug treatments which share well studied mechanism of action [16]. The dopamine hypothesis of schizophrenia, the defects in attention seen in patients with schizophrenia, and the dopamine antagonist properties of antipsychotic drugs are all aspects of the illness which lend themselves to animal model development. Animal behavioral models applied to research on schizophrenia can be divided into models of antipsychotic drug action and models of the disease state.

10.2.1 Models of antipsychotic drug action

Animal models of antipsychotic drug action include, for purposes of this discussion, only those models in which the effect of antipsychotic drugs are studied on intact, untreated animals. They can be separated into those which study changes in motor behavior, and those whose intent is to measure changes in cognitive variables such as motivation, reward, attention, and learning due to antipsychotic drug treatment.

10.2.1.1 Antipsychotic drug-induced changes in motor behavior
Catalepsy
Perhaps the simplest animal behavioral test used for screening antipsychotic drugs is the induction of catalepsy in the rat or mouse. Typical antipsychotic drugs given acutely to experimental animals induce a waxy immobility referred to as catalepsy [17]. Because this test can be quickly and easily performed in rats without special equipment, it has been widely used as a screening tool. This is unfortunate, as it fails on every count to meet the requirements of an animal model of drug action. As noted, typical antipsychotic drugs induce catalepsy in rats. Atypical antipsychotic drugs such as thioridazine [18], clozapine [19], savoxepine [20], and sulpiride [17] show no cataleptogenic activity. In addition to lacking antipsychotic drug sensitivity, this test is not specific for antipsychotic drugs. Morphine [21], beta-endorphin [14], and the cholinomimetics arecoline and eserine [17] have been reported to induce catalepsy. Catalepsy also shows poor pharmacologic isomorphism with the clinical pharmacology of schizophrenia. Antipsychotic drugs attain maximal therapeutic benefit after chronic treatment, while their side effects (primarily sedation, and extrapyramidal symptoms) diminish over time [22]. Catalepsy in rats occurs with acute drug administration, and with many antipsychotic drugs, tolerance to this effect occurs over time [23,24]. Finally, the clinical potency of antipsychotic drugs does not correlate with their cataleptic potency [17]. Antipsychotic drug-induced catalepsy may be a good model for the extrapyramidal side-effect potential of these drugs. It should not be used, however, in attempts to discover new antipsychotic agents.

Open field behavior
Antipsychotic drug-induced changes in rat open field behavior is a potentially useful, but incompletely characterized, test for antipsychotic activity. Rats placed in a large enclosed space can be rated by observers on behaviors including exploring, immobility, rearing, grooming, and defecating [17]. Photocell arrays or video cameras linked to computers can automate some of this data collection. Antipsychotic drugs decrease most open field behaviors and increase immobility at doses which generally do not cause catalepsy. Conversely anxiolytics increase open field activity generally [17,25]. It is probable that this test better models the antipsychotic drug-induced

bradykinesia seen in humans rather than their antipsychotic effects. More complete evaluation is required before the model's full potential as a drug development tool is known.

10.2.1.2   Drug-induced changes in learning

Efforts to generate models based on cognitive changes in animals caused by antipsychotic drugs are motivated by a desire to simulate effects on brain function with underlie therapeutic changes seen in schizophrenic patients treated with these drugs. The earliest and most widely used of these models is the conditioned avoidance responding (CAR) paradigm.

Conditioned avoidance responding
Of the variety of paradigm used for measuring CAR, the one most commonly employed now is shuttle box shock avoidance (Fig. 10.1). In this paradigm a rat is

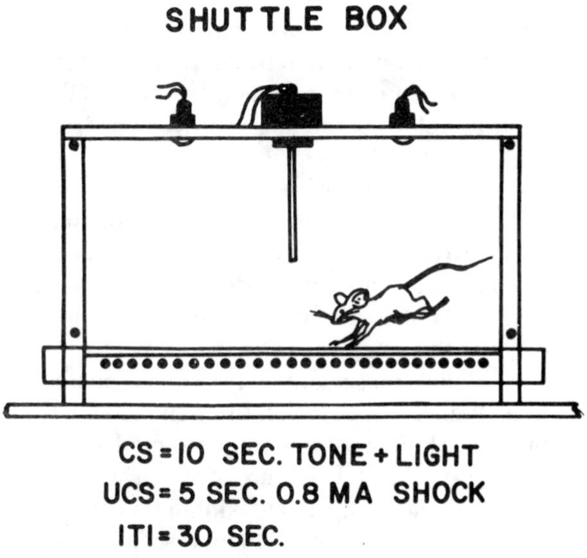

SHUTTLE BOX

CS = 10 SEC. TONE + LIGHT
UCS = 5 SEC. 0.8 MA SHOCK
ITI = 30 SEC.

Fig. 10.1 — Conditioned avoidance responding: the shuttle box consists of 2 compartments. The rat may pass freely between them. On CS presentation, the rat must pass to the opposite compartment to avoid a foot shock. If then rat fails to avoid the shock, it can terminate the shock by escaping into the opposite compartment. The succeeding trial automatically begins in whichever compartment the rat occupies. Separate scores are recorded for number of avoidance responses and number of escape responses.

placed in a cage with two compartments connected by an open doorway. A light or tone comes on for 10 s to signal the rat to make an avoidance response. If the rat passes through the door on cue, it avoids a shock. If it remains in the starting compartment, it receives a 10 s foot shock. The rat can escape this unavoided foot shock by passing through the door as well. Once having learned the paradigm, subjects virtually always avoid the shock. Any unavoided shocks result in rapid escape. Antipsychotic drug-treated rats exhibit a deficit in shock avoidance, but are unimpaired in their ability to escape shocks once they begin [17,26]. A recent series of experiments [27] demonstrated that drug potency for inhibition of shock avoidance consistently exceeded that for escape avoidance for typical antipsychotic drugs such as haloperidol and fluphenazine as well as for the atypical antipsychotic drugs clozapine, thioridazine, and sulpiride. The potency of the drug effect in this model correlated well with clinical potency [27–29]. In the same study, serotonin receptor antagonists, norpinephrine receptor antagonists, monoamine oxidase inhibitors, opiates, benzodiazepines, barbiturates, and an anticonvulsant were shown to be inactive in the paradigm. These drugs inhibited both escape and avoidance to equal degrees. Moreover, neurotensin, an endogenous tridecapeptide with pharmacologic properties similar to atypical antipsychotics, inhibits avoidance without affecting escape response in the CAR [30]. However, not all studies report a similar profile of drug sensitivity and specificity for CAR paradigms. The model has been reported to be ineffective with prolonged administration of clozapine, a clinically effective atypical antipsychotic drug [31]. The effects usually observed in this model represent those of acute drug doses. CAR inhibition by antipsychotic drugs has been noted to exhibit tolerance with repeated drug treatment [23,24,31,32]. Despite these flaws this model does appear useful for predicting antipsychotic drug effects.

Latent inhibition of conditioned emotional responding
While having some degree of predictive validity, the aforementioned models lack phenomenological similarity to the clinical condition of schizophrenia. An animal model with such similarity currently under development in our laboratory is the antipsychotic drug-induced enhancement of latent inhibition (Figs 10.2 and 10.3). Our purpose in developing this animal behavioral model is to provide a drug effect on brain functions which parallels those mediating the therapeutic effect of the drug in its clinical application. We have focused on the well recognized defect in selective attention present in schizophrenia as a symptom to model because it is ubiquitous and drug-responsive [33,34]. A useful measure of selective attention which is present across species is a phenomenon known as latent inhibition of conditioned responding [35]. Repeated representation of a neutral stimulus such as a symbol, light, tone, or smell, that is uncorrelated with other events in the environment, causes a subject to learn to ignore the stimulus. This learned irrelevance is similar to, but distinct from, the process of habituation in that it lasts for days rather than hours, is dependent on integrated brain function, and shows behavioral thresholds different from those of habituation [36]. Subsequent conditioned response training using this now irrelevant stimulus is severely retarded. The subject must first unlearn the irrelevance assigned to the stimulus, and then learn the association for it. Latent inhibition is observed across species and in humans [37]. Latent inhibition has been shown to be decreased in schizophrenic patients compared to controls and to increase following antipsychotic drug treatment in schizophrenic patients [38–40]. Latent inhibition measured in rats is decreased by amphetamine administration [41,42]. Haloperidol administration increases latent inhibition in rats [43,44] and antagonizes the effect of amphetamine on latent inhibition [45]. We have found that latent inhibition is enhanced by

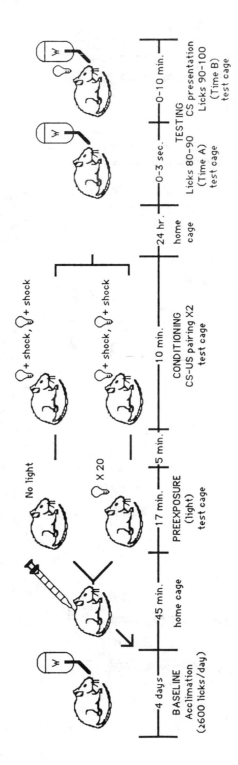

Fig. 10.2 — Latent inhibition: this is the conditioned emotional response paradigm for measurement of LI. The schematic outlines subject manipulation and data recording.

Data Transformation for Measurement of Latent Inhibition

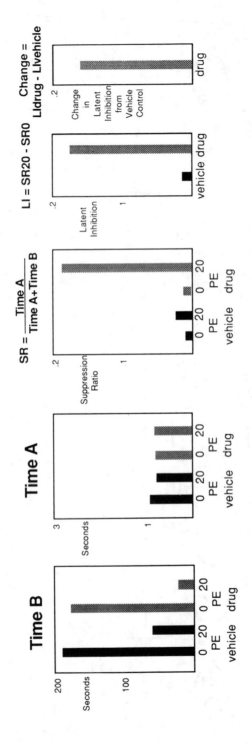

Fig. 10.3 — (a) Raw data in seconds recorded for each rat is individually converted to a unitless suppression ratio by the formula: SR=Time A/(Time A+Time B). (b) Means and standard deviations are estimated for each group using a modified bootstrap technique. (c) Latent inhibition is calculated for groups by the formulas: LI drug=(SR drug 20)−(SR drug 0), and LI vehicle=(SR vehicle 20)−(SR vehicle 0). (d) Drug-induced charge in latent inhibition is calculated by the formula: Charge=(LI vehicle)−(LI drug).

the repeated administration of typical antipsychotic drugs but not by tricyclic antidepressants or anxiolytics [46].

The enhancement of latent inhibition by antipsychotic drugs could be an excellent animal model of antipsychotic drug action. Because it uses normal rats, it makes no unwarranted assumptions about the etiology of psychosis, or the mechanism of action of antipsychotic drugs. The observed effect is maximally present after chronic drug administration, and shows no apparent tolerance. The model is drug responsive at clinically relevant doses. Further development of the model is needed, however, to better characterize its drug sensitivity and specificity prior to its use as an animal model of antipsychotic drug action.

Inhibition of self-stimulation
Intracranial electrical self-stimulation represents another behavioral paradigm proposed for use as an animal model of antipsychotic drug action that uses relatively intact subjects. Species used in this model vary from rats to primates. Operationally, subjects are implanted with an intracranial electrode in an area for which electrical stimulation is positively reinforcing. Such areas include the lateral hypothalamus, substantia nigra, ventral tegmental area, dorsal noradrenergic fiber tract, hippocampus, septum, nucleus accumbens, and central gray matter [17]. Animals are trained to self-stimulate via operantly conditioned lever pressing for electrical pulses. A broad range of antipsychotic drugs including haloperidol, pimozide, butaclamol, chlorpromazine, clozapine, thioridazine, and spiperone inhibit self-stimulation at clinical drug doses [17]. It is hypothesized that these drugs decrease self-stimulation performance by inducing an anhedonic state in which the electrical stimulation which rewards lever pressing is no longer positively reinforcing. This suggests that what is actually being modeled is not antipsychotic drug effects, but rather the ability of a drug to interfere with dopaminergically mediated reward mechanism(s). It has been found that the decreased responding is, in some instances, due to bradykinesia induced by the antipsychotic drug, rather than by a drug-induced anhedonic state. Ettentberg *et al.* [47] found that they could prevent flupenthixol inhibition of intracranial self-simulation by using rats trained to respond by nose poking, a motorically simple task, rather than the more demanding lever-pressing task. This finding, however, would not explain the inhibition of self-simulation behavior reported for clozapine, and thioridazine, drugs which do not cause catalepsy in rats.

Another type of self-stimulation paradigm used as a behavioral screen for antipsychotic activity involves assessment of drug effects on the self-administration of cocaine. Rats trained to lever-press for food reinforcement are implanted with intravenous (i.v.) catheters. They are subsequently rewarded with small i.v. doses of cocaine for lever pressing. Low, acute doses of the typical antipsychotic drugs haloperidol, chlorpromazine, pimozide, and flupenthixol increase self-administration of cocaine, as do the atypical antipsychotic drugs sulpiride, metoclopramide, and thioridazine [48]. An excellent correlation ($r=0.94$) between drug potency in the model and clinical drug potencies was reported [48]. Since the observed drug effect is an increase in responding, bradykinetic effects of the drugs do not underlie the effects in this model. One reported false negative was clozapine, which actually decreased cocaine self-administration. It was hypothesized that this was due to clozapine's interference with cocaine metabolism in the rats. A criticism that applies to both of these models is that they appear to most directly model dopaminergic pharmacology of central reward mechanisms, effects which may turn out to be incidental to the antipsychotic effect of these drugs. They do, none the less, appear promising in terms of their antipsychotic drug sensitivity and correlation with clinical potency. The effects of chronic drug administration on performance in these self-simulation paradigms have not been examined.

10.2.2   Models of disease states
The major group of animal behavioral models relevant to antipsychotic drug development is that which attempts to artificially simulate a presumed etiology of schizophrenia or symptoms of schizophrenia in animals. These attempts rely on either pretreatments with pharmacologic agents or surgical brain lesions to manufacture their effects.

10.2.2.1   Dopamine agonist paradigms
The earliest and still one of the most widely used of these techniques is the antagonism of apomorphine effects by antipsychotic drugs. Very early in the search for antipsychotic drug screening tests it was noted that antipsychotic drugs effectively blocked apomorphine-induced emesis in dogs [17].

Apomorphine, a direct acting, mixed agonist of D_1 and D_2 receptors, produces other readily observable effects in animals as well. Mice given 1.25 mg/kg apomorphine subcutaneously (s.c.) exhibit within minutes a compulsive climbing behavior. This behavior is very reliably extinguished by pretreatment of the mice with an antipsychotic drug. The suppression of apomorphine-induced climbing test is rapid, uses simple equipment, and is reported to possess good antipsychotic drug sensitivity, specificity, and correlation with clinical potency [20]. Because this effect is manifested following acute rather than chronic drug administration, its pharmacological isomorphism is incomplete. The test also does not possess behavioral homology. If the dopamine hypothesis of schizophrenia is correct, then this test, using a dopamine agonist, may be said to have some degree of etiologic homology with schizophrenia. It is of interest to note that SCH 23390, a selective D_1 receptor antagonist which is believed to be devoid of antipsychotic effects, though not yet tested in man, is effective in this model [49].

Apomorphine is used as a behavioral precipitant in other antipsychotic drug screening tests as well. Rats, within 30 min of receiving 0.3 mg/kg apomorphine s.c., exhibit stereotyped sniffing, licking, gnawing and movement behavior. Pretreatment of the rats with a broad variety of antipsychotic drugs inhibits these stereotypies [17,50]. Although some researchers have reported good sensitivity and specificity for this test, it has also been reported to be insensitive to the atypical antipsychotic drugs thioridazine, clozapine, and sulpiride [17,19,51,52]. The stereotypies observed in this model can be augmented by scopolamine, a centrally acting anticholinergic. Cholinergic receptor agonists also inhibit apomorphine stereotypies [50,53]. In addition, chronic administration of antipsychotic drugs produce enhanced stereotypies in response to an acute apomorphine challenge, rather than an inhibition as is seen acutely [50]. These findings seem to indicate that what are being modeled in this apomorphine challenge test are motoric side effects of antipsychotic drugs which develop tolerance over time, are responsive to anticholinergic drugs, and are much less evident with atypical antipsychotic drugs.

The same criticism can be raised for the nearly identical screening tests using antipsychotic drug inhibition of *d*-amphetamine-induced hyperactivity and stereotyped behaviors in lab animals [17]. A potentially more informative approach to animal model development using dopamine agonists involves the assessment of drug effects on cognitive and attentional measures in animals.

10.2.2.2 Neural lesion paradigms

One such model reproduces in rats an abnormal startle response typically seen in schizophrenic patients [39,54]. A normal human subject displays a startle response, such as an eye blink, on presentation of a loud noise. This response can be sharply attenuated by preceding it by 500 ms with a soft tone. This pre-pulse inhibition of acoustic startle is not present in schizophrenic subjects. They cannot suppress a startle response which is preceded by a warning tone.

A very similar defect in pre-pulse inhibition can be created in rats by causing brain region selective dopamine receptor supersensitivity. Rats are stereotaxically injected with the catecholamine neurotoxin 6-hydroxydopamine (6OHDA). This treatment selectively destroys pre-synaptic catecholamine containing neurons. Post-synaptic dopaminoreceptive neurons are functionally upregulated in response to this loss of stimulation in the region of the injection. As a result, when a direct-acting dopamine agonist such as apomorphine is administered systemically, it has a disproportionately powerful effect on the lesioned area, causing a local dopamine hyperfunctional state.

A defect in pre-pulse inhibition was created in rats by inducing this dopamine hyperfunction in the nucleus accumbens, or the substantia nigra. Pre-pulse inhibition was not altered by lesions in the frontal cortex. Important to this discussion, haloperidol 0.2 mg/kg reversed the effect of apomorphine on pre-pulse inhibition in 6OHDA lesioned rats [39].

This model has not been evaluated for antipsychotic drug sensitivity, specificity, or potency. Because it involves specialized skills and equipment, and is very labor intensive, it will likely have limited application as a drug screening test. Its real importance lies in the fact that it creates in rats a sensory gating, or information processing deficit seen in schizophrenic patients. It also provides information as to the possible neuroanatomic substrates of these brain functions and thus may prove useful in identifying the neural circuitry involved in schizophrenia-related cognitive deficits. A better understanding of the disease will allow more informed antipsychotic drug development.

10.3 ANXIETY DISORDERS

Anxiety disorders are a diverse group of diseases which share the common symptom presentation of anxiety. Rather than discuss the questionable success of attempts to model directly this complex group of illnesses, we will focus specifically on the more fruitful area of animal models of anxiolytic drug action. These models can be divided into those animal models which use changes in ongoing, non-evoked behavior as a measure of anxiolytic drug effects, those which set up an artificial conflict in which an animal's behavior changes with anxiolytic drug treatment, and those which use anticonvulsant activity as a measure of anxiolytic drug potential.

10.3.1 Anticonvulsant activity

The measurement of the ability of a compound to prevent pentylenetetrazol (metrazol)-induced seizures in mice is often used as a primary screen for anxiolytic drug potential. Most compounds used clinically in the treatment of anxiety, including benzodiazepines, barbiturates, and meprobamate block metrazol-induced seizures in mice [55]. The test procedure is simple. Metrazol (82 mg/kg, s.c.) produces seizures in 99% of mice. Animals are given oral doses of test compounds, followed by metrazol 45 min later. They are observed over the next 30 min for the onset of seizures [56]. There is also an excellent correlation between clinical anxiolytic drug potency and anti-seizure activity in mice [56].

A criticism of this technique is that there is no fundamental link between anticonvulsant and anxiolytic properties. This is most apparent in the case of buspirone, a clinically effective anxiolytic [57] which does not antagonize the convulsant action of metrazol [58]. In addition, not all anticonvulsant drugs are useful in treating anxiety. The lack of specificity of this test for anxiolytics encourages the use of other paradigms as primary anxiolytic drug screening tests.

10.3.2 Shock-induced suppression of drinking

The effects of anxiolytics on punished responding in animals has good behavioral homology with anxiolytic drug effects in humans. An anxiolytic-treated animal will readily execute behaviors that will produce an aversive stimulus (i.e. electrical shock) in order to obtain a reward. In humans, anxiolytic drugs will also disinhibit behaviors which have feared consequences such as going outside for an agoraphobic, or boarding a plane for an individual who is afraid of flying. A representative anxiolytic drug screening test which exploits this effect on punished responding is shock-induced suppression of drinking. In the prototype of this paradigm [59], a rat is water-deprived for 48 h and then placed in a test cage containing a shock floor, and a drinking tube. On every twentieth lick of the drinking tube, the rat receives a shock through the tube. Untreated control animals lick only enough to receive 2 to 5 shocks on average during daily 3 min sessions. Animals dosed with benzodiazepines, barbiturates, meprobamate, or ethanol continue to lick and receive significantly more shocks. Animals treated with other psychotropic agents including chlorpromazine, morphine, meperidine, or *d*-amphetamine do not receive more shocks than controls [56]. This test is rapid, uses naive animals, and provides sensitive, specific results making it a useful initial screening test for anxiolytic drugs. The paradigm, however, lacks an important component of unpunished responding by which nonspecific drug effects may be assessed. Such a two-component (or schedule) paradigm is a feature of other conflict [60,61] or conditioned emotional response [62] tasks.

10.3.3 Geller–Seifter conflict

One additional type of conflict paradigm based upon response-contingent foot shock that uses operant conditioning is the Geller–Seifter test [61]. In this procedure, rats are trained to lever press for food on a multiple variable interval (VI) 2 min fixed ratio (FR) reinforcement schedule. During 60 min sessions, the schedule components are alternated. During the VI segment, rats are rewarded on a variable interval with food pellets for lever pressing. The FR segments are signaled by a white cue light, or tone, during which each lever press is rewarded with food and punished with a shock. Rats are typically trained for 2 or more weeks before obtaining stable behavioral baselines in this paradigm. Rats trained to criteria receive very few shocks, because they learn to lever press only during the VI segments. These same rats, when treated with anxiolytic drugs, begin lever pressing for reward during the FR segment and receive significantly more shocks at doses which do not affect VI performance [56,61,63]. This test has been found to be both sensitive to and specific for anxiolytic drugs [60,63]. Some studies have found that the antipsychotic drugs clozapine, haloperidol, and sulpiride demonstrate anxiolytic action in this model [64,65]. These effects are observed over very narrow dose ranges and probably indicate some limited anxiolytic action of these drugs rather than lack of drug specificity for this model. Although this paradigm is technically demanding, it appears to offer greater precision in studying subtle drug effects than the simpler anxiolytic drug screens.

10.3.4 Neophobic suppression of drinking

A simple but effective animal model of anxiolytic drug action takes advantage of the neophobic response of rats toward unfamiliar food [56,66]. Rats will consume only small portions of a novel food for several days before accepting it into their diet. This behavior makes wild rats difficult to poison, as any illness caused by or even temporarily associated with a new food will powerfully inhibit further consumption of that food. This same behavior in humans is lightly referred to as the 'sauce bernaise effect'. It has been shown that food neophobia in rats is decreased by anxiolytic drugs [67].

In practice, rats are treated orally with vehicle or a test compound and, 30 mins later, given free access to dilute, sweetened, condensed milk. Vehicle-treated rats will drink 1 to 2 ml on first experience with the novel food source. Consumption of greater than 5 ml indicates an anxiolytic effect of the test compound [56,68]. The test has been positive for all benzodiazepines tested and meprobamate, but not pentobarbital or phenobarbital [56]. This screening test is advantageous in that it requires no pretraining of subjects, is rapid and requires no sophisticated equipment. Although it appears to possess good anxiolytic drug sensitivity, its specificity requires further characterization. This paradigm is pharmacologically isomorphic in that the drug effects in this paradigm and in clinical use are both observed with acute administration and in comparable dose ranges.

10.3.5 Conditioned taste aversion

Another model of anxiolytic drug effect which exploits the consummatory behavior of rats is a conditioned-taste-aversion paradigm. In this model, water-deprived rats are given a single opportunity to drink a saccharin solution. Following consumption, rats are given an aversive stimulus consisting of intraperitoneal (i.p.) injections of either 25 mg/kg 1-5-hydroxytryptophan, or 30 mg/kg lithium chloride. Both of these drugs cause abdominal pain after i.p. injection. Normal rats develop a strong aversion to saccharin and will consume very little of it upon retesting even when water deprived for 24 h. The expression of the taste aversion to saccharin is antagonized by treatment with lorazepam, diazepam, chlordiazepoxide, oxazepam, phenobarbital, meprobamate, chlormezanone, and the atypical anxiolytic, buspirone. No inhibition of conditioned taste aversion is observed with the non-anxiolytic antidepressants imipramine, desipramine and phenelzine, or chlorpromazine, scopolamine and d-amphetamine [58,69]. This paradigm can also be rapidly performed with minimal equipment. Its excellent sensitivity and specificity, particularly its sensitivity to buspirone, recommend this paradigm as an initial screening tool.

10.4 DEPRESSION

Animal behavioral models have, as yet, contributed little to efforts at novel antidepressant drug development. Drug discovery in this field, from its beginnings with iproniazid and imipramine, to the current generation of antidepressant drugs, such as fluoxetine, has relied on a combination of serendipity and astute chemical observation for its advances [70]. Current methods for screening potential antidepressant drugs rely primarily on multiple behavioral tests to achieve a level of accuracy in predicting clinical activity that is not available with any one test. The most effective of these tests make no assumptions about the etiology of the disorder or the mechanism underlying drug effects. In fact, the etiologies of the cardinal symptoms of depression reproduced by these models are themselves actively pursued.

10.4.1 Learned helplessness

The learned-helplessness model of depression is one of the most intuitively satisfying of the current approaches and has been studied intensively by Weiss and Simson [71] as well as others [72–75]. This model is based on the observation that exposure to uncontrollable stress produces performance deficits in subsequent learning tasks [7]. In this model [72], rats are placed individually in chambers with shock grid floors. Over a 1 h period, subjects receive 60 inescapable shocks (0.8 ma), each of 15 s duration, at a rate of one per minute. Forty-eight hours following this procedure, subjects are tested for shock-escape performance in a conditioned-avoidance-responding paradigm using a shuttle box, as previously described (Fig. 10.1). The number of shock-escape failures are recorded. Control rats that had received no pre-conditioning shocks averaged 4 shock-escape failures in 30 shuttle box trials. In contrast, rats pre-exposed to inescapable shock averaged 20 shock-escape failures in 30 trials. This performance deficit is suggested to result from the subject having learned that its behavior does not control its environment; that it is helpless [72]. Such deficits are reversed by a variety of antidepressant treatments [72–77]. In this particular study, escape failures were shown to be decreased by treatment with 5-HT$_{1a}$ agonists including buspirone, gepirone, and ipsapirone [72].

In a similar learned-helplessness paradigm, rats are exposed to randomly presented inescapable foot shock for a cumulative total shock time of 20 min in a 40 min session. One day later they are tested in a Skinner box with a shock floor, cue light, and lever press. Illumination of the light cues a 20 second shock which can be terminated by a lever press. The subjects receive 15 trials. Animals which score 10 to 15 escape failures are considered to have developed a 'learned helplessness' and are used in subsequent studies as 'depressed' subjects. If not re-exposed to inescapable shock, these animals recover to a normal level of shock-escape performance in 3 to 5 weeks. Animals treated with antidepressant drugs demonstrate behavioral recovery in 5 days [73]. Tricyclic antidepressants, and monoamine oxidase inhibitors at clinically used doses, as well as electroconvulsive therapy, reversed escape failures in this model [76]. Antipsychotic drugs, benzodiazepines, sedative-hypnotics, ethanol and stimulants were not effective [73].

A recent study examined the relationship between learned helplessness and the serum corticosterone response to dexamethasone in rats. It was found that inescapably shocked rats do not suppress plasma corticosterone secretion in response to dexamethasone as effectively as unshocked rats. Thus, learned-helplessness paradigms may have use as animal models for the dexamethasone suppression test used as an adjunct to diagnose depression in humans [78]. The learned-helplessness model of depression exhibits sensitivity and specificity for antidepressant drugs. It has good pharmacological isomorphism, and behavioral and possibly etiologic homology for depression.

10.4.2 Forced swimming

A similar type of model to learned helplessness is the Porsolt forced-swim model of depression [79]. In this model, rats are placed in a cylinder of water for 15 min. During this time they swim about, struggling and trying to escape. Eventually they give up and float motionless, displaying what is termed behavioral despair. Rats returned to the water on subsequent days spend most of their time floating motionless. This immobility is assumed to be analogous to escape failure in the learned-helplessness model. The time spent immobile upon retesting is reduced by treatment with tricyclic antidepressants (imipramine, desipramine, amitriptyline, and nortriptyline), monamine oxidase inhibitors (ipronazid, nialimide, and tranylcypromine), and atypical antidepressant drugs (iprindole, mianserin, nomifensin, and viloxazine). This test is also positive, however, for the psychostimulants amphetamine and caffeine [79–81]. Anxiolytics have no effect in this model, and antipsychotic drugs increase immobility rather than decreasing it [79,82]. In that this test is similar to the inescapable-shock paradigms, it has good behavioral homology with symptoms of depression. Its antidepressant sensitivity is excellent. The specificity of this paradigm is called into question by action of psychostimulants in this model. It should be noted, in assessing the severity of this flaw, that psychostimulants, such as amphetamine, are known to provide short-term symptomatic relief of depressive symptoms [83]. The forced-swim paradigm may therefore be quite useful as a rapid, simple antidepressant drug screening test.

10.4.3 Operant conditioning

In general, operant behavior is not altered in a sensitive and specific way by antidepressant drugs. However, a specific operant paradigm, the differential reinforcement of low-rate 72-s schedule (DRL 72-s), has been developed which does not appear to be sensitive to antidepressant drug effects. In a DRL 72-s paradigm, a response is reinforced (rewarded with food or water) only if at least 72 s has elapsed since the last response. Both the reinforcement rate (the number of rewards per trial), and the response rate (the number of lever presses per trial) are recorded. The paradigm is time-consuming, as it takes approximately 9 weeks to shape the behavior of subjects to performance criteria. Tricyclic antidepressant drugs (desipramine, chlorimipramine, protriptyline, nortriptyline, amitriptyline, and doxepin), monoamine oxidase inhibitors (tranylcypromine, iproniazid, isocarboxazid, and phenelzine), atypical antidepressant drugs (mianserin, iprindole, zimelidine, trazodone, fluoxetine, and alaproclate), and electroconvulsive treatments have all resulted in an increase in reinforcement rate, and a decrease in response rate on this schedule [80,84]. In effect, antidepressant drugs improve performance in this complex response task. Antipsychotic drugs, antihistamines, anticholinergics, stimulants, anxiolytics, alcohol, and narcotic analgesics all have effects on performance in a DRL 72-s schedule which qualitatively differs from that of antidepressants [84]. Although this model does not possess the behavioral or etiologic homology, or pharmacologic isomorphism of some of the other antidepressant drug screens, its sensitivity and specificity for antidepressant treatments make it a useful screening tool.

10.4.4   Other models of antidepressant drug action

There are a plethora of behavioral tests that have been proposed as screening tools for antidepressant drug discovery. Few of them can be said to have much reliability at this task. Two of them, antidepressant drug reversal of clonidine-induced hypothermia in rats [80] and antidepressant drug reversal of clonidine-induced social submission in rats [80], are more probably behavioral measures of alpha$_2$-adrenoreceptor agonist properties, rather than true models of antidepressant drug action.

Another model of depression, the olfactory bulbectomized rat, meets many of the validity criteria previously discussed. It shows behavioral and neuroendocrine changes paralleling those seen in human depression. These changes are responsive to chronic, but not acute, antidepressant drugs of different types. This model obviously lacks etiologic homology with human depression [81].

Currently no one animal behavioral model of depression can be relied on to identify a potential antidepressant drug. The most useful approach to screening potential drugs would be to select a group of screens to broadly characterize the behavioral activity profile of a compound.

10.5   CONCLUSION: FUTURE DIRECTIONS

The trend in animal behavioral models of drug efficacy has been toward more emphasis on modeling the psychiatric diseases being treated and less on using arbitrary animal reactions to existing drug treatments as models. The impact of that trend is brought into focus more clearly by a glance at the history of pharmacotherapy in psychiatry. A gap spanning centuries existed between the realization that much of what is called madness is actually physical disease, and the first effective therapies for these diseases [85]. The search for agents to treat these diseases had become nearly desperate. Up until the late 1950s, for example, virtually every drug used in surgical anesthesia had also been tried as a treatment for schizophrenia [86]. The first effective and specific agents discovered, chlorpromazine for schizophrenia, ɔniazid and then imipramine for depression, and diazepam for anxiety, became ᴉtype drugs. Their metabolites and structurally related compounds were studied, tested, and marketed where appropriate. These 'me too' drugs added tremendous power to the psychopharmacologic armamentarium. Early animal models such as neuroleptic-induced catalepsy in rats played a role in screening for compounds that would have the same actions, side effects, and mechanism of action as these prototypical drugs.

More sophisticated efforts to model disease states and therapeutic drug effects promise tools for drug discovery that are not limited to one drug class, or bound by preconceptions about etiology or mechanism of action. The model of antipsychotic drug action represented by latent inhibition is one such model which makes no assumptions about the mechanism by which antipsychotic drugs act. The learned-helplessness model of depression, with its broad avenues for environmental induction, similarly has no inherent limitations as to the types of treatment that it can be used to test. Animal behavioral tools for anxiolytic drug screening such as punished responding, Geller–Seifter conflict, conditioned taste aversion and others which do not unnecessarily limit the chemical scope of drug response are already in use.

The perfect animal behavioral model of drug efficacy would provide a complete parallel to the human drug response. It would be sensitive to all of the drug regimens to which the human disease responds, and to none which are ineffective in human treatment. The differences in psychobiology between laboratory animals and humans ensure that such a model will never exist. The degree to which it can be approximated will, however, continue to surprise and profit researchers in drug discovery in psychopharmacology.

REFERENCES

[1] Coryell, W. (1988). Secondary depression. In: J. O. Cavenar (ed.) *Psychiatry*. J. B. Lippincott Company, Basic Books, New York, Volume 1, Chapter 66.

[2] Risch, S. C. & Janowsky, D. S. (1988). Limbic-hypothalamic-pituitary-adrenal axis dysfunction in melancholia. In: J. O. Cavenar (ed.) *Psychiatry*. J. B. Lippincott Company, Basic Books, New York, Volume 3, Chapter 54.

[3] Carroll, J. B. (1983). Biologic markers and treatment response. *J. Clin. Psychiatry* **44**, 30.

[4] Mckinney, W. T. & Bunney W. E. (1969). Animal model of depression. I. Review of evidence: implications for research. *Arch. Gen. Psychiatry* **21**, 240.

[5] Abromson, L. Y. & Seligman, M. P. (1977). Modeling psychopathology in the laboratory: history and rationale. In: J. D. Moser & M. P. Seligman (eds) *Psychopathology: Experimental Models*. W. H. Freeman, San Francisco, p. 1.

[6] Jessberger, J. A., & Richardson, J. S. (1985) Animal models of depression: parallels and correlates to severe depression in humans. *Biol. Psychiatry* **20**, 764.

[7] Wilner, P. (1984). The validity of animal models of depression. *Psychopharmacology* **83**, 1.

[8] Segal, D. S. & Geyer, M. A. (1988). Animal models of psychopathology. In: J. O. Cavenar (ed.) *Psychiatry*, J. B. Lippincott Company, Basic Books, New York, Volume 3, Chapter 46.

[9] Matthyse, S. (1986). Animal models in psychiatric research. In: J. M. Van Ree & S. Matthyse (eds) *Progress in Brain Research*. Elsevier, Amsterdam, p. 259.

[10] Akiskal, H. S. (1988). The clinical management of affective disorder. In: J. O.

Cavenar (ed.) *Psychiatry*. J. B. Lippincott Company, Basic Books, New York, Volume 1, Chapter 61.

[11] Bleuler, E. (1950). *Dementia Praecox or the Group of Schizophrenias*. International Universities Press, New York.

[12] American Psychiatric Association (1982). *Diagnostic and Statistical Manual of Mental Disorders, 3rd edn*. APA, Washington, D.C.

[13] Holzman, R. S., Kringlen, E., Matthyse, S., Flanagon, K., & Levy, D. L. (1988). A single dominant gene can account for eye tracking dysfunction and schizophrenia in offspring of discordant twins. *Arch. Gen. Psychiatry* **45**; 641.

[14] Evenden, J. C. & Ryan, C. N. (1988). Order and disorder of behavior: the dopamine connection. In: P. Simon, P. Soubrie, & D. Widlocher (eds) *Animal Models of Psychiatric Disorders*. Karger Basel, Volume 2, p. 49.

[15] Joyce, E. M. (1988). The amphetamine model of schizophrenia; a critique. In: P. Simon, P. Soubrie, & D. Widlocher (eds) *Animal Models of Psychiatric Disorders*. Karger, Basel, Volume 2, p. 89.

[16] Bernstein, J. G. (1982). Rational use of antipsychotic drugs. In: J. G. Bernstein (ed.) *Clinical Psychopharmacology, 2nd edn*. John Wright-PSG, Littleton, MA, p. 145.

[17] Worms, P., Broekkamp, C. L. E., & Lloyd, K. G. (1983). Behavioral effects of neuroleptics. In: J. T. Coyle & S. J. Enna (eds) *Neuroleptics: Neurochemical, Behavioral, and Clinical Perspectives*. Raven Press, New York, p. 93.

[18] Roberts, D. C. S. & Vickers, G. (1984). Atypical neuroleptics increase self administration of cocaine: an evaluation of a behavioral screen for antipsychotic drug activity. *Psychopharmacology* **82**, 135.

[19] Sayers, A. C. & Amster, H. A. (1977). Clozapine. *Pharmacol. Biochem. Prop. Drug Subst.* **1**, 1.

[20] Bischoff, S., Christen, P., & Vassout, A. (1988). Blockade of hippocampal dopamine (DA) receptors: a tool for antipsychotic drugs with low extrapyramidal side effects. *Prog. Neuro-psychopharmacol. Biol. Psychiat.* **12**, 455.

[21] Dunstan, R., Broekkamp, C. L., & Lloyd, K. G. (1981). Involvement of caudate nucleus, amygdala, or reticular formation in neuroleptic and narcotic catalepsy. *Pharmacol. Biochem. Behav.* **14**, 169.

[22] Ridhelson, E. (1988). Schizophrenia: treatment. In: J. O. Cavenar (ed.) *Psychiatry*. J. B. Lippincott Company, Basic Books, New York, Volume 1, Chapter 55.

[23] Danneskold-Samsoe, P. & Pedersen, V. (1976). Inhibition of conditional avoidance response by neuroleptics upon repeated administration. *Psychopharmacology* **51**, 9.

[24] Nielsen, M., Fjalland, B., Pedersen, V., & Nymark, M. (1974). Pharmacology of neuroleptics upon repeated administration. *Psychopharmacologia* **34**, 95.

[25] Cunha, J. M. & Masur, J. (1978). Evaluation of psychotropic drugs with a modified open field test. *Pharmacology* **16**, 259.

[26] Petty, F., Mott, J., & Sherman, A. D. (1984). Potential locus and mechanisms of blockade of conditioned avoidance responding of neuroleptics. *Neuropharmacology* **23**, 73.

　ı der Heyden, J. A. M., Tulp, M. T. M., & Oliver, B. (1988). The use of conditioned avoidance behavior in predicting antipsychotic activity. *Soc. Neurosci. Abstr.* **14** (151.14) 371.

[28] Kuribara, H. & Tadokoro, S. (1981). Correlation between antiavoidance activities of antipsychotic drugs in rats and daily clinical doses. *Pharmacol. Biochem. Behav.* **14**, 181.

[29] Nishibe, Y., Matsuo, Y., Toshio, Y., Masami, E., Teuruo, S., & Katsumi, H. (1982). Differential effects of sulpiride and metoclopramide on brain homovanillic acid levels and shuttle box avoidance after systemic and intracerebral administration. *Arch. Pharmacol.* **321**, 190.

[30] Luttinger, D., Nemeroff, C. B., & Prange, Jr., A. J. (1982). The effects of neuropeptides on discrete-trial conditioned avoidance responding. *Brain Res.* **237**, 183.

[31] Sanger, D. J. (1985). The effect of clozapine on shuttle box avoidance responding in rats: comparison with haloperidol and chlordiazepoxide. *Pharmacol. Biochem. Behav.* **23**, 231.

[32] Bregnan, G. B. & Chieli, T. (1980). Classical neuroleptics and deconditioning activity after single or repeated treatments. *Arzneim.-Forsch./Drug Res.* **30**, 1865.

[33] Lubow, R. E. & Feldon, J. An animal model of attention. In: M. Y. Spiegelstein & A. Lagy (eds) *Proceedings of the 27th OHOLO Conf.* Elsevier, Amsterdam, p. 89.

[34] Schnur, P. (1971). Selective attention: effect of element preexposure on compound conditioning in rats. *J. Comp. Physiol. Psychol.* **76**, 123.

[35] Lubow, R. E. & Moore, A. U. (1959). Latent inhibition: the effect of non-reinforced preexposure to the conditioned stimulus. *J. Comp. Physiol. Psychol.* **52**, 415.

[36] Hall, G. & Channell, S. (1985). Differential effect of contextual changes on latent inhibition and on the habituation of an orienting response. *J. Exp. Psychol.: Anim. Behav. Processes* **11**, 470.

[37] Lubow, R. E. (1973). Latent inhibition. *Psychol. Bull.* **79**, 389.

[38] Lubow, R. E., Feldon, J., & Weiner, I. (1988). Attentional deficits in schizophrenics as assessed by latent inhibition magnitude. *Schizoph. Res.* **1**, 193.

[39] Swerdlow, N. R., Koob, G. F., Geyer, M. A., Mansbach, B., & Braff, D. L. (1988). A cross species model of psychosis. In: P. Simon, P. Soubrie, & D. Widlocher (eds) *Animal Models of Psychiatric Disorders*. Karger, Basel, Volume 2, p. 1.

[40] Baruch, I., Hemsley, D. R., & Gray, J. A. (1988). Different performance of acute and chronic schizophrenics in a latent inhibition task. *J. Nerv. Mental Dis.* **176**, 598.

[41] Weiner, I., Lubow, R. E., & Feldon, J. (1988). Disruption of latent inhibition by acute administration of low dose amphetamine. *Pharmacol. Biochem. Behav.* **30**, 871.

[42] Weiner, I., Lubow, R. E., & Feldon, J. (1984). Abolition of expression but not acquisition of latent inhibition by chronic amphetamine in rats. *Psychopharmacology* **83**, 194

[43] Christison, G. W., Atwater, G. E., Dunn, L. A., & Kilts, C. D. (1988).

Haloperidol enhancement of latent inhibition: relationship to therapeutic drug action. *Biol. Psychiatry* **23**, 746.

[44] Weiner, I. & Feldon, J. (1987). Facilitation of latent inhibition by haloperidol in rats. *Psychopharmacology* **91**, 248.

[45] Solomon, C. R., Crider, A., Winkleman, J. W., Turi, A., Kamer, R. M., & Kaplan, L. J. (1981). Disrupted latent inhibition in the rat with chronic amphetamine or haloperidol-induced supersensitivity: relationship to schizophrenic attention disorder. *Biol. Psychiatry* **16**, 519.

[46] Dunn, L. A., Atwater, G. E., Christison, G. W., & Kilts, C. D. (1988). Selective enhancement of latent inhibition by antipsychotic drugs in the rat: a possible model for clinical action. *Soc. Neurosci. Abstr.* **14**, (506.15) 1263.

[47] Ettentberg, A., Koob, G. F., & Bloom, F. E. (1981). Response artifact in the measurement of neuroleptic induced anhedonia. *Science* **213**, 357.

[48] Roberts, D. C. S. & Vickers, G. (1984). Atypical neuroleptics increase self-administration of cocaine: an evaluation of a behavioral screen for antipsychotic activity. *Psychopharmacology* **82**, 135.

[49] Vasse, M., Cahgraoui, A., & Protais, P. (1988). Climbing the stereotyped behaviors in mice require the stimulation of D-1 dopamine receptors. *Eur. J. Pharmacol.* **148**, 221.

[50] Butkerait, P. & Friedman, E. (1988). Scopolamine modulates apomorphine-induced behavior in rats treated with haloperidol or SCH 23390. *Eur. J. Pharmacol.* **148**, 269.

[51] Jenner, P., Clow, A., Reavill, C., Theodorou, A., & Marsden, C. D. (1980). Stereoselective actions of substituted benzamide rings on cerebral dopamine mechanisms. *J. Pharm. Pharmacol.* **32**, 39.

[52] Schmutz, J. & Eichenberger, E. (1982). Cloxapine. In: J. S. Bindra & D. Lednicer (eds) *Chronicles of Drug Discovery*, Volume 1. Wiley, New York, p. 39.

[53] Arnfred, T. & Randrup, A. (1968). Cholinergic mechanism in brain inhibiting amphetamine-induced stereotyped behavior. *Acta Pharmacol. Toxicol.* **26**, 384.

[54] Swerdlow, N. R., Braff, D. L., Geyer, M. A., & Koob, G. F. (1986). Central dopamine hyperactivity in rats mimics abnormal acoustic startle response in schizophrenics. *Biol. Psychiatry* **21**, 23.

[55] Zhinder, G. & Rondell, L. O. (1967). Pharmacology of benzodiazepines: laboratory and clinical considerations. *Adv. Pharmacol.* **5**, 213.

[56] Patel, J. B. & Malick, J. B. (1983). Neuropharmacological profile of an anxiolytic. In: J. B. Malick, S. J. Enna, & H. I. Yamamura (eds) *Anxiolytics: Neurochemical, Behavioral, and Clinical Perspectives*. Raven Press, New York, p. 173.

[57] Goldberg, H. L. & Finnerty, R. J. (1979) Comparative efficacy of buspirone and diazepam in treatment of anxiety. *Am. J. Psychiatry* **136**, 1184.

[58] Ervin, G. N., Soroko, F. S., & Cooper, B. R. (1987) Buspirone antagonizes the expression of conditioned taste aversion in rats. *Drug Dev. Res.* **11**, 87.

Vogel, J. R., Beer, B., & Clody, D. E. (1971). A simple and reliable conflict cedure for testing antianxiety agents. *Psychopharmacologia* **21**, 1.

C., D., Commissaris, R. L., & Rech, R. H. (1981). Comparison of anticonflict drug effects in three experimental animal models of anxiety. *Psychopharmacology* **74**, 290.

[61] Geller, I. & Seifter, J. (1960). The effects of meprobamate, barbiturate, *d*-amphetamine, and promazine on experimentally induced conflict in the rat. *Psychopharmacologia* **1**, 482.

[62] Estes, W. K. & Skinner, B. F. (1941). Some quantitative properties of anxiety. *J. Exp. Psych.* **29**, 390.

[63] Young, Y., Urbancic, A., Emrey, T. A., Hall, P. C., & Metcalf, G. (1987). Behavioral effects of several anxiolytics and putative anxiolytics. *Eur. J. Pharmacol.* **143**, 361.

[64] Pich, E. M. & Samanin, R. (1986). Disinhibitory effects of buspirone and low doses of sulpiride and haloperidol in two experimental anxiety models in rats: possible role of dopamine. *Psychopharmacology* **89**, 125.

[65] Spealman, R. D. & Katz, J. L. (1980). Some effects of clozapine on punished responding by mice and squirrel monkeys. *J. Pharmacol. Exp. Ther.* **212**, 435.

[66] Barnett, S. A. (1981). *The Rat: a Study in Behavior*. The University of Chicago Press, Chicago.

[67] Poschel, B. P. H. (1971). A simple and specific screen for benzodiazepine-like drugs. *Psychopharmacologia* **19**, 193.

[68] Malick, J. B. & Enna, S. J. (1979). Comparative effects of benzodiazepines and non-benzodiazepine anxiolytics on biochemical and behavioral tests predictive of anxiolytic activity. *Commun. Psychopharmacol.* **3**, 245.

[69] Ervin, G. N. & Cooper, B. R. (1988). The use of conditioned taste aversion as a conflict model: effects of anxiolytic drugs. *J. Pharmacol. Exp. Ther.*, in press.

[70] Natraj, S. & Gershon, S. (1983). From animal models to clinical testing — promises and pitfalls. *Prog. Neuro-psychopharmacol. Biol. Psychiat.* **7**, 227.

[71] Weiss, J. M. & Simson, P. G. (1986). Depression in an animal model: focus of the locus ceruleus. In: R. Porter, G. Bock, & S. Clark (eds) *Antidepressants and Receptor Function*. Wiley, Chichester, p. 191.

[72] Giral, P., Martin, P., Soubrie, P., & Simon, P. (1988). Reversal of helpless behavior in rats by putative 5-HT1A agonists. *Biol. Psychiatry* **23**, 237.

[73] Henn, F. A., Johnson, J., Edwards, E., Anderson, D. (1985) Melancholia in rodents: neurobiology and pharmacology. *Psychopharm. Bull.* **21**, 443.

[74] Telner, J. E. & Singhal, R. L. (1981). Effects of nortriptyline treatment on learned helplessness in the rat. *Pharmacol. Biochem. Behav.* **14**, 823–826.

[75] Overmier, J. B. & Hellhammer, D. H. (1988). The learned helplessness model of human depression. In: P. Simon, P. Soubrie, & D. Widlocher (eds) *Animal Models of Psychiatric Disorders*, Karger, Basel, Volume 2, pp. 177–202.

[76] Sherman, A. D., Sacquitine, J. L., & Petty, F. (1982). Pharmacological specificity of the learned helplessness model of depression. *Pharmacol. Biochem. Behav.*, **16**, 449–454.

[77] Martin, P., Soubrie, P., & Simon, P. (1986). Shuttle box deficits induced by inescapable shocks in rats: reversal by beta-adrenoreceptor stimulants clenbuterol and salbutamol. *Pharmacol. Biochem. Behav.* **24**, 177–181.

[78] Haracz, J. L., Minor, T. R., Wilkins, J. N., & Zimmerman, E. G. (1988). Learned helplessness: An experimental model of the DST in rats. *Biol. Psychiatry*, **23**, 388–396.

[79] Porsolt, R. D. (1979). Animal model of depression. *Biomedicine* **30**, 139–140.

[80] Daysz, W., Plaznik, A., Kostowski, W., Malatynska, E., Jarbe, T. U. C., Hiltonen, A. J., & Archer, T. (1988). Comparison of desipramine, amitriptyline, zimelidine and alaproclate in six animal models used to investigate antidepressant drugs. *Pharmacol. Toxicol.* **62**, 42–50.

[81] Jesberger, J. A. & Richardson, J. S. (1985). Animal models of depression: parallels and correlates to severe depression in humans. *Biol. Psychiatry* **20**, 764.

[82] Porsolt, R. D., Anton, G., Blavet, N., & Jalfre, M. (1978). Behavioral despair in rats: a new model sensitive to antidepressant treatments. *Eur. J. Pharmacol.* **47**, 379.

[83] Schukit, M. A. (1988). Trait (and state) markers of a predisposition of psychopathology. In: J. O. Cavenar (ed.) *Psychiatry*. J. B. Lippincott Company, Basic Books, New York, Volume 3, Chapter 53.

[84] Seiden, L. S., Dahms, J. L., & Shaughnessy, R. A. (1985). Behavioral screen for antidepressants: the effect of drugs and electroconvulsive shock on performance under a differential-reinforcement-of-low-rate schedule. *Psychopharmacology* **86**, 55.

[85] Baldessarini, R. J. (1980). Drugs and the treatment of psychiatric disorders. In: A. G. Gilman, L. S. Goodman, & A. Gilman (eds.) *The Pharmacologic Basis of Therapeutics*, 6th edn. MacMillan, New York, p. 391.

[86] Caldwell, A. E. (1978). History of psychopharmacology. In: W. G. Clark & J. del Guidice (eds) *Principles of Psychopharmacology*. Academic Press, New York, p. 417.

Index